BIODIVERSITY: THE UK STEERING G

VOLUME 2: ACTION PLANS

LONDON: HMSO

Produced by DDP Services
Printed in Great Britain on recycled paper

B2154

ANNEX F
LISTS OF KEY SPECIES, KEY HABITATS AND BROAD HABITATS

ANNEX F: LISTS OF KEY SPECIES, KEY HABITATS AND BROAD HABITATS

SPECIES LISTS

1. This section contains three lists: a long list of some 1250 species; a middle list of just under 300 species (for which action plans will be produced during the next three years), and a short list of 116 species (for which action plans have been produced). The criteria used in compiling these lists are explained in Chapter 2 of the report.

2. It was agreed that species which qualified for one or more of the following categories should be considered for the long list:

- threatened endemic and globally threatened species;
- species where the UK has more than 25% of the world or appropriate biogeographical population;
- species where numbers or range have declined by more than 25% in the last 25 years;
- in some instances where the species is found in fewer than 15 ten km squares in the UK; and
- species which are listed in the EC Birds or Habitats Directives, the Bern, Bonn or CITES Conventions, or under the Wildlife and Countryside Act 1981 or the Nature Conservation and Amenity Lands (Northern Ireland) Order 1985.

The middle and short lists contain species which are either globally threatened or are rapidly declining in the UK (ie by more than 50% in the last 25 years).

3. The long list does not claim to be a comprehensive record of species of conservation concern. It lacks several thousand nationally threatened (Red List), rare and scarce species. We did not think it appropriate to add all these species to the long list, especially as the process of re-assessing national Red Lists, to bring them into line with the revised threat criteria issued by IUCN in 1994, has only just begun. Also, more information is needed about the international status of most invertebrates and many lower plants before definitive statements on the status of species can be made for these groups. The long list will be reviewed as more information becomes available and as changes are made to the species protected under UK and international legislation.

4. Selection of species for the middle list was carried out using the criteria of "international threat" and "rapid decline in the UK". This is only one of a number of approaches which could have been used. The international threat criterion is difficult to apply to invertebrates and some lower plants because of the dearth of collated information on the status of these groups in other countries. Decline is difficult to quantify for most invertebrates and many plants, except in terms of distribution. Legislative responsibilities, Red List status and endemism are also important factors to be taken into consideration.

5. Care was taken to include the plants, invertebrates and vertebrates for which the UK has obligations under international legislation, as well as our endemic species and other species in urgent need of action.

HABITAT LISTS

6. Key habitats were selected using one or more of the following criteria: habitats for which the UK has international obligations; habitats at risk, such as those with a high rate of decline especially over the last 20 years, or which are rare; areas, particularly marine areas, which may be functionally critical, and areas important for key species.

7. This gave a list of 38 key habitats, for which costed plans have been prepared for 14 (see Annex G). We propose that the remaining 24 costed habitat action plans be written within three years, with the great majority within two years.

8. In addition, a classification of 37 broad habitat types, to include the whole land surface of the UK, and the surrounding sea to the edge of the continental shelf in the Atlantic Ocean has been developed as a basic framework. Further work is required to fill gaps, eg caves and natural rock exposures. A brief habitat statement has been prepared for each of these to inform national and local policy and action. These are set out in Annex G.

KEY TO BIODIVERSITY LISTS

The following lists are not intended to be comprehensive but to provide an indication of how each species qualifies for inclusion under the selection process. Thus, the information does not provide a full synopsis of all the Directives and Conventions on which species are listed, but is restricted to those relevant to their inclusion under this process.

In order to present the information concisely, abbreviations have been used. The following provides a key to interpret these:

STATUS:

RDB = Red Data Book
    (RDB 1 = Endangered, RDB 2 = Vunerable, RDB 3 = Rare) } (using original IUCN Red list categories)
pRDB = Proposed for British Red Data list

CR = Critically endangered
EN = Endangered } (using 1994 IUCN Red list categories)
VU = Vulnerable

INTERNATIONAL THREAT:

2	Species of global conservation concern
2?	Status uncertain - possibly 2
I	Unfavourable conservation status in Europe
0	Favourable conservation status in Europe

INTERNATIONAL IMPORTANCE:

3	75+% of the world population in the UK
3*	Believed endemic
3*?	Possible endemic
2	50 - 74% of the world population in the UK
I	25 - 49% of the world population in the UK
0	0 - 24% of the world population in the UK

DECLINE:

2	50 - 100% decline in numbers/range in GB in last 25 years
I	25 - 49% decline in numbers/range in GB in last 25 years
0	0 - 24% decline in numbers/range in GB in last 25 years
0	0 - 24% increase in numbers/range in GB in last 25 years
-I	25 - 49% increase in numbers/range in GB in last 25 years
-2	50+% increase in numbers/range in GB in last 25 years

LOCALISATION

2	Currently occurs in 1 - 5 10km squares in GB		2	Currently occurs in 1 - 3 10km squares in GB
I	Currently occurs in 6 - 15 10km squares in GB		I	Currently occurs in 4 - 8 10km squares in GB
+	Currently occurs in 16 - 100 10km squares in GB		+	Currently occurs in 9 - 55 10km squares in GB
0	Currently occurs in 101+ 10km squares in GB		0	Currently occurs in 56+ 10km squares in GB

Values for marine species are as follows:

(BR = Breeding numbers)
(W = Winter numbers)
(S = Numbers at sea)

For species occuring in Northern Ireland only, the values apply to that Province only.

EC DIRECTIVES   Birds Directive Annex I (native species only)
    EC Habitats Directive Annex II and/or IV (native species only)

BERN CONVENTION   Appendices I and II (native species only)

BONN CONVENTION   Appendices I and II (native species only)

UK ACT SCHEDS.

I	Schedule I	} **Wildlife and Countryside Act 1981**	(a)	Schedule I	} **Wildlife (Northern Ireland) Order 1985**
5	Schedule 5		(b)	Schedule 5	
8	Schedule 8		(c)	Schedule 8	
5*	Schedule 5 but protection against sale only				

EXTINCTION   Denoted by X
    X(C) indicates a species which has gone extinct in the wild but is held in captivity
    X(R) indicates a species which has gone extinct in the wild but has been re-introduced

Short list of Globally Threatened/Declining Species

Group	Scientific name	Common name	Family
Mammal	*Arvicola terrestris*	water vole	Muridae
Mammal	*Lepus europaeus*	brown hare	Leporidae
Mammal	*Lutra lutra lutra*	European otter	Mustelidae
Mammal	*Muscardinus avellanarius*	dormouse	Gliridae
Mammal	*Myotis myotis*	greater mouse-eared bat	Vespertilionidae
Mammal	*Phocoena phocoena*	harbour porpoise	Phocoenidae
Mammal	*Pipistrellus pipistrellus*	pipistrelle bat	Vespertilionidae
Mammal	*Rhinolophus ferrumequinum*	greater horseshoe bat	Rhinolophidae
Mammal	*Sciurus vulgaris*	red squirrel	Aplodontidae
Bird	*Acrocephalus paludicola*	aquatic warbler	Sylviidae
Bird	*Alauda arvensis*	skylark	Alaudidae
Bird	*Botaurus stellaris*	bittern	Ardeidae
Bird	*Burhinus oedicnemus*	stone curlew	Burhinidae
Bird	*Crex crex*	corncrake	Rallidae
Bird	*Loxia scotica*	Scottish crossbill	Fringillidae
Bird	*Perdix perdix*	grey partridge	Phasianidae
Bird	*Tetrao urogallus*	capercaillie	Tetraonidae
Bird	*Turdus philomelos*	song thrush	Turdidae
Amphibian	*Bufo calamita*	natterjack toad	Bufonidae
Amphibian	*Triturus cristatus*	great crested newt	Salamandridae
Reptile	*Lacerta agilis*	sand lizard	Lacertidae
Fish	*Alosa alosa*	allis shad	Clupeidae
Fish	*Alosa fallax*	twaite shad	Clupeidae
Fish	*Coregonus albula*	vendace	Coregonidae
Fish	*Coregonus autumnalis*	pollan	Coregonidae
Ants	*Formica candica (transkaucasica)*	bog ant	Formicidae
Ants	*Formica exsecta*	narrow-headed ant	Formicidae
Ants	*Formica pratensis (nigricans)*	black-backed meadow ant	Formicidae
Bees	*Bombus sylvarum*	shrill carder bee, knapweed carder bee	Apidae
Beetle	*Aphodius niger*	a scarab beetle	Scarabaeidae
Beetle	*Bembidion argentoleum*	a ground beetle	Carabidae
Beetle	*Carabus intricatus*	blue ground beetle	Carabidae
Beetle	*Cathormiocerus brittanicus*	a weevil	Curculionidae
Beetle	*Cryptocephalus coryli*	a leaf beetle	Chrysomelidae
Beetle	*Cryptocephalus exiguus*	a leaf beetle	Chrysomelidae
Beetle	*Limoniscus violaceus*	violet click beetle	Elateridae
Beetle	*Lucanus cervus*	stag beetle	Lucanidae
Beetle	*Obera oculata*	a longhorn beetle	Cerambycidae
Beetle	*Panagaeus crux-major*	a ground beetle	Carabidae
Beetle	*Stenus palposus*	a ground beetle	Staphylinidae
Beetle	*Tachys edmondsi*	a ground beetle	Carabidae
Butterfly	*Argynnis adippe*	high brown fritillary	Nymphalidae
Butterfly	*Boloria euphrosyne*	pearl-bordered fritillary	Nymphalidae
Butterfly	*Eurodryas aurinia*	marsh fritillary	Nymphalidae
Butterfly	*Hesperia comma*	silver-spotted skipper	Hesperiidae
Butterfly	*Lycaena dispar*	large copper	Lycaenidae
Butterfly	*Maculinea arion*	large blue	Lycaenidae
Butterfly	*Mellicta athalia*	heath fritillary	Nymphalidae
Cricket/Grasshopper	*Gryllotalpa gryllotalpa*	mole cricket	Gryllotalpidae
Crustacean	*Austropotamobius pallipes*	freshwater white-clawed crayfish	Astacidae

Status	Int. threat	Int. import.	Decline	Local.	EC Annex	Bern App.	Bonn App.	UK Act Sched.	Extinct
	0	0	1	0					
	0	0	1	0					
	2?	0	-1	0	IIa IVa	II		5	
	1	0	1	0	IVa			5(b)	
	2?	0	2	2	IIa IVa	II		5	X
	2	0	0	1	IIa IVa	II	II	5(b)	
	1	0	1	0	IVa		II	5(b)	
	1	0	1	+	IIa IVa	II	II	5	
	0	0	1	0				5(b)	
	2	0	0	1	I				
	1	0	2	0					
	1	0	2	2	I	II	II	1	
	1	0	2	+	I	II	II	1	
	2	0	2	+	I	II		1	
	2	3	0	+	I	II		1	
	1	0	2	0					
	0	0	2	+	I				
	0	0	2	0					
	1	0	1	+	IVa	II		5	
	1	0	1	0	IIa IVa	II		5	
	1	0	1	+	IVa	II		5	
	1	0	2	1	IIa			5	
	1	0	2	1+	IIa				
	1	0	2	2				5	
RDB 1	2?	1?	0	2?					
RDB 1	1	0	1	2					
RDB 1	1?	0	2	2					?
	1?	0	2?	1?					
RDB 1	?	?	0	2					
									X?
RDB 1	2	0	2	2					
RDB 1	2?	3*	0	2					
RDB 1	?	?	2	2					
RDB 1	?	?	2	2					
RDB 1	2?	2?	0	2	IIa			5	
	1	?	0	+	IIa	III			
RDB 1	?	?	2	2					
pRDB 1	1?	?	2	2					
pRDB 1	2?	3*?	0?	2					
RDB 2	0	0	2	0				5	
	0	0	1	0				5*	
	1	0	2	+	IIa	II		5*(b)	
RDB 3	0	0	2	1				5*	
	2?	0	0	2	IIa IVa	II		5*	
	2	0	2	2	IVa	II		5	X(R)
RDB 2	0	0	2	1				5	
RDB 1	1?	0	2	2				5	X?
	2	0	1	0	IIa			5	

Damsel/Dragonfly	*Coenagrion mercuriale*	southern damselfly	Coenagriidae
Fly	*Asilus crabroniformis*	a robber fly	Asilidae
Fly	*Callicera spinolae*	a hoverfly	Syrphidae
Fly	*Chrysotoxum octomaculatum*	a hoverfly	Syrphidae
Mollusc	*Anisus vorticulus*	a snail	Planorbidae
Mollusc	*Catinella arenaria*	sandbowl snail	Succineidae
Mollusc	*Margaritifera margaritifera*	a freshwater pearl mussel	Margaritiferidae
Mollusc	*Myxas glutinosa*	glutinous snail	Lymnaeidae
Mollusc	*Pisidium tenuilineatum*	a freshwater bivalve	Sphaeriidae
Mollusc	*Pseudanodonta complanata*	a freshwater mussel	Unionidae
Mollusc	*Segmentina nitida*	a freshwater snail	Planorbidae
Mollusc	*Vertigo angustior*	a snail	Vertiginidae
Mollusc	*Vertigo genesii*	a snail	Vertiginidae
Mollusc	*Vertigo geyeri*	a snail	Vertiginidae
Mollusc	*Vertigo moulinsiana*	a snail	Vertiginidae
Moth	*Coscinia cribraria bivittata*	speckled footman	Arctiidae
Moth	*Eustroma reticulata*	netted carpet	Geometridae
Moth	*Idaea ochrata cantiata*	bright wave	Geometridae
Sea Anemone Group	*Edwardsia ivelli*	Ivell's sea anemone	Edwardsiidae
Sea Anemone Group	*Nematostella vectensis*	starlet sea anemone	Edwardsiidae
Worm	*Hirudo medicinalis*	medicinal leech	Hirudinidae
Fungus	*Battarraea phalloides*	a phalloid	Tulastomataceae
Fungus	*Boletus satanas*	Devil's bolete	Boletaceae
Fungus	*Poronia punctata*	nail fungus	Xylaniaceae
Fungus	*Tulostoma niveum*	a stalked puffball	Talastomataceae
Lichen	*Buellia asterella*	starry Breck-lichen	Physciaceae
Lichen	*Caloplaca luteoalba*	orange-fruited elm-lichen	Teloschistaceae
Lichen	*Collema dichotomum*	river jelly lichen	Collemataceae
Lichen	*Gyalecta ulmi*	Elm's gyalecta	Gyalectaceae
Lichen	*Pseudocyphellaria aurata*	a lichen	Lobariaceae
Lichen	*Pseudocyphellaria norvegica*	a lichen	Lobariaceae
Lichen	*Schismatomma graphidioides*	a lichen	Opegraphaceae
Liverwort	*Jamesoniella undulifolia*	marsh earwort	Jungermanniaceae
Liverwort	*Lejeunea mandonii*	a liverwort	Lejeuneaceae
Liverwort	*Lophozia (Lieocolea) rutheana*	Norfolk flapwort	Lophoziaceae
Liverwort	*Marsupella profunda*	western rustwort	Gymnomitriaceae
Liverwort	*Petalophyllum ralfsii*	petalwort	Codoniaceae
Moss	*Buxbaumia viridis*	green shield moss	Archidiaceae
Moss	*Didymodon (Barbula) glaucus*	glaucous beard-moss	Pottiaceae
Moss	*Ditrichum cornubicum*	Cornish path moss	Ditrichaceae
Moss	*Hamatocaulis (Drepanocladus) vernicosus*	slender green feather-moss	Amblystegiaceae
Moss	*Thamnobryum angustifolium*	Derbyshire feather-moss	Thamniaceae
Moss	*Weissia multicapsularis*	a moss	Pottiaceae
Stonewort	*Chara muscosa*	mossy stonewort	Characeae
Vascular Plant	*Alisma graminea*	ribbon-leaved water-plantain	Alismataceae
Vascular Plant	*Apium repens*	creeping marshwort	Apiaceae
Vascular Plant	*Artemisia norvegica*	Norwegian mugwort	Asteraceae
Vascular Plant	*Athyrium flexile*	Newman's lady-fern	Woodsiaceae
Vascular Plant	*Cochlearia micacea*	mountain scurvy-grass	Brassicaceae
Vascular Plant	*Coincya wrightii*	Lundy cabbage	Brassicaceae
Vascular Plant	*Cotoneaster cambricus*	wild cotoneaster	Rosaceae
Vascular Plant	*Cypripedium calceolus*	Lady's-slipper orchid	Orchidaceae
Vascular Plant	*Damasonium alisma*	starfruit	Alismataceae

RDB 3	2?	0	0	+	IIa	II	
	1?	0	2	1			
RDB 1	2?	0	2?	2			
RDB 2	1	0	1	1			
RDB 2	2?	0	2	1			
RDB 1	2	0	0	2			5
	2	0	0	2	IIa		5
RDB 1	2	0	0	2			5
RDB 3	2?	0	2	1			
	2	0	0	+			
RDB 1	1	0	2	2			
RDB 1	2	0	0	2	IIa		
RDB 1	2	0	0	2	IIa		
RDB 1	2	0	0	2	IIa		
RDB 3	?	?	0	1	IIa		
RDB 2	?	?	2	2			
RDB 2	1	0	1	1			
RDB 3	0	0	1?	1			
	2	3?	2	2			5
RDB 3	2?	?	0?	+			5
RDB 3	2?	?	0	1			5
EN	2?	2	1	2			
VU	2	1	1	1			
EN	2	0	0	2			
CR	2	1	-1	2			
CR	1?	0	2?	2			8
VU	1	1?	2	1?			8
VU	2	2?	1?	2			8
EN	1?	0?	2?	1			8
CR	1	0	2	2			
	1	1?	0	+			
VU	2	1?	0?	1			
EN	2	0?	2	2			8
EN	2	1?	0?	2			
CR	0	0	2?	2			8
CR	2	1?	2	2	IIb	I	8
VU	1	1?	1?	+	IIb	I	8
CR	1	0	2?	2	IIb	I	8
CR	2?	0?	0	2			8
CR	2	3*	0?	2			8
DD	1?	0?	?	?	IIb	I	8
CR	2	3*	1?	2			8
VU	2?	3	1?	1			
DD	2	2	?	?			
CR	1	0	2	2			8
CR	1	0	2	2	IIb IVb	I	8
VU	2	0	0	2			
VU	1	3*	0	2			
LR	2	3*	0	1			
VU	2	3*	0	2			8
EN	2?	3*?	0	2			8
CR	1	0	0	2	IIb IVb	I	8
EN	1	1	2	2			8

Vascular Plant	*Epipactis youngiana*	Young's helleborine	Orchidaceae
Vascular Plant	*Euphrasia cambrica*	an eyebright	Scrophulariaceae
Vascular Plant	*Euphrasia campbelliae*	an eyebright	Scrophulariaceae
Vascular Plant	*Euphrasia heslop-harrisonii*	an eyebright	Scrophulariaceae
Vascular Plant	*Euphrasia rivularis*	an eyebright	Scrophulariaceae
Vascular Plant	*Euphrasia rotundifolia*	an eyebright	Scrophulariaceae
Vascular Plant	*Euphrasia vigursii*	an eyebright	Scrophulariaceae
Vascular Plant	*Fumaria occidentalis*	western ramping-fumitory	Fumariaceae
Vascular Plant	*Gentianella anglica*	early gentian	Gentianaceae
Vascular Plant	*Liparis loeselii*	fen orchid	Orchidaceae
Vascular Plant	*Luronium natans*	floating water plantain	Alismataceae
Vascular Plant	*Najas flexilis*	slender naiad	Najadaceae
Vascular Plant	*Najas marina*	holly-leaved naiad	Najadaceae
Vascular Plant	*Potamogeton rutilus*	Shetland pondweed	Potamogetonace
Vascular Plant	*Ranunculus tripartitus*	three-lobed water-crowfoot	Ranunculaceae
Vascular Plant	*Rumex rupestris*	shore dock	Polygonaceae
Vascular Plant	*Saxifraga hirculus*	yellow marsh saxifrage	Saxifragaceae
Vascular Plant	*Trichomanes speciosum*	Killarney fern	Hymenophyllace

EN	2?	3*	0	2			8
	2	3*	0	1			
	2	3*	0	1			
	2	3*	0	1			
	2	3*	0	1			
VU	2	3*	0	2			
	2	3*	0	+			
VU	2	3*	0	+			
	1	3*	1	+	IIb IVb	1	8
EN	1	0	2	2	IIb IVb	1	8
	1	1	0	+	IIb IVb	1	8
	1	0	0	+	IIb IVb	1	8
VU	1	0	0	2			8
	1	0	0	1			
VU	1	1	2	1			
EN	2	1	2	1	IIb IVb	1	8
	1	0	0	1	IIb IVb	1	8
VU	2	0	0	1	IIb IVb	1	8(C)

Middle list of Globally Threatened/Declining Species

Group	Scientific name	Common name	Family
Mammal	Balaena glacialis (Eubalaena glacialis)	northern/black right whale	Balaenidae
Mammal	Balaenoptera acutorostrata	minke whale	Balaenopteridae
Mammal	Balaenoptera borealis	Sei whale	Balaenopteridae
Mammal	Balaenoptera musculus (Sibbaldus musculus)	blue whale	Balaenopteridae
Mammal	Balaenoptera physalus	fin whale	Balaenopteridae
Mammal	Hyperoodon ampullatus	northern bottlenosed whale	Ziphiidae
Mammal	Megaptera novaeangliae	humpback whale	Balaenopteridae
Mammal	Myotis bechsteinii	Bechstein's bat	Vespertilionidae
Mammal	Physeter catodon (P. macrocephalus)	sperm whale	Physeteridae
Bird	Acrocephalus palustris	marsh warbler	Sylviidae
Bird	Caprimulgus europaeus	nightjar	Caprimulgidae
Bird	Carduelis cannabina	linnet	Fringillidae
Bird	Emberiza cirlus	cirl bunting	Emberizidae
Bird	Emberiza schoeniclus	reed bunting	Emberizidae
Bird	Jynx torquilla	wryneck	Picidae
Bird	Lanius collurio	red-backed shrike	Laridae
Bird	Lullula arborea	woodlark	Alaudidae
Bird	Melanitta nigra	common scoter	Anatidae
Bird	Miliaria calandra	corn bunting	Emberizidae
Bird	Muscicapa striata	spotted flycatcher	Muscicapidae
Bird	Passer montanus	tree sparrow	Passeridae
Bird	Phalaropus lobatus	red-necked phalarope	Scolopacidae
Bird	Pyrrhula pyrrhula	bullfinch	Fringillidae
Bird	Sterna dougallii	roseate tern	Sternidae
Bird	Streptopelia turtur	turtle dove	Columbidae
Amphibian	Rana lessonae	pool frog	Ranidae
Reptile	Caretta caretta	loggerhead turtle	Cheloniidae
Reptile	Chelonia mydas	green turtle	Cheloniidae
Reptile	Dermochelys coriacea	leatherback turtle	Dermochelyidae
Reptile	Eretmochelys imbricata	hawksbill turtle	Cheloniidae
Reptile	Lepidochelys kempii	Kemp's ridley turtle	Cheloniidae
Fish	Acipenser sturio	sturgeon	Acipenseridae
Fish	Coregonus oxyrhynchus	houting	Coregonidae
Fish	Lota lota	burbot	Gadidae
Ant	Formica rufibarbis	red barbed ant	Formicidae
Bee	Andrena floricola	a mining bee	Andrenidae
Bee	Andrena gravida	banded mining bee	Andrenidae
Bee	Andrena lathyri	a mining bee	Andrenidae
Bee	Andrena lepida	a mining bee	Andrenidae
Bee	Bombus distinguendus	great yellow bumble bee	Apidae
Bee	Bombus humilis	brown-banded carder bee	Apidae
Bee	Bombus ruderatus	large garden bumble bee	Apidae
Bee	Bombus subterraneus	short haired bumble bee	Apidae
Bee	Osmia xanthomelana	a mason bee	Megachilidae
Beetle	Agabus brunneus	a water beetle	Dytiscidae
Beetle	Amara famelica	a ground beetle	Carabidae
Beetle	Amara strenua	a ground beetle	Carabidae
Beetle	Anisodactylus nemorivagus	a ground beetle	Carabidae
Beetle	Anisodactylus poeciloides	a ground beetle	Carabidae
Beetle	Badister anomalus	a ground beetle	Carabidae
Beetle	Badister peltatus	a ground beetle	Carabidae

Status	Int. threat	Int. import.	Decline	Local.	EC Annex	Bern App.	Bonn App.	UK Act Sched.	Extinct
	2	0	0?		IVa	II	I	5(b)	
	2?	0	?	0	IVa			5(b)	
	2?	0	?		IVa			5(b)	
	2	0	?		IVa	II	I	5(b)	
	2?	0	?		IVa			5(b)	
	2?	0	?	0	IVa		II	5(b)	
	2	0	0		IVa	II	I	5(b)	
	2?	0	0	+	IIa IVa	II	II	5	
	2?	0	?		IVa			5(b)	
	0	0	2	2		II		I	
	I	0	2	0	I	II		(a)	
	0	0	2	0		II			
	0	0	2	I		II		I	
	0	0	2	0		II			
	I	0	2	2		II		I	
	I	0	2	2	I	II		I	
	I	0	2	+	I			I	
	0	0	2	+			II	I	
	0	0	2	0				(a)	
	I	0	2	0		II	II		
	0	0	2	0					
	0	0	2	2	I	II	II	I	
	0	0	2	0					
	I	0	2	+	I	II	II	I	
	I	0	2	0				(a)	
			2	2	IVa				
	2?	0	?		IIa IVa	II	I II	5	
	2?	0	?		IVa	II	I II	5	
	2?	0	?		IVa	II	I II	5	
	2?	0	?		IVa	II	I II	5	
	2?	0	?		IVa	II	I II	5	
	2	0	2	2	IIa IVa			5	
	2	0	2	2	IIa IVa				
	I	0	2	2				5	
RDB I	I	0	2	2					
RDB I	I?	0	2	2					
RDB I	I?	0	2	2					
RDB I	0	0?	2	2					
RDB I	I?	0	2	2					
	I?	0	2?	I?					
	I?	0	2?	I?					
	I?	0	2?	I?					
	I?	0	2?	I?					
RDB I	0	0	2	2					
RDB 2	I	?	2	2					
pRDB 3	?	?	2	2					
pRDB 3	I?	?	2	2					
	I?	?	2	2					
pRDB 3	I?	?	2	2					
pRDB I	?	?	2	2					
	?	?	2	2					

Beetle	*Bagous arduus*	a weevil	Curculionidae
Beetle	*Bembidion nigropiceum*	a ground beetle	Carabidae
Beetle	*Bembidion testaceum*	a ground beetle	Carabidae
Beetle	*Bidessus minutissimus*	a water beetle	
Beetle	*Bidessus unistriatus*	a water beetle	Dytiscidae
Beetle	*Ceutorhynchus insularis*	a weevil	Curculionidae
Beetle	*Cicindela germanica*	a tiger beetle	Carabidae
Beetle	*Cicindela hybrida*	a ground beetle	Carabidae
Beetle	*Cicindela maritima*	a dune tiger beetle	Carabidae
Beetle	*Dromius quadrisignatus*	a ground beetle	Carabidae
Beetle	*Dromius sigma*	a ground beetle	Carabidae
Beetle	*Dyschirius angustus*	a ground beetle	Carabidae
Beetle	*Ernoporus caucasicus*	a beetle	Scolytidae
Beetle	*Harpalus cordatus*	a ground beetle	Carabidae
Beetle	*Harpalus dimidiatus*	a ground beetle	Carabidae l
Beetle	*Harpalus froehlichi*	a ground beetle	Carabidae
Beetle	*Harpalus obscurus*	a ground beetle	Carabidae
Beetle	*Harpalus parallelus*	a ground beetle	Carabidae
Beetle	*Harpalus punctatulus*	a ground beetle	Carabidae l
Beetle	*Helophorus laticollis*	a water beetle	Hydrophilidae
Beetle	*Hydrochus nitidicollis*		Hydrophilidae
Beetle	*Hydroporus cantabricus*	a water beetle	Dytiscidae
Beetle	*Hydroporus rufifrons*	a water beetle	Dytiscidae
Beetle	*Laccophilus (obsoletus) ponticus*	a water beetle	Dytiscidae
Beetle	*Lebia cyanocephala*	a ground beetle	Carabidae
Beetle	*Lionychus quadrillum*	a ground beetle	Carabidae
Beetle	*Octhebius poweri*	a water beetle	Hydraenidae
Beetle	*Perileptus areolatus*	a ground beetle	Carabidae
Beetle	*Procas granulicollis*	a weevil	Curculionidae
Beetle	*Psylliodes luridipennis*	a flea beetle	Chrysomelidae
Beetle	*Pterostichus aterrimus*	a ground beetle	Carabidae
Beetle	*Pterostichus kugelanni*	a ground beetle	Carabidae
Beetle	*Tachys micros*	a ground beetle	Carabidae l
Beetle	*Thinobius newberyi*	a rove beetle	Staphylinidae
Butterfly	*Carterocephalus palaemon*	chequered skipper	Hesperiidae
Butterfly	*Lysandra bellargus*	adonis blue	Lycaenidae
Butterfly	*Plebejus argus*	silver-studded blue	Lycaenidae
Cricket/Grasshopper	*Decticus verrucivorus*	wart-biter grasshopper	Tettigoniidae
Cricket/Grasshopper	*Gryllus campestris*	field cricket	Gryllidae
Cricket/Grasshopper	*Stethophyma grossum*	large marsh grasshopper	Acrididae
Crustacean	*Metatrichoniscoides celticus*	an isopod	Trichoniscidae
Crustacean	*Niphargellus glenniei*	a freshwater amphipod	Niphargidae
Fly	*Bombylius discolor*	a beefly	Bombyliidae
Fly	*Bombylius minor*	a beefly	Bombyliidae
Fly	*Dorycera graminum*	a large otitid	Otitidae
Fly	*Lipsothrix nervosa*	a cranefly	Tipulidae
Fly	*Metasyrphus lapponicus*		Syrphidae
Fly	*Myolepta potens*		Syrphidae
Fly	*Rhabdomastix hilaris*	a cranefly	Tipulidae
Fly	*Tipula serrulifera*	a cranefly	
Mayfly	*Heptagenia longicauda*		Heptageniidae
Mollusc	*Thyasira gouldi*	northern hatchet-shell	Thyasiridae
Moth	*Acosmetia caliginosa*	reddish buff	Noctuidae

	2?	3*?	0	2		
	?	?	2	2		
	?	?	2	2		
pRDB 2	0	0	2	1		
RDB 1	i	?	2	2		
RDB 1	2?	1	0	2		
RDB 3	?	?	2	2		
pRDB 2	?	?	2	2		
	?	?	2	1		
pRDB 1	1?	?	2	2		
	?	?	2	2		
RDB 3	?	?	2	2		
RDB 1	?	?	2	2		
pRDB 3	1?	?	2	2		
	?	?	2	2		
pRDB 2	1?	?	2	2		
pRDB 1	1?	?	2	2		
pRDB 3	1?	?	2	2		
	?	?	2	2		
RDB 2	1	?	2	2		
RDB 3	1	?	2	2		
pRDB 2	0	0	2	2		
RDB 2	?	?	2?	1		
RDB 2	1	?	2	2		X?
pRDB 1	1?	?	2	2		
RDB 3	1?	?	2	2		
RDB 3	1	?	2	2		
	?	?	2	2		
RDB 1	2?	3*?	0	2		
pRDB 2	2?	3*	0	2		
RDB 1	?	?	2	2		
pRDB 1	1?	?	2	2		
	?	?	2	2		
RDB 1	2?	3*?	0	1		
	1	0	2	+	5*	
	0	0	2	+	5*	
	0	0	2	0	5*	
RDB 2	0	0	2	2	5	
RDB 1	1	0	2	2	5	
RDB 2	1?	0	2	1		
RDB K	2?	3*?	0	2		
RDB K	2?	3*	0?	1		
	1	0	2?	+		
pRDB 2	1	0	2?	1		
RDB 3	0	0	2	1		
Local	2?	3	?	0		
	?	?	2	2		
RDB 1	1	0	2	2		X?
RDB 3	?	?	2?	1		
RDB 1	?	?	2	2		
pRDB 1	?	?	2	2		
	0	0?	2?	2?	5	
RDB 1	1	0	2	2	5	

Moth	Agrotis cinerea	light feathered rustic	Noctuidae
Moth	Aspitates gilvaria gilvaria	straw belle	Geometridae
Moth	Athetis pallustris	marsh	Noctuidae
Moth	Calophasia lunula	toadflax brocade	Noctuidae
Moth	Catocala promissa	light crimson underwing	Noctuidae
Moth	Catocala sponsa	dark crimson underwing	Noctuidae
Moth	Cosmia diffinis	white-spotted pinion	Noctuidae
Moth	Cucullia asteris	starwort	Noctuidae
Moth	Cucullia lychnitis	striped lychnis	Noctuidae
Moth	Cyclophora pendularia	dingy mocha	Geometridae
Moth	Dicycla oo	heart	Noctuidae
Moth	Dyscia fagaria	grey scalloped bar	Geometridae
Moth	Epione parallelaria	dark bordered beauty	Geometridae
Moth	Hadena albimacula	white spot	Noctuidae
Moth	Heliophobus reticulata	bordered gothic	Noctuidae
Moth	Hemaris tityus	narrow-bordered bee hawk	Sphingidae
Moth	Hydraecia osseola hucherardi	marsh mallow	Noctuidae
Moth	Hydrelia sylvata	waved carpet	Geometridae
Moth	Hypena rostralis	buttoned snout	Noctuidae
Moth	Idaea dilutaria	silky wave	Geometridae
Moth	Idaea serpentata	ochraceous wave	Geometridae
Moth	Jodia croceago	orange upperwing	Noctuidae
Moth	Lygephila craccae	scarce blackneck	Noctuidae
Moth	Minoa murinata	drab looper	Geometridae
Moth	Moma alpium	scarce Merveille du Jour	Noctuidae
Moth	Mythimnia turca	double line	Noctuidae
Moth	Noctua orbona	lunar yellow underwing	Noctuidae
Moth	Oria musculosa	Brighton wainscot	Noctuidae
Moth	Paracolax derivalis	clay fan-foot	Noctuidae
Moth	Paradiarsia sobrina	cousin German	Noctuidae
Moth	Pareulype berberata	barberry carpet	Geometridae
Moth	Pechipogo strigilata	common fan-foot	Noctuidae
Moth	Phyllodesma ilicifolia	small lappet	Lasiocampidae
Moth	Polia bombycina	pale shining brown	Noctuidae
Moth	Polymixis xanthomista	black-banded	Noctuidae
Moth	Rheumaptera hasta	argent and sable	Geometridae
Moth	Schrankia taenialis	white-line snout	Noctuidae
Moth	Scotopteryx bipunctaria	chalk carpet	Geometridae
Moth	Semiothisa carbonaria	netted mountain	Geometridae
Moth	Siona lineata	black-veined	Geometridae
Moth	Thetidia smaragdaria maritima	Essex emerald	Geometridae
Moth	Trichopteryx polycommata	barred toothed stripe	Geometridae
Moth	Trisateles emortualis	olive crescent	Noctuidae
Moth	Tyta luctuosa	four-spotted	Noctuidae
Moth	Xestia alpicola alpina	northern dart	Noctuidae
Moth	Xestia ashworthi	Ashworth's rustic	Noctuidae
Moth	Xestia rhomboidea	square-spotted clay	Noctuidae
Moth	Xylena exsoleta	sword grass	Noctuidae
Moth	Zygaena viciae argyllensis	New Forest burnet moth	Zygaenidae
Spider	Centromerus albidus	a spider	Linyphiidae
Spider	Dipoena melanogaster	a spider	Theridiidae
True Bug	Hydrometra gracilis	the lesser water measurer	Hydrometridae
True Bug	Orthotylus rubidus	a capsid bug	Miridae

	I	0	2?	+		
	I	0	2	I		
RDB 3	0	0	2	I		
RDB 3	0	0	2	I		
RDB 3	0	0	2?	I		
RDB 3	0	0	2?	I		
	I	0	2	+		
	0	0	2	+		
	0	0	2	I		
RDB 3	I	0	2	I		
	0	0	2	I		
	I	0	2	+		
RDB 3	0	0	2?	2		
RDB 3	0	0	2?	I		
	I	0	2	+		
	I	0	2	+		
RDB 3	I	I	2?	2		
	0	0	2	+		
	0	0	2	+		
RDB 3	0	0	2?	2		
	0	0	2?	2?		
RDB 3	I	0	2	I		
RDB 3	0	0	2?	2		
	0	0	2	+		
RDB 3	0	0	2	I		
	I	0	2	+		
	I	0	2	+		
	I	0	2	I		
	0	0	2	I		
	0	0	2	I		
RDB I	I	0	2	I	5	
	0	0	2	+		
RDB 3	?	?	2	2		
	0	0	2	I		
	0	0	2	+		
	0	0	2	+		
	0	0	2	+		
	I	0	2	+		
RDB 3	0	0	2	I		
RDB I	0	0	2	2	5	
RDB I	I	0	2	2	5	X(C)
	0	0	2	+		
RDB 3	0	0	2	I		
RDB 2	0	0	2	+		
	?	?	2	I		
	I	I	2	I		
	0	I	2	+		
	I	0	2	+		
RDB I	I?	0	2	2	5	
RDB 2	I?	I?	2	I		
RDB 2	0	0	2	I		
pRDB 3	I	0	2	I		
pRDB 3	I	I	2	I		

Worm	*Armandia cirrhosa*	lagoon sandworm	Opheliidae
Worm	*Prostoma jenningsi*	a nemertean	Tetrastemmidae
Alga	*Anotrichium barbatum*	a red alga	Ceramiacaea
Fungus	*Armillaria ectypa*	an agaric	Tricholomatacea
Fungus	*Boletopsis leucomelaena*	a bracket fungus	Boletaceae
Fungus	*Boletus regius*	the Royal bolete	Boletaceae
Fungus	*Buglossoporus pulvinus*	oak polypore	Polyparaceae
Fungus	*Squamanita schreieri*	an agaric	Tricholomatacea
Lichen	*Arthothelium dictyosporum*	a lichen	Arthoniaceae
Lichen	*Arthothelium macounii (A. reagens)*	a lichen	Arthoniaceae
Lichen	*Bacidia incompta*	a lichen	Bacidiaceae
Lichen	*Belonia calcicola*	a lichen	Gyalectaceae
Lichen	*Calicium corynellum*	a lichen	Caliciaceae
Lichen	*Caloplaca aractina*	a lichen	Teloschistaceae
Lichen	*Catapyrenium psoromoides*	tree catapyrenium	Verrucaruaceae
Lichen	*Catillaria aphana (Lecidea aphana)*	a lichen	Lecideaceae
Lichen	*Catillaria subviridis*	a lichen	Catillariaceae
Lichen	*Chaenotheca phaeocephala*	a lichen	Coniocybaceae
Lichen	*Cladonia botrytes*	a lichen	Cladoniaceae
Lichen	*Cladonia fragilissima*	a lichen	Cladoniaceae
Lichen	*Cladonia peziziformis*	a lichen	Cladoniaceae
Lichen	*Enterographa sorediata*	a lichen	Opegraphaceae
Lichen	*Graphina pauciloculata*	a lichen	Graphidaceae
Lichen	*Gyalideopsis scotica*	a lichen	Gomphillaceae
Lichen	*Halecania rhypodiza*	a lichen	Catillariaceae
Lichen	*Heterodermia leucomelos*	ciliate strap-lichen	Physciaceae
Lichen	*Hypogymnia intestiniformis*	a lichen	Parmeliaceae
Lichen	*Lecanactis hemisphaerica*	churchyard lecanactis	Opegraphaceae
Lichen	*Lempholemma intricatum*	a lichen	Lichinaceae
Lichen	*Melaspilea interjecta*	a lichen	No family
Lichen	*Opegrapha fumosa*	a lichen	Opegraphaceae
Lichen	*Opegrapha paraxanthoides*	a lichen	Opegraphaceae
Lichen	*Peltigera lepidophora*	ear-lobed dog-lichen	Peltigeraceae
Lichen	*Pertusaria bryontha*	Alpine moss pertusaria	Pertusariaceae
Lichen	*Squamarina lentigera*	scaly breck-lichen	Bacidiaceae
Lichen	*Teloschistes chrysophthalmus*	a lichen	Teloschistaceae
Lichen	*Thelenella modesta*	a lichen	Thelenellaceaa
Lichen	*Zamenhofia rosei*	Francis' blue-green lichen	Trichotheliacea
Liverwort	*Acrobolbus wilsonii*	a liverwort	Acrobolbaceae
Liverwort	*Cephaloziella nicholsonii*	a liverwort	Cephaloziellacea
Liverwort	*Fossombronia crozalsii*	a liverwort	Codoniaceae
Liverwort	*Herbertus borealis*	a liverwort	Herbertaceae
Liverwort	*Marsupella stableri*	a liverwort	Gymnomitriacea
Moss	*Acaulon triquetrum*	triangular pigmy moss	Pottiaceae
Moss	*Andreaea frigida*	a moss	Andreaeaceae
Moss	*Bartramia stricta*	rigid apple moss	Bartramiaceae
Moss	*Brachythecium appleyardiae*	a moss	Brachytheciacea
Moss	*Bryoerythrophyllum caledonicum*	a moss	Pottiaceae
Moss	*Bryum calophyllum*	a moss	Bryaceae
Moss	*Bryum mamillatum*	dune thread moss	Bryaceae
Moss	*Bryum neodamense*	a moss	Bryaceae
Moss	*Bryum turbinatum*	a moss	Bryaceae
Moss	*Bryum uliginosum*	a moss	Bryaceae

	2?	?	2?	2?	5
RDB K	2?	3*?	0?	1?	
	0?	0?	2?	2?	
EN	2?	0	1	2	
VU	2?	0	1	1	
EN	1	0	2	2	
EN	2	?	?	1	
VU	2?	0	0	1	
	2?	3*?	0	2	
VU	2?	3?	0	1	
VU	2?	0?	2?	0	
	2?	3*?	0	2	
CR	0	0	2	2	
CR	0?	0?	2?	2	
CR	2?	0?	0	2	8
	2?	3*?	0	2	
VU	2?	3*?	0	2	
CR	0	0	2?	2	
CR	0	0	2?	1?	
LR	2?	2?	0	0?	
CR	2?	0?	2?	2	
	2?	3*?	0	2	
VU	2?	3*?	0	2	
	2?	3*?	0	2	
VU	2?	3*?	0	2	
EN	0	0	2?	1	8
CR	0	0	2?	2	
	2?	3?	0	1?	8
	2?	3?	0	2	
	2?	3*?	0	2?	
	2?	3*?	0?	1	
	2?	3*?	0?	1?	
CR	0	0	2?	2	8
CR	0	0	2?	2	8
EN	0	0	2	2	8
CR	1	0	2	2	
CR	2?	0	2?	2	
VU	2?	2?	0	1	
	2?	2?	0	+	
	2	3*	0?	1	
CR	1	?	2?	2	
VU	2?	3	0	2	
LR	2?	2?	0	+	
EN	0	0	2?	2	8
VU	2?	0?	0?	2	
EN	0	0	2	2	8
	2	3*	0?	2	
	2?	3*	0?	1	
VU	1	0	2?	2	
CR	2?	0	2?	2	8
EN	1	0	2?	2	
CR	0	0	2?	2	
CR	0?	0	2?	2	

Moss	*Bryum warneum*	a moss	Bryaceae
Moss	*Campylopus setifolius*	a moss	Dicranaceae
Moss	*Cryphaea lamyana*	multi-fruited river moss	Cryphaeaceae
Moss	*Desmatodon cernuus*	a moss	Pottiaceae
Moss	*Didymodon (Barbula) mamillosus*	a moss	Pottiaceae
Moss	*Didymodon (Barbula) tomaculosus*	a moss	Pottiaceae
Moss	*Ditrichum plumbicola*	a moss	Ditrichaceae
Moss	*Ephemerum cohaerens*	a moss	Ephemeraceae
Moss	*Ephemerum stellatum*	a moss	Ephemeraceae
Moss	*Fissidens exiguus*	a moss	Fissidentaceae
Moss	*Leptodontium gemmascens*	thatch moss	Pottiaceae
Moss	*Micromitrium tenerum*	millimetre moss	Ephemeraceae
Moss	*Orthodontium gracile*	a moss	Bryaceae
Moss	*Orthotrichum gymnostomum*	a moss	Orthotrichaceae
Moss	*Orthotrichum obtusifolium*	blunt-leaved bristle-moss	Orthotrichaceae
Moss	*Orthotrichum pallens*	a moss	Orthotrichaceae
Moss	*Orthotrichum sprucei*	a moss	Orthotrichaceae
Moss	*Pictus scoticus*	a moss	Amblystegiaceae
Moss	*Plagiothecium piliferum*	hair silk moss	Plagiotheciaceae
Moss	*Pohlia scotica*	a moss	Bryaceae
Moss	*Rhynchostegium rotundifolium*	round-leaved feather-moss	Brachytheciaceae
Moss	*Seligeria paucifolia*	a moss	Seligeriaceae
Moss	*Sphagnum skyense*	a bog moss	Sphagnaceae
Moss	*Tetrodontium repandum*	a moss	Tetraphidaceae
Moss	*Thamnobryum cataractarum*	a feather-moss	Thamniaceae
Moss	*Tortula freibergii*	a moss	Pottiaceae
Moss	*Trochobryum carniolicum (Seligeria carniolica)*	a moss	Seligeriaceae
Moss	*Weissia rostellata*	a moss	Pottiaceae
Moss	*Weissia squarrosa*	a moss	Pottiaceae
Moss	*Weissia sterilis*	a moss	Pottiaceae
Moss	*Zygodon forsteri*	knothole moss	Orthotrichaceae
Moss	*Zygodon gracilis*	Nowell's limestone moss	Orthotrichaceae
Stonewort	*Chara baltica*	Baltic stonewort	Characeae
Stonewort	*Chara canescens*	bearded stonewort	Characeae
Stonewort	*Chara curta*	lesser bearded stonewort	Characeae
Stonewort	*Lamprothamnium papulosum*	foxtail stonewort	Characeae
Stonewort	*Nitella gracilis*	slender stonewort	Characeae
Stonewort	*Nitella tenuissima*	dwarf stonewort	Characeae
Stonewort	*Nitellopsis obtusa*	starry stonewort	Characeae
Stonewort	*Tolypella intricata*	tassel stonewort	Characeae
Stonewort	*Tolypella nidifica*	bird's nest stonewort	Characeae
Stonewort	*Tolypella prolifera*	great tassel stonewort	Characeae
Vascular Plant	*Alchemilla minima*	an alchemilla	Rosaceae
Vascular Plant	*Alyssum alyssoides*	small alison	Brassicaceae
Vascular Plant	*Arabis glabra*	tower mustard	Brassicaceae
Vascular Plant	*Calamagrostis scotica*	Scottish small-reed	Poaceae
Vascular Plant	*Carex muricata ssp. muricata*	prickly sedge	Cyperaceae
Vascular Plant	*Carex vulpina*	true fox-sedge	Cyperaceae
Vascular Plant	*Centaurea cyanus*	cornflower	Asteraceae
Vascular Plant	*Cerastium nigrescens*	Shetland mouse-ear	Caryophyllaceae
Vascular Plant	*Cochlearia scotica*	Scottish scurvy-grass	Brassicaceae
Vascular Plant	*Crepis foetida*	stinking hawk's-beard	Asteraceae
Vascular Plant	*Dianthus armeria*	Deptford pink	Carophyllaceae

VU	I	0?	2?	2	
	2?	3?	0	+	
VU	2?	0?	0?	2	8
EN	I	0	2	2	
	2?	I?	0?	2	
	2?	3?	0	I	
	2?	3	0	2	
CR	I	0	2?	2	
EN	2	I?	2?	2	
	2?	2?	0	I	
EN	2?	0?	2?	I	
EN	I	0	2?	2	8
EN	I	0	2?	2	
CR	0?	0	2?	2	
CR	0	0	2?	2	8
CR	0	0	2?	2	
	2?	3	0?	+	
	2?	3*	0	2	
EN	0	0	2?	2	8
	2	3*	0	I	
CR	2?	0?	0	2	8
	2?	3	0?	0	
	2?	3*	0?	2	
CR	0	0	2?	2	
VU	2	3*	0?	2	
	2?	I?	0	2	
CR	2	0?	2?	2	
	2?	I?	I?	+	
EN	2?	0?	2?	I	
	2?	3	I?	+	
EN	2?	0	0?	2	8
EN	2?	0?	I?	2	8
EN	2?	0?	2?	2	
CR	0	0	2	2	8
	2?	I?	I?	I	
	2?	I?	0?	+	8
EN	0	0	2?	2	
EN	0?	?	2?	2	
EN	2?	0?	2?	2	
EN	2?	0?	2?	2	
	2?	0?	2?	2	
EN	I?	0?	2?	2	
VU	2	3*?	0	2	
CR	0	0	2	2	8
VU?	0	0	2	I?	
VU	2	3*	0	2	
	0	0	2	2	
VU	0	0	2	I	
EN	0	0	2	2	
VU	2	3*	0	2	
	I	3	2	+?	
EN	0	0	2	2	8
VU	0	0	2	+	

Vascular Plant	*Filago lutescens*	red-tipped cudweed	Asteraceae
Vascular Plant	*Filago pyramidata*	broad-leaved cudweed	Asteraceae
Vascular Plant	*Fumaria purpurea*	purple ramping-fumitory	Fumariaceae
Vascular Plant	*Galeopsis angustifolia*	red hemp-nettle	Lamiaceae
Vascular Plant	*Galium tricornutum*	corn cleavers	Rubiaceae
Vascular Plant	*Gladiolus illyricus*	wild gladiolus	Iridaceae
Vascular Plant	*Hieracium Sect. Alpestria (13 Shetland spp only)*	hawkweeds	Asteraceae
Vascular Plant	*Juncus pygmaeus*	pygmy rush	Juncaceae
Vascular Plant	*Leersia oryzoides*	cut-grass	Poaceae
Vascular Plant	*Limonium (endemic taxa)*	sea lavender	Plumbaginaceae
Vascular Plant	*Linnaea borealis*	twinflower	Caprifoliaceae
Vascular Plant	*Lycopodiella inundata*	marsh clubmoss	Lycopodiaceae
Vascular Plant	*Mentha pulegium*	pennyroyal	Lamiaceae
Vascular Plant	*Potamogeton compressus*	grass-wrack pondweed	Potamogetonacea
Vascular Plant	*Salix lanata*	woolly willow	Salicaceae
Vascular Plant	*Scandix pecten-veneris*	shepherd's needle	Apiaceae
Vascular Plant	*Scirpus triqueter*	triangular club-rush	Cyperaceae
Vascular Plant	*Scleranthus perennis ssp prostratus*	prostrate perennial knawel	Caryophyllaceae
Vascular Plant	*Silene gallica*	small-flowered catchfly	Caryophyllaceae
Vascular Plant	*Sorbus leyana*	a whitebeam	Rosaseae
Vascular Plant	*Thlaspi perfoliatum*	perfoliate pennycress	Brassicaceae
Vascular Plant	*Valerianella rimosa*	broad-fruited corn salad	Valerianaceae
Vascular Plant	*Woodsia ilvensis*	oblong woodsia	Woodsiaceae

VU	1	0	2	1	8
EN	0	0	2	2	8
	2?	3	0	+	
	0	0	2?	1?	
CR	0	0	2	2	
	2?	3*?	0	1	8
VU	2	3*	?	2	8 (3 spp)
EN	0?	?	2	2	
EN	0?	0	2	2	
VU	2	3*	0	2	
	0	0	2	+	
	0	0	2	+	
VU	0	0	2	1	8
	0	0	2	+	
EN	0	?	2	1	
VU?	0	0	2	+	
CR	0	0	2	2	8
EN	2	3*	0	2	8
	0	0	2	+	
EN	2	3*	0	2	
VU	0	0	2	1	8
EN	?	0	2	3?	
EN	0	0	2	1	8

Long list of Globally Threatened/Declining Species

Group	Scientific name	Common name	Family
Mammal	*Arvicola terrestris*	water vole	Muridae
Mammal	*Balaena glacialis (Eubalaena glacialis)*	northern/black right whale	Balaenidae
Mammal	*Balaenoptera acutorostrata*	minke whale	Balaenopteridae
Mammal	*Balaenoptera borealis*	Sei whale	Balaenopteridae
Mammal	*Balaenoptera musculus (Sibbaldus musculus)*	blue whale	Balaenopteridae
Mammal	*Balaenoptera physalus*	fin whale	Balaenopteridae
Mammal	*Barbastella barbastellus*	barbastelle	Vespertilionidae
Mammal	*Capreolus capreolus*	roe deer	Cervidae
Mammal	*Cervus elaphus*	red deer	Cervidae
Mammal	*Crocidura suaveolens*	lesser white-toothed shrew	Soricidae
Mammal	*Dama dama*	fallow deer	Cervidae
Mammal	*Delphinapterus leucas*	white whale	Monodontidae
Mammal	*Delphinus delphis*	common dolphin	Delphinidae
Mammal	*Eptesicus nilssonii*	northern bat	Vespertilionidae
Mammal	*Eptesicus serotinus*	serotine	Vespertilionidae
Mammal	*Erinaceus europaeus*	hedgehog	Erinaceidae
Mammal	*Felis sylvestris*	wildcat	Felidae
Mammal	*Globicephala melas*	long-finned pilot whale	Delphinidae
Mammal	*Grampus griseus*	Risso's dolphin	Delphinidae
Mammal	*Halichoerus grypha*	grey seal	Phocidae
Mammal	*Hyperoodon ampullatus*	northern bottlenosed whale	Ziphiidae
Mammal	*Kogia breviceps (Physeter breviceps)*	pygmy sperm whale	Physeteridae
Mammal	*Lagenorhynchus acutus*	Atlantic white-sided dolphin	Delphinidae
Mammal	*Lagenorhynchus albirostris*	white-beaked dolphin	Delphinidae
Mammal	*Lepus europaeus*	brown hare	Leporidae
Mammal	*Lepus timidus*	mountain hare	Leporidae
Mammal	*Lutra lutra lutra*	European otter	Mustelidae
Mammal	*Martes martes*	pine marten	Mustelidae
Mammal	*Megaptera novaeangliae*	humpback whale	Balaenopteridae
Mammal	*Meles meles*	badger	Mustelidae
Mammal	*Mesoplodon bidens*	Sowerby's beaked whale	Ziphiidae
Mammal	*Mesoplodon europaeus*	Gervais' beaked whale	Ziphiidae
Mammal	*Mesoplodon mirus*	True's beaked whale	Ziphiidae
Mammal	*Monodon monocerus*	narwhal	Monodontidae
Mammal	*Muscardinus avellanarius*	dormouse	Gliridae
Mammal	*Mustela erminea*	stoat	Mustelidae
Mammal	*Mustela nivalis*	weasel	Mustelidae
Mammal	*Mustela putorius*	polecat	Mustelidae
Mammal	*Myotis bechsteinii*	Bechstein's bat	Vespertilionidae
Mammal	*Myotis brantii*	Brandt's bat	Vespertilionidae
Mammal	*Myotis daubentonii*	Daubenton's bat	Vespertilionidae
Mammal	*Myotis myotis*	greater mouse-eared bat	Vespertilionidae
Mammal	*Myotis mystacinus*	whiskered bat	Vespertilionidae
Mammal	*Myotis nattereri*	Natterer's bat	Vespertilionidae
Mammal	*Neomys fodiens*	water shrew	Soricidae
Mammal	*Nyctalus leisleri*	Leisler's bat	Vespertilionidae
Mammal	*Nyctalus noctula*	noctule	Vespertilionidae
Mammal	*Odobenus rosmarus*	walrus	Odobenidae
Mammal	*Orcinus orca*	killer whale	Delphinidae
Mammal	*Phoca vitulina*	common seal	Phocidae
Mammal	*Phocoena phocoena*	harbour porpoise	Phocoenidae

Status	Int. threat	Int. import.	Decline	Local.	EC Annex	Bern App.	Bonn App.	UK Act Sched.	Extinct
	0	0	1	0					
	2	0	0?		IVa	II	I	5(b)	
	2?	0	?	0	IVa			5(b)	
	2?	0	?		IVa			5(b)	
	2	0	?		IVa	II	I	5(b)	
	2?	0	?		IVa			5(b)	
	1	0	0	+	IIa IVa	II	II	5	
	0	0	-2	0					
	0	1	-2	0					
	0	0	1						
	0	0	0	0					
	0	0	?		IVa		II	5(b)	
	0	0	?	0	IVa	II	II	5(b)	
	1	0	?	?	IVa	II	II	5	
	1	0	0	0	IVa	II	II	5	
	0	0	0	0					
	0	0	0	0	IVa	II		5	
	0	0	?	0	IVa	II	II	5(b)	
	0	0	?	0	IVa	II	II	5(b)	
	0	2	-1	0	II			(b)	
	2?	0	?	0	IVa		II	5(b)	
	0	0	?		IVa			5(b)	
	0	0	?		IVa	II	II	5(b)	
	0	0	?	0	IVa	II	II	5(b)	
	0	0	1	0					
	1	0	0	0					
	2?	0	-1	0	IIa IVa	II		5(b)	
	0	0	0	0				5(b)	
	2	0	0		IVa	II	I	5(b)	
	0	0	0	0				(b)	
	0	0	?		IVa	II		5(b)	
	0	0	?		IVa			5(b)	
	0	0	?		IVa	II		5(b)	
	0	0	?		IVa		II	5(b)	
	1	0	1	0	IVa			5	
	0	0	0	0					
	0	0	1	0					
	1	0	0	0					
	2?	0	0	+	IIa IVa	II	II	5	
	1	0	0	0	IVa	II	II	5	
	1	0	0	0	IVa	II	II	5(b)	
	2?	0	2	2	IIa IVa	II		5	X
	1	0	0	0	IVa	II	II	5(b)	
	1	0	0	0	IVa	II	II	5(b)	
	1	0	0	0					
	1	0	0	+	IVa	II	II	5(b)	
	1	0	1	0	IVa	II	II	5	
	1?	0	?			II		5	
	0	0	?	0	IVa	II	II	5(b)	
	0	0	0	0	IIa			(b)	
	2	0	0	1	IIa IVa	II	II	5(b)	

Mammal	*Physeter catodon (P. macrocephalus)*	sperm whale	Physeteridae
Mammal	*Pipistrellus nathusii*	Nathusius' pipistrelle	Vespertilionidae
Mammal	*Pipistrellus pipistrellus*	pipistrelle bat	Vespertilionidae
Mammal	*Plecotus auritus*	brown long-eared bat	Vespertilionidae
Mammal	*Plecotus austriacus*	grey long-eared bat	Vespertilionidae
Mammal	*Pseudorca crassidens*	false killer whale	Delphinidae
Mammal	*Rhinolophus ferrumequinum*	greater horseshoe bat	Rhinolophidae
Mammal	*Rhinolophus hipposideros*	lesser horseshoe bat	Rhinolophidae
Mammal	*Sciurus vulgaris*	red squirrel	Aplodontidae
Mammal	*Sorex araneus*	common shrew	Soricidae
Mammal	*Sorex minutus*	pygmy shrew	Soricidae
Mammal	*Stenella coeruleoalba*	striped dolphin	Delphinidae
Mammal	*Tursiops truncatus*	bottlenose dolphin	Delphinidae
Mammal	*Vespertillio murinus*	parti-coloured bat	Vespertilionidae
Mammal	*Ziphius cavirostris*	Cuvier's beaked whale	Ziphiidae
Bird	*Accipiter gentilis*	goshawk	Accipitridae
Bird	*Accipiter nisus*	sparrowhawk	Accipitridae
Bird	*Acrocephalus paludicola*	aquatic warbler (on migration only)	Sylviidae
Bird	*Acrocephalus palustris*	marsh warbler	Sylviidae
Bird	*Acrocephalus schoenobaenus*	sedge warbler	Sylviidae
Bird	*Acrocephalus scirpaceus*	reed warbler	Sylviidae
Bird	*Alauda arvensis*	skylark	Alaudidae
Bird	*Alca torda*	razorbill	Alcidae
Bird	*Alcedo atthis*	kingfisher	Alcedinidae
Bird	*Anas acuta*	pintail	Anatidae
Bird	*Anas clypeata*	shoveler	Anatidae
Bird	*Anas crecca*	teal	Anatidae
Bird	*Anas penelope*	wigeon	Anatidae
Bird	*Anas platyrhynchos*	mallard	Anatidae
Bird	*Anas querquedula*	garganey	Anatidae
Bird	*Anas strepera*	gadwall	Anatidae
Bird	*Anser albifrons*	white-fronted goose	Anatidae
Bird	*Anser anser*	greylag goose	Anatidae
Bird	*Anser brachyrhynchos*	pink-footed goose	Anatidae
Bird	*Anser fabilis*	bean goose	Anatidae
Bird	*Anthus petrosus*	rock pipit	Motacillidae
Bird	*Anthus pratensis*	meadow pipit	Motacillidae
Bird	*Anthus trivialis*	tree pipit	Motacillidae
Bird	*Aquila chrysaetos*	golden eagle	Acciptridae
Bird	*Arenaria interpres*	turnstone	Scolopacidae
Bird	*Asio flammeus*	short-eared owl	Strigidae
Bird	*Asio otus*	long-eared owl	Strigidae
Bird	*Aythya ferina*	pochard	Anatidae
Bird	*Aythya fuligula*	tufted duck	Anatidae
Bird	*Aythya marila*	scaup	Anatidae
Bird	*Bombycilla garrulus*	waxwing	Bombicyllidae
Bird	*Botaurus stellaris*	bittern	Ardeidae
Bird	*Branta bernicla*	Brent goose	Anatidae
Bird	*Branta leucopsis*	barnacle goose	Anatidae
Bird	*Bucephala clangula*	goldeneye	Anatidae
Bird	*Burhinus oedicnemus*	stone curlew	Burhinidae
Bird	*Buteo buteo*	buzzard	Accipitridae
Bird	*Calcarius lapponicus*	Lapland bunting	Emberizidae

2?	0	?		IVa			5(b)
I	0	0	+	IVa	II	II	5(b)
I	0	I	0	IVa		II	5(b)
I	0	I	0	IVa	II	II	5(b)
I	0	0	+	IVa	II	II	5
0	0	?		IVa	II		5(b)
I	0	I	+	IIa IVa	II	II	5
I	0	0	0	IIa IVa	II	II	5
0	0	I	0				5(b)
0	0	0	0				
0	0	0	0				
0	0	?		IVa	II		5(b)
0	0	?		IIa IVa	II	II	5(b)
				IVa	II	II	5
0	0	?		IVa	II		5(b)
0	0	-2	+		II	II	I
0	0	-1	0		II	II	
2	0	0	I	I			
0	0	2	2		II		I
0	0	0	0		II		
0	0	0	0		II		(a)
I	0	2	0				
0	0	0	0				
I	0	0	0	I	II		I
I	0	0	+			II	I
0	0	0	0			II	(a)
0	0	0	0			II	(a)
0	0	0	0			II	(a)
0	0	0	0			II	
I	0	0	+			II	I
I	0	0	0			II	(a)
0	0	0	I	I		II	
0	0	-2	0			II	I
0	3	-2	0			II	
0	0	0	I			II	
0	0	0	0		II		
0	0	0	0		II		
0	0	0	0		II		(a)
I	0	0	0	I	II	II	I
0	0	0	0		II	II	
I	0	0	0	I	II		(a)
0	0	0	0		II		(a)
0	0	0	0			II	(a)
0	0	0	0			II	
I	0	0	2			II	I
0	0	0	0		II		
I	0	2	2	I	II	II	I
I	2	-1	0			II	
I	3	-1	+	I	II	II	
0	0	-2	I			II	I
I	0	2	+	I	II	II	I
0	0	0	0		II	II	(a)
0	0	0	2		II		I

Bird	*Calidris alba*	sanderling	Scolopacidae
Bird	*Calidris alpina*	dunlin	Scolopacidae
Bird	*Calidris canutus*	knot	Scolopacidae
Bird	*Calidris ferruginea*	curlew sandpiper	Scolopacidae
Bird	*Calidris maritima*	purple sandpiper	Scolopacidae
Bird	*Calidris minuta*	little stint	Scolopacidae
Bird	*Calidris temmincki*	Temminck's stint	Scolopacidae
Bird	*Caprimulgus europaeus*	nightjar	Caprimulgidae
Bird	*Carduelis cannabina*	linnet	Fringillidae
Bird	*Carduelis carduelis*	goldfinch	Fringillidae
Bird	*Carduelis chloris*	greenfinch	Fringillidae
Bird	*Carduelis flammea*	lesser redpoll	Fringillidae
Bird	*Carduelis flavirostris*	twite	Fringillidae
Bird	*Carduelis spinus*	siskin	Fringillidae
Bird	*Carpodacus erythrinus*	scarlet rosefinch	Fringillidae
Bird	*Cepphus grylle*	black guillemot	Alcidae
Bird	*Certhia brachydactyla*	short-toed treecreeper	Certhiidae
Bird	*Certhia familiaris*	treecreeper	Certhiidae
Bird	*Cettia cetti*	Cetti's warbler	Sylviidae
Bird	*Charadrius dubius*	little ringed plover	Charadriidae
Bird	*Charadrius hiaticula*	ringed plover	Charadriidae
Bird	*Charadrius morinellus*	dotterel	Charadriidae
Bird	*Childonias niger*	black tern	Sternidae
Bird	*Cinclus cinclus*	dipper	Cinclidae
Bird	*Circus aeruginosus*	marsh harrier	Accipitridae
Bird	*Circus cyaenus*	hen harrier	Accipitridae
Bird	*Circus pygargus*	Montagu's harrier	Accipitridae
Bird	*Clangula hyemalis*	long-tailed duck	Anatidae
Bird	*Coccothraustes coccothraustes*	hawfinch	Fringillidae
Bird	*Coturnix coturnix*	quail	Phasianidae
Bird	*Crex crex*	corncrake	Rallidae
Bird	*Cygnus columbianus bewickii*	Bewick's swan	Anatidae
Bird	*Cygnus cygnus*	whooper swan	Anatidae
Bird	*Cygnus olor*	mute swan	Anatidae
Bird	*Delichon urbica*	house martin	Hirundinidae
Bird	*Dendrocopos major*	great spotted woodpecker	Picidae
Bird	*Dendrocopos minor*	lesser spotted woodpecker	Picidae
Bird	*Egretta garzetta*	little egret	Ardeidae
Bird	*Emberiza cirlus*	cirl bunting	Emberizidae
Bird	*Emberiza citrinella*	yellowhammer	Emberizidae
Bird	*Emberiza schoeniclus*	reed bunting	Emberizidae
Bird	*Eremophila alpestris*	shore lark	Alaudidae
Bird	*Falco columbarius*	merlin	Falconidae
Bird	*Falco peregrinus*	peregrine	Falconidae
Bird	*Falco subbuteo*	hobby	Falconidae
Bird	*Falco tinnunculus*	kestrel	Falconidae
Bird	*Ficedula hypoleuca*	pied flycatcher	Muscicapidae
Bird	*Fratercula arctica*	puffin	Alcidae
Bird	*Fringilla montifringilla*	brambling	Fringillidae
Bird	*Gallinago gallinago*	snipe	Scolopacidae
Bird	*Gavia arctica*	black-throated diver	Gaviidae
Bird	*Gavia immer*	great northern diver	Gaviidae
Bird	*Gavia stellata*	red-throated diver	Gaviidae

0	0	0	0		II	II		
I	0	0	0		II	II	(a)	
I	0	0	0			II		
0	0	0	0		II	II		
0	0	0	2 (BR)		II	II	I	
0	0	0	0		II	II		
0	0	0	2 (BR)		II	II	I	
I	0	2	0	I	II		(a)	
0	0	2	0		II			
0	0	I	0		II			
0	0	0	0		II			
0	0	0	0		II			
0	0	0	0		II		(a)	
0	0	-I	0		II			
0	0	-I	2		II		I	
I	0	0	0					
0	0	0	2		II		I	
0	0	0	0		II			
0	0	-2	+		II		I	
0	0	0	0		II	II	I	
0	0	0	0		II	II		
0	0	0	+	I	II	II	I	
I	0	0	0 (W)	I	II		I	X
0	0	0	0		II			
0	0	-I	+	I	II	II	I	
I	0	0	0	I	II	II	I	
0	0	I	2	I	II	II	I	
0	0	0				II	I	
0	0	I	0		II			
I	0	0	0			II	I	
2	0	2	+	I	II		I	
I	2	-I	+	I	II	II	I	
0	0	0	2	I	II	II	I	
0	0	0	0			II		
0	0	0	0		II			
0	0	-I	0		II			
0	0	0	0		II			
0	0	0	I	I	II			
0	0	2	I		II		I	
0	0	0	0		II			
0	0	2	0		II			
0	0	0	2		II		I	
0	0	0	0	I	II	II	I	
I	0	-I	0	I	II	II	I	
0	0	-I	0		II	II	I	
I	0	I	0		II	II		
0	0	0	0		II	II	(a)	
I	0	0	0					
0	0	0	2				I	
0	0	0	0			II		
I	0	0	I (W = 0)	I	II	II	I	
0	0	0		I	II	II	I	
I	0	0	0	I	II	II	I	

Bird	Grus grus	crane	Gruidae
Bird	Haliaeetus albicilla	white-tailed eagle	Accipitridae
Bird	Himantopus himantopus	black-winged stilt	Recurvirostridae
Bird	Hirundo rustica	swallow	Hirundinidae
Bird	Hydrobates pelagicus	storm petrel	Hydrobatidae
Bird	Ixobrychus minutus	little bittern	Ardeidae
Bird	Jynx torquilla	wryneck	Picidae
Bird	Lanius collurio	red-backed shrike	Laridae
Bird	Larus argentatus	herring gull	Laridae
Bird	Larus fuscus	lesser black-backed gull	Laridae
Bird	Larus melanocephalus	Mediterranean gull	Laridae
Bird	Larus minutus	little gull	Laridae
Bird	Limosa lapponica	bar-tailed godwit	Scolopacidae
Bird	Limosa limosa	black-tailed godwit	Scolopacidae
Bird	Locustella luscinioides	Savi's warbler	Sylviidae
Bird	Locustella naevia	grasshopper warbler	Sylviidae
Bird	Loxia curvirostra	common crossbill	Fringillidae
Bird	Loxia pytyopsittacus	parrot crossbill	Fringillidae
Bird	Loxia scotica	Scottish crossbill	Fringillidae
Bird	Lullula arborea	woodlark	Alaudidae
Bird	Luscinia megarhynchos	nightingale	Turdidae
Bird	Lymnocryptes minimus	jack snipe	Scolopacidae
Bird	Melanitta fusca	velvet scoter	Anatidae
Bird	Melanitta nigra	common scoter	Anatidae
Bird	Mergus albellus	smew	Anatidae
Bird	Mergus merganser	goosander	Anatidae
Bird	Mergus serrator	red-breasted merganser	Anatidae
Bird	Miliaria calandra	corn bunting	Emberizidae
Bird	Milvus milvus	red kite	Accipitridae
Bird	Morus bassanus	gannet	Sulidae
Bird	Motacilla alba	pied wagtail	Motacillidae
Bird	Motacilla cinerea	grey wagtail	Motacillidae
Bird	Motacilla flava	yellow wagtail	Motacillidae
Bird	Muscicapa striata	spotted flycatcher	Muscicapidae
Bird	Numenius arquata	curlew	Scolopacidae
Bird	Numenius phaeopus	whimbrel	Scolopacidae
Bird	Nyctea scandiaca	snowy owl	Strigidae
Bird	Oceanodroma leucorhoa	Leach's petrel	Hydrobatidae
Bird	Oenanthe oenanthe	wheatear	Turdidae
Bird	Oriolus oriolus	golden oriole	Oriolidae
Bird	Pandion haliaetus	osprey	Pandionidae
Bird	Panurus biarmicus	bearded tit	Paradoxornithid
Bird	Parus ater	coal tit	Paridae
Bird	Parus caeruleus	blue tit	Paridae
Bird	Parus cristatus	crested tit	Paridae
Bird	Parus major	great tit	Paridae
Bird	Parus montanus	willow tit	Paridae
Bird	Parus palustris	marsh tit	Paridae
Bird	Passer montanus	tree sparrow	Passeridae
Bird	Perdix perdix	grey partridge	Phasianidae
Bird	Pernis apivorus	honey buzzard	Accipitridae
Bird	Phalacrocorax aristotelis	shag	Phalacrocoracid
Bird	Phalacrocorax carbo	cormorant	Phalacrocora

I	0	-I	2	I	II	II	
I	0	0	2	I	II	I II	I
0	0	0	2	I	II	II	I
I	0	I	0		II		
I	0	?	+	I	II		(a)
I	0	0	2	I	II		I
I	0	2	2		II		I
I	0	2	2	I	II		I
0	0	I	0				
0	I	0	0				
0	0	0	2	I	II		I
I	0	0	2 (S = 0)		II		I
I	2	0	0			II	
I	0	0	I			II	I
0	0	0	I		II		I
0	0	I	0		II		
0	0	-I	0		II		I
0	0	0	2		II		I
2	3	0	+	I	II		I
I	0	2	+	I			I
0	0	I	0		II		
I	0	0	0			II	
I	0	0	0			II	I
0	0	2	+			II	I
I	0	0	0		II	II	
0	0	-I	0			II	(a)
0	0	0	0			II	
0	0	2	0				(a)
0	0	-2	+	I	II	II	I
I	2	-2	+				
0	0	0	0		II		
0	0	0	0		II		
0	0	0	0		II		(a)
I	0	2	0		II	II	
I	0	0	0			II	
0	0	0	+			II	I
I	0	0	2	I	II		I
I	0	?	I	I	II		I
0	0	0	0		II		
0	0	0	2		II		I
I	0	-I	2	I	II	II	I
0	0	0	+		II		I
0	0	0	0		II		
0	0	0	0		II		
0	0	0	+		II		I
0	0	0	0		II		
0	0	I	0		II		
0	0	I	0		II		
0	0	2	0				
I	0	2	0				
0	0	0	I	I	II	II	I
0	I	0	0				
0	0	0	0	I			

Bird	*Phalaropus lobatus*	red-necked phalarope	Scolopacidae
Bird	*Philomachus pugnax*	ruff	Scolopacidae
Bird	*Phoenicurus ochruros*	black redstart	Turdidae
Bird	*Phoenicurus phoenicurus*	redstart	Turdidae
Bird	*Phylloscopus collybita*	chiffchaff	Sylviidae
Bird	*Phylloscopus sibilatrix*	wood warbler	Sylviidae
Bird	*Phylloscopus trochilus*	willow warbler	Sylviidae
Bird	*Picus viridis*	green woodpecker	Picidae
Bird	*Platalea leucorodia*	spoonbill	Threskiornithidae
Bird	*Plectrophenax nivalis*	snow bunting	Emberizidae
Bird	*Pluvialis apricaria*	golden plover	Charadriidae
Bird	*Pluvialis squatarola*	grey plover	Charadriidae
Bird	*Podiceps auritus*	Slavonian grebe	Podicipedidae
Bird	*Podiceps grisegena*	red-necked grebe	Podicipedidae
Bird	*Podiceps nigricollis*	black-necked grebe	Podicipedidae
Bird	*Porzana porzana*	spotted crake	Rallidae
Bird	*Prunella modularis*	dunnock	Prunellidae
Bird	*Puffinus puffinus*	Manx shearwater	Procellariidae
Bird	*Pyrrhocorax pyrrhocorax*	chough	Corvidae
Bird	*Pyrrhula pyrrhula*	bullfinch	Fringillidae
Bird	*Rallus aquaticus*	water rail	Rallidae
Bird	*Recurvirostra avosetta*	avocet	Recurvirostridae
Bird	*Regulus ignicapillus*	firecrest	Sylviidae
Bird	*Regulus regulus*	goldcrest	Sylviidae
Bird	*Riparia riparia*	sand martin	Hirundinidae
Bird	*Saxicola rubetra*	whinchat	Turdidae
Bird	*Saxicola torquata*	stonechat	Turdidae
Bird	*Scolopax rusticola*	woodcock	Scolopacidae
Bird	*Serinus serinus*	serin	Fringillidae
Bird	*Sitta europaea*	nuthatch	Sittidae
Bird	*Somateria mollissima*	eider	Anatidae
Bird	*Stercorarius parasiticus*	arctic skua	Stercorariidae
Bird	*Stercorarius skua*	great skua	Stercorariidae
Bird	*Sterna albifrons*	little tern	Sternidae
Bird	*Sterna dougallii*	roseate tern	Sternidae
Bird	*Sterna hirundo*	common tern	Sternidae
Bird	*Sterna paradisaea*	arctic tern	Sternidae
Bird	*Sterna sandvicensis*	Sandwich tern	Sternidae
Bird	*Streptopelia turtur*	turtle dove	Columbidae
Bird	*Strix aluco*	tawny owl	Strigidae
Bird	*Sylvia atricapilla*	blackcap	Sylviidae
Bird	*Sylvia borin*	garden warbler	Sylviidae
Bird	*Sylvia carruca*	lesser whitethroat	Sylviidae
Bird	*Sylvia communis*	whitethroat	Sylviidae
Bird	*Sylvia undata*	Dartford warbler	Sylviidae
Bird	*Tadorna tadorna*	shelduck	Anatidae
Bird	*Tetrao tetrix*	black grouse	Tetraonidae
Bird	*Tetrao urogallus*	capercaillie	Tetraonidae
Bird	*Tringa erythropus*	spotted redshank	Scolopacidae
Bird	*Tringa glareola*	wood sandpiper	Scolopacidae
Bird	*Tringa nebularia*	greenshank	Scolopacidae
Bird	*Tringa ochropus*	green sandpiper	Scolopacidae
Bird	*Tringa totanus*	redshank	Scolopacidae

0	0	2	2	I	II	II	I
0	0	0	I	I		II	I
0	0	0	I		II		I
I	0	0	0		II	(a)	
0	0	0	0		II		
0	0	0	0		II		
0	0	0	0		II		
I	0	0	0		II		
I	0	0	0	I		II	I
0	0	0	I		II		I
0	0	0	0	I		II	(a)
0	0	0	0		II		
0	0	-I	I	I	II	II	I
0	0	0	2		II	II	
0	0	0	I		II		I
0	0	I	2	I	II	II	I
0	0	I	0		II		
I	2	0	+		II		
I	0	0	+	I	II		I
0	0	2	0				
0	0	I	0				
I	0	-I	+	I	II	II	I
0	0	-I	+		II		I
0	0	0	0		II		
I	0	0	0		II		
0	0	0	0		II		
I	0	0	0		II		
I	0	I	0			II	
0	0	0	2		II		I
0	0	0	0		II		
0	0	0	0			II	
0	0	-2	0				
0	I	0	+				
I	0	0	0	I	II	II	I
I	0	2	+	I	II	II	I
0	0	0	0	I	II	II	(a)
0	0	0	0	I	II	II	(a)
I	0	0	+	I	II	II	
I	0	2	0				(a)
0	0	0	0		II		
0	0	-I	0		II		
0	0	0	0		II		(a)
0	0	0	0		II		
0	0	0	0		II		
I	0	-2	0	I	II		I
0	0	0	0		II	II	
I	0	I	0				
0	0	2	+	I			
0	0	0	0		II		
I	0	0	2	I	II	II	I
0	0	0	0		II		I
0	0	0	0	I	II	II	I
I	0	0	0		II		

Bird	*Troglodytes troglodytes fidarensis*	wren (Fair Isle race)	Trogloditidae
Bird	*Turdus iliacus*	redwing	Turdidae
Bird	*Turdus philomelos*	song thrush	Turdidae
Bird	*Turdus pilaris*	fieldfare	Turdidae
Bird	*Turdus torquatus*	ring ousel	Turdidae
Bird	*Tyto alba*	barn owl	Tytonidae
Bird	*Vanellus vanellus*	lapwing	Charadriidae
Amphibian	*Bufo bufo*	common toad	Bufonidae
Amphibian	*Bufo calamita*	natterjack toad	Bufonidae
Amphibian	*Rana lessonae*	pool frog	Ranidae
Amphibian	*Rana temporaria*	common frog	Ranidae
Amphibian	*Triturus cristatus*	great crested newt	Salamandridae
Amphibian	*Triturus helveticus*	palmate newt	Salamandridae
Amphibian	*Triturus vulgaris*	smooth newt	Salamandridae
Reptile	*Anguis fragilis*	slow-worm	Abguidae
Reptile	*Caretta caretta*	loggerhead turtle	Cheloniidae
Reptile	*Chelonia mydas*	green turtle	Cheloniidae
Reptile	*Coronella austriaca*	smooth snake	Colubridae
Reptile	*Dermochelys coriacea*	leatherback turtle	Dermochelyidae
Reptile	*Eretmochelys imbricata*	hawksbill turtle	Cheloniidae
Reptile	*Lacerta agilis*	sand lizard	Lacertidae
Reptile	*Lepidochelys kempii*	Kemp's ridley turtle	Cheloniidae
Reptile	*Natrix natrix*	grass snake	Colubridae
Reptile	*Vipera berus*	adder	Viperidae
Fish	*Acipenser sturio*	sturgeon	Acipenseridae
Fish	*Alosa alosa*	allis shad	Clupeidae
Fish	*Alosa fallax*	twaite shad	Clupeidae
Fish	*Cetorhinus maximus*	basking shark	Cetorhinidae
Fish	*Cobitis taenia*	spined loach	Cobitidae
Fish	*Coregonus albula*	vendace	Coregonidae
Fish	*Coregonus autumnalis*	pollan	Coregonidae
Fish	*Coregonus lavaretus*	powan	Coregonidae
Fish	*Coregonus oxyrhynchus*	houting	Coregonidae
Fish	*Cottus gobio*	bullhead	Cottidae
Fish	*Galeorhinus galeus*	tope	Carcharinidae
Fish	*Gobius couchi*	Couch's goby	Gobiidae
Fish	*Gobius gasteveni*	Steven's goby	Gobiidae
Fish	*Lamna nasus*	porbeagle shark	Lamnidae
Fish	*Lampetra fluviatilis*	river lamprey	Petromyzonidae
Fish	*Lampetra planeri*	brook lamprey	Petromyzonidae
Fish	*Lota lota*	burbot	Gadidae
Fish	*Osmerus eperlanus*	smelt	Osmeridae
Fish	*Petromyzon marinus*	sea lamprey	Petromyzonidae
Fish	*Pomatoschistus microps*	common goby	Gobiidae
Fish	*Pomatoschistus minutus*	sand goby	Gobiidae
Fish	*Prionace glauca*	blue shark	Carcharinidae
Fish	*Salmo salar*	atlantic salmon	Salmonidae
Fish	*Salvelinus alpinus*	arctic charr	Salmonidae
Fish	*Thymallus thymallus*	grayling	Thymallidae
Ants	*Formica aquilonia*	Scottish wood ant	Formicidae
Ants	*Formica candica (transkaucasica)*	bog ant	Formicidae
Ants	*Formica exsecta*	narrow-headed ant	Formicidae
Ants	*Formica pratensis (nigricans)*	black-backed meadow ant	Formicidae

	0	3	0	2	I	II		
	0	0	0	+				I
	0	0	2	0				
	0	0	0	+				I
	0	0	I	0				(a)
	I	0	I	0				I
	0	0	I	0			II	
	0	0	0	0				5*
	I	0	I	+	IVa	II		5
			2	2	IVa			
	0	0	0	0				5*
	I	0	I	0	IIa IVa	II		5
	0	0	0	0				5*
	0	0	0	0				5*(b)
	I	0	0	0				5
	2?	0	?		IIa IVa	II	I II	5
	2?	0	?		IVa	II	I II	5
	0	0	0	I	IVa	II		5
	2?	0	?		IVa	II	I II	5
	2?	0	?		IVa	II	I II	5
	I	0	I	+	IVa	II		5
	2?	0	?		IVa	II	I II	5
	I	0	0	0				5
	I	0	0	0				5
	2	0	2	2	IIa IVa			5
	I	0	2	I	IIa			5
	I	0	2	I+	IIa			
	0?	0	?	0				
	I	0	0	I+	IIa			
	I	0	2	2				5
	I	0	0	2				5
	2	0	2	2	IIa IVa			
	I	0	0	0	IIa			
	I?	I?	I?	2				
	0	0	0	I?				
	I?	?	I?	I?				
	I	0	0	0	IIa			
	I	0	0	I+	IIa			
	I	0	2	2				5
	I	0	0	I+				
	I	0	0	I+	IIa			
	I?	0	I?	?				
	0	0	0	0	IIa			
	0	0	0	I+				
	0	0	0	0				
	I?	0	0?	+				
RDB I	2?	I?	0	2?				
RDB I	I	0	I	2				
RDB I	I?	0	2	2				X?

Ants	*Formica rufibarbis*	red barbed ant	Formicidae
Bee	*Andrena floricola*	a mining bee	Andrenidae
Bee	*Andrena gravida*	banded mining bee	Andrenidae
Bee	*Andrena lathyri*	a mining bee	Andrenidae
Bee	*Andrena lepida*	a mining bee	Andrenidae
Bee	*Anthophora retusa*	potter flower bee	Anthophoridae
Bee	*Bombus distinguendus*	great yellow bumble bee	Apidae
Bee	*Bombus humilis*	brown-banded carder bee	Apidae
Bee	*Bombus ruderatus*	large garden bumble bee	Apidae
Bee	*Bombus subterraneus*	short haired bumble bee	Apidae
Bee	*Bombus sylvarum*	shrill carder bee, knapweed carder bee	Apidae
Bee	*Colletes cunicularis*	the vernal colletes	Colletidae
Bee	*Lasioglossum angusticeps*	a mining bee	Halictidae
Bee	*Lasioglossum pauperatum*	a mining bee	Halictidae
Bee	*Lasioglossum sexnotatum*	a mining bee	Halictidae
Bee	*Nomada errans*	a nomad bee	Anthophoridae
Bee	*Nomada sexfasciata*	a cuckoo bee	Anthophoridae
Bee	*Osmia inermis*	a mason bee	Megachilidae
Bee	*Osmia xanthomelana*	a mason bee	Megachilidae
Bee	*Psithyrus rupestris*	hill cuckoo bee	Apidae
Beetle	*Aegialia rufa*	a beetle	Scarabaeidae
Beetle	*Aepus marinus*	a small ground beetle	Carabidae
Beetle	*Agabus brunneus*	a water beetle	Dytiscidae
Beetle	*Agabus striolatus*	a water beetle	Dytiscidae
Beetle	*Amara alpina*	a ground beetle	Carabidae
Beetle	*Amara famelica*	a ground beetle	Carabidae
Beetle	*Amara strenua*	a ground beetle	Carabidae
Beetle	*Ampedus cardinalis*	a click beetle	Elateridae
Beetle	*Ampedus nigerrimus*	a click beetle	Elateridae
Beetle	*Ampedus ruficeps*	a click beetle	Elateridae
Beetle	*Ampedus rufipennis*	a click beetle	Elateridae
Beetle	*Anisodactylus nemorivagus*	a ground beetle	Carabidae
Beetle	*Anisodactylus poeciloides*	a ground beetle	Carabidae
Beetle	*Aphodius niger*	a scarab beetle	Scarabaeidae
Beetle	*Badister anomalus*	a ground beetle	Carabidae
Beetle	*Badister peltatus*	a ground beetle	Carabidae
Beetle	*Bagous arduus*	a weevil	Curculionidae
Beetle	*Bembidion argentoleum*	a ground beetle	Carabidae
Beetle	*Bembidion humerale*	a ground beetle	Carabidae
Beetle	*Bembidion nigropiceum*	a ground beetle	Carabidae
Beetle	*Bembidion testaceum*	a ground beetle	Carabidae
Beetle	*Bidessus minutissimus*	a water beetle	
Beetle	*Bidessus unistriatus*	a water beetle	Dytiscidae
Beetle	*Bledius furcatus*	a rove beetle	Staphylinidae
Beetle	*Carabus intricatus*	blue ground beetle	Carabidae
Beetle	*Cathormiocerus brittanicus*	a weevil	Curculionidae
Beetle	*Ceutorhynchus insularis*	a weevil	Curculionidae
Beetle	*Ceutorhynchus verrucatus*	a weevil	Curculionidae
Beetle	*Chrysolina cerealis*	rainbow leaf beetle	Chrysomelidae
Beetle	*Chrysolina crassicornis*	a leaf beetle	
Beetle	*Cicindela germanica*	a tiger beetle	Carabidae
Beetle	*Cicindela hybrida*	a ground beetle	Carabidae
Beetle	*Cicindela maritima*	a dune tiger beetle	Carabidae

RDB 1	I	0	2	2	
RDB 1	I?	0	2	2	
RDB 1	I?	0	2	2	
RDB 1	0	0?	2	2	
RDB 1	I?	0	2	2	
RDB 1	0	0?	0?	2	
	I?	0	2?	I?	
	I?	0	2?	I?	
	I?	0	2?	I?	
	I?	0	2?	I?	
	I?	0	2?	I?	
RDB 3	I?	0	0?	I?	
RDB 3	I?	0	I	2	
RDB 3	I?	?	I?	2	
pRDB 1	?	?	0	2	
RDB 1	0	0	0	2	
	I?	0	0	2	
RDB 2	0?	0	0	I	
RDB 1	0	0	2	2	
	I	0	I?	+	
RDB 1	?	?	0?	2	
	?	?	I	+	
RDB 2	I	?	2	2	
RDB 2	I	?	I?	2	
RDB 3	?	?	0	2	
pRDB 3	?	?	2	2	
pRDB 3	I?	?	2	2	
RDB 2	?	?	0?	I	
RDB 1	?	?	0	2	
RDB 1	?	?	I?	2	
RDB 2	?	?	0?	I	
	I?	?	2	2	
pRDB 3	I?	?	2	2	
RDB 1	?	?	0	2	
pRDB 1	?	?	2	2	
	?	?	2	2	
	2?	3*?	0	2	
					X?
RDB 1	?	?	0	2	
	?	?	2	2	
	?	?	2	2	
pRDB 2	0	0	2	I	
RDB 1	I	?	2	2	
RDB 1	?	?	0?	2	
RDB 1	2	0	2	2	
RDB 1	2?	3*	0	2	
RDB 1	2?	I	0	2	
pRDB 3	?	?	I?	I	
RDB 1	I	0	0	2	5
pRDB 2	?	?	I?	2	
RDB 3	?	?	2	2	
pRDB 2	?	?	2	2	
	?	?	2	I	

Beetle	*Cryptocephalus coryli*	a leaf beetle	Chrysomelidae
Beetle	*Cryptocephalus exiguus*	a leaf beetle	Chrysomelidae
Beetle	*Curimopsis nigrita*	mire pill beetle	Byrrhidae
Beetle	*Dromius quadrisignatus*	a ground beetle	Carabidae
Beetle	*Dromius sigma*	a ground beetle	Carabidae
Beetle	*Dyschirius angustus*	a ground beetle	Carabidae
Beetle	*Ernoporus caucasicus*	a beetle	Scolytidae
Beetle	*Gastrallus immarginatus*	a beetle	Anobiidae
Beetle	*Graphoderus zonatus*	spangled water beetle	Dytiscidae
Beetle	*Harpalus cordatus*	a ground beetle	Carabidae
Beetle	*Harpalus dimidiatus*	a ground beetle	Carabidae
Beetle	*Harpalus froehlichi*	a ground beetle	Carabidae
Beetle	*Harpalus obscurus*	a ground beetle	Carabidae
Beetle	*Harpalus parallelus*	a ground beetle	Carabidae
Beetle	*Harpalus punctatulus*	a ground beetle	Carabidae
Beetle	*Helophorus laticollis*	a water beetle	Hydrophilidae
Beetle	*Hydrochara caraboides*	lesser silver water beetle	Hydrophilidae
Beetle	*Hydrochus nitidicollis*		Hydrophilidae
Beetle	*Hydrophilus piceus*	great silver water beetle	Hydrophilidae
Beetle	*Hydroporus cantabricus*	a water beetle	
Beetle	*Hydroporus rufifrons*	a water beetle	Dytiscidae
Beetle	*Hypebaeus flavipes*	Moccas beetle	Melyridae
Beetle	*Laccophilus (obsoletus) ponticus*	a water beetle	Dytiscidae
Beetle	*Lebia cyanocephala*	a ground beetle	Carabidae
Beetle	*Limoniscus violaceus*	violet click beetle	Elateridae
Beetle	*Lionychus quadrillum*	a ground beetle	Carabidae
Beetle	*Lucanus cervus*	stag beetle	Lucanidae
Beetle	*Meotica anglica*	a rove beetle	Staphylinidae
Beetle	*Negastrius puchellus*	a click beetle	Elateridae
Beetle	*Obera oculata*	a longhorn beetle	Cerambycidae
Beetle	*Octhebius poweri*	a water beetle	Hydraenidae
Beetle	*Panagaeus crux-major*	a ground beetle	Carabidae
Beetle	*Paracymus aeneus*	a water beetle	Hydrophilidae
Beetle	*Perileptus areolatus*	a ground beetle	Carabidae
Beetle	*Procas granulicollis*	a weevil	Curculionidae
Beetle	*Psylliodes luridipennis*	a flea beetle	Chrysomelidae
Beetle	*Pterostichus aterrimus*	a ground beetle	Carabidae
Beetle	*Pterostichus kugelanni*	a ground beetle	Carabidae
Beetle	*Stenus palposus*	a rove beetle	Staphylinidae
Beetle	*Tachys edmondsi*	a ground beetle	Carabidae
Beetle	*Tachys micros*	a ground beetle	Carabidae
Beetle	*Thinobius newberyi*	a rove beetle	Staphylinidae
Butterfly	*Apatura iris*	purple emperor	Nymphalidae
Butterfly	*Argynnis adippe*	high brown fritillary	Nymphalidae
Butterfly	*Argynnis paphia*	silver-washed fritillary	Nymphalidae
Butterfly	*Aricia artaxerxes*	northern brown argus	Lycaenidae
Butterfly	*Boloria euphrosyne*	pearl-bordered fritillary	Nymphalidae
Butterfly	*Boloria selene*	small pearl-bordered fritillary	Nymphalidae
Butterfly	*Carterocephalus palaemon*	chequered skipper	Hesperiidae
Butterfly	*Coenonympha tullia*	large heath	Satyridae
Butterfly	*Cupido minimus*	small blue	Lycaenidae
Butterfly	*Erebia epiphron*	mountain ringlet	Satyridae
Butterfly	*Eurodryas aurinia*	marsh fritillary	Nymphalidae

RDB 1	?	?	2	2			
RDB 1	?	?	2	2			
RDB 1	?	?	0	2			5
pRDB 1	1?	?	2	2			
	?	?	2	2			
RDB 3	?	?	2	2			
RDB 1	?	?	2	2			
RDB 1	?	?	0	2			
RDB 1	1	0	0	2			5
pRDB 3	1?	?	2	2			
	1?	?	2	2			
pRDB 2	1?	?	2	2			
pRDB 1	1?	?	2	2			
pRDB 3	1?	?	2	2			
	1?	?	2	2			
RDB 2	1	?	2	2			
RDB 1	1	?	1?	2			5
RDB 3	1	?	2	2			
RDB 3	?	?	1	1			
pRDB 2	0	0	2	2			
RDB 2	?	?	2?	1			
RDB 1	?	?	0	2			5
RDB 2	1	?	2	2			X?
pRDB 1	1?	?	2	2			
RDB 1	2?	2?	0	2	IIa		5
RDB 3	1?	?	2	2			
	1	?	0	+	IIa	III	
	?	3*?	0?	+			
pRDB 2	?	?	1?	1			
RDB 1	?	?	2	2			
RDB 3	1	?	2	2			
pRDB 1	1?	?	2	2			
RDB 1	1	?	1?	2			5
	?	?	2	2			
RDB 1	2?	3*?	0	2			
pRDB 2	2?	3*	0	2			
RDB 1	?	?	2	2			
pRDB 1	1?	?	2	2			
pRDB 1	2?	3*?	0?	2			
	1?	?	2	2			
RDB 1	2?	3*?	0	1			
	1	0	1	+			5*
RDB 2	0	0	2	0			5
	0	0	1	0			
	0	2	1	+			5*
	0	0	1	0			5*
	0	0	1	0			
	1	0	2	+			5*
	1	0	0	0			5*(b)
	0	0	1	0			5*(b)
	0	0	1?	+			5*
	1	0	2	+	IIa	II	5*(b)

Butterfly	*Hamearis lucina*	Duke of Burgundy	Nemeobiidae
Butterfly	*Hesperia comma*	silver-spotted skipper	Hesperiidae
Butterfly	*Leptidea sinapis*	wood white	
Butterfly	*Lycaena dispar*	large copper	Lycaenidae
Butterfly	*Lysandra bellargus*	adonis blue	Lycaenidae
Butterfly	*Lysandra coridon*	chalkhill blue	Lycaenidae
Butterfly	*Maculinea arion*	large blue	Lycaenidae
Butterfly	*Melitaea cinxia*	Glanville fritillary	Nymphalidae
Butterfly	*Mellicta athalia*	heath fritillary	Nymphalidae
Butterfly	*Papilio machaon britannicus*	swallowtail	Papilionidae
Butterfly	*Plebejus argus*	silver-studded blue	Lycaenidae
Butterfly	*Strymonidia pruni*	black hairstreak	Lycaenidae
Butterfly	*Thecla betulae*	brown hairstreak	Lycaenidae
Butterfly	*Thymelicus acteon*	Lulworth skipper	Hesperiidae
Caddis fly	*Glossosoma intermedium*	a caddisfly	Glossosomatidae
Caddis fly	*Ithytrichia clavata*	a caddisfly	Hydroptilidae
Coral	*Balanophyllia regia*	a star coral	Dendrophylliidae
Cricket/Grasshopper	*Chorthippus vagans*	heath grasshopper	Acrididae
Cricket/Grasshopper	*Decticus verrucivorus*	wart-biter grasshopper	Tettigoniidae
Cricket/Grasshopper	*Gomphocerripus rufus*	a grasshopper	
Cricket/Grasshopper	*Gryllotalpa gryllotalpa*	mole cricket	Gryllotalpidae
Cricket/Grasshopper	*Gryllus campestris*	field cricket	Gryllidae
Cricket/Grasshopper	*Pseudomogoplistes squamiger*	scaly cricket	Mogoplistidae
Cricket/Grasshopper	*Stethophyma grossum*	large marsh grasshopper	Acrididae
Crustacean	*Allomelita pellucida*	a brackish water crustacean	Melitidae
Crustacean	*Armadillidium pictum*	a land woodlouse	Armadillidiidae
Crustacean	*Austropotamobius pallipes*	freshwater white-clawed crayfish	Astacidae
Crustacean	*Chirocephalus diaphanus*	a freshwater fairy shrimp	Chirocephalidae
Crustacean	*Corophium lacustre*	a brackish water crustacean	Corophidae
Crustacean	*Crangonyx subterraneus*	a freshwater crustacean	Crangonictidae
Crustacean	*Gammarus insensibilis*	lagoon sand shrimp	Gammaridae
Crustacean	*Metatrichoniscoides celticus*	a woodlouse	Trichoniscidae
Crustacean	*Mysis relicta*	a freshwater opossum shrimp	Mysidae
Crustacean	*Niphargellus glenniei*	a freshwater amphipod	Niphargidae
Crustacean	*Niphargus fontanus*	a freshwater crustacean	Niphargidae
Crustacean	*Proasellus cavaticus*	a freshwater woodlouse	Asellidae
Crustacean	*Triops cancriformis*	freshwater tadpole shrimp	Triopsidae
Damsel/Dragonfly	*Aeshna isosceles*	Norfolk hawker	Aeshnidae
Damsel/Dragonfly	*Coenagrion hastulatum*	northern blue damselfly	Coenagriidae
Damsel/Dragonfly	*Coenagrion mercuriale*	southern damselfly	Coenagriidae
Damsel/Dragonfly	*Lestes dryas*	scarce emerald damselfly	Lestidae
Damsel/Dragonfly	*Leucorrhina dubia*	white-faced dragonfly	Libellulidae
Damsel/Dragonfly	*Libellula fulva*	scarce chaser dragonfly	Libellulidae
Damsel/Dragonfly	*Oxygastra curtisii*	orange-spotted emerald dragonfly	Corduliidae
Fly	*Asilus crabroniformis*	a robber fly	Asilidae
Fly	*Atrichops crassipes*	an aquatic snipe fly	Rhagionidae
Fly	*Atylotus plebeius*	a horsefly	Tabanidae
Fly	*Atylotus rusticus*	a horsefly	Tabanidae
Fly	*Blera fallax*	a hoverfly	Syrphidae
Fly	*Bombylius canescens*	a beefly	Bombyliidae
Fly	*Bombylius discolor*	a beefly	Bombyliidae
Fly	*Bombylius minor*	a beefly	Bombyliidae
Fly	*Callicera spinolae*	a hoverfly	Syrphidae

	0	0	I	+		5*	
RDB 3	0	0	2	1		5*	
	0	0	I	+		5*	
	2?	0	0	2	IIa IVa II	5*	X(R)
	0	0	2	+		5*	
	0	0	I	0		5*	
	2	0	2	2	IVa II	5	X(R)
RDB 3	0	0	0	1		5*	
RDB 2	0	0	2	1		5	
RDB 2	I	3*	0	2		5	
	0	0	2	0		5*	
	0	0	I	+		5*	
	0	0	I	0		5*	
	I?	0	-2	1		5*	
RDB 3	?	?	0?	1			
RDB 3	?	?	0?	1			
	0?	0?	0?	+?			
RDB 3	0	0	I?	2			
RDB 2	0	0	2	2		5	
	0?	0	I	+			
RDB I	I?	0	2	2		5	X?
RDB I	I	0	2	2		5	
RDB I	I?	0	0	2			
RDB 2	I?	0	2	1			
	I	2	0	2?			
RDB 3	0	0	0	1			
	2	0	I	0	IIa	5	
	0	0	0	1		5	
	I	0	I?	1			
	0	0	0	1			
RDB 3	0?	0?	0?	+?		5	
	2?	3*?	0	2			
RDB I	0	0	0	2			
	2?	3*	0?	1			
	0	0	0	1			
	0	0	0	1			
RDB I	0	0	I?	2		5	
RDB I	I?	0	0	1		5	
RDB 2	I?	0	0	1			
RDB 3	2?	0	0	+	IIa II		
RDB 2	I?	0	0	+			
	0?	0	I	+			
RDB 3	I?	0	I	+			
RDB I	2?	0	0	2	IIa IVa II		X
	I?	0	2	1			
RDB 3	?	?	0?	1			
RDB I	I?	?	I	2			
RDB I	?	0	I	2			
RDB I	?	?	?	2			
	I	0	0?	+			
	I	0	2?	+			
pRDB 2	I	0	2?	1			
RDB I	2?	0	2?	2			

Fly	Chrysopilus laetus	a snipefly	Rhagionidae
Fly	Chrysops sepulchralis	a horsefly	Tabanidae
Fly	Chrysotoxum octomaculatum	a hoverfly	Syrphidae
Fly	Clorismia rustica	a stiletto fly	Therevidae
Fly	Ctenophora flaveolata	a cranefly	Tipulidae
Fly	Dasyhelea lithotelmatica	a midge	Ceratopogonidae
Fly	Didea alneti	a hoverfly	Syrphidae
Fly	Doros conopseus	a hoverfly	Syrphidae
Fly	Dorycera graminum	a large otitid	Otitidae
Fly	Erioptera bivittata	a cranefly	Tipulidae
Fly	Eristalis cryptarum	a hoverfly	Syrphidae
Fly	Eumerus ornata	a hoverfly	Syrphidae
Fly	Geranomyia bezzia	a cranefly	Tipulidae
Fly	Gonomyia bradleyi	a cranefly	Tipulidae
Fly	Hammerschmitidia ferruginea	a hoverfly	Tipulidae
Fly	Laphria flava	a robber fly	Asilidae
Fly	Lejops vittata	a hoverfly	Syrphidae
Fly	Limonia goritiensis	a cranefly	Tipulidae
Fly	Lipsothrix nervosa	a cranefly	Tipulidae
Fly	Machinus coweni	a robber fly	Asilidae
Fly	Metasyrphus lapponicus	a hoverfly	Syrphidae
Fly	Microdon devius	a hoverfly	Syrphidae
Fly	Molophilus pusillus	a cranefly	Tipulidae
Fly	Myolepta potens	a hoverfly	Syrphidae
Fly	Nephrotoma quadristriata	a cranefly	Tipulidae
Fly	Odontomyia angulata	a soldier fly	Stratiomyidae
Fly	Odontomyia argentata	a soldier fly	Stratiomyidae
Fly	Odontomyia hydroleon	a soldier fly	Stratiomyidae
Fly	Odontomyia ornata	a soldier fly	Stratiomyidae
Fly	Oxycera analis	a soldier fly	Stratiomyidae
Fly	Oxycera leonina	a soldier fly	Stratiomyidae
Fly	Oxycera terminata	a soldier fly	Stratiomyidae
Fly	Oxycere varipes	a soldier fly	Stratiomyidae
Fly	Pamponerus germanicus	a robber fly	Asilidae
Fly	Pandivirilia melaleuca	a stiletto fly	Therevidae
Fly	Parasyrphus nigritarsis	a hoverfly	Syrphidae
Fly	Pherbellia knutsoni	snail-killing fly	Sciomyzidae
Fly	Pocota personata	a hoverfly	Syrphidae
Fly	Poecilobothrus ducalis	a fly	Dolichopodidae
Fly	Rhabdomastix hilaris	a cranefly	Tipulidae
Fly	Spilogona alpica	a muscid fly	Muscidae
Fly	Stratiomys chamaeleon	a soldier fly	Stratiomyidae
Fly	Thyridanthrax fenestratus	a beefly	Bombyliidae
Fly	Tipula serrulifera	a cranefly	Tipulidae
Fly	Trichocera maculipennis	winter gnat	Trichoceridae
Fly	Urophora quadrifasciata	a tephritid fly	Tephritidae
Fly	Xylomyia maculata	a fly	Xylomyiidae
Mayfly	Heptagenia longicauda	a mayfly	Heptageniidae
Millipede	Chordeuma proximum	a millipede	Chordeumatidae
Millipede	Chordeuma sylvestre	a land millipede	Chordeumatidae
Millipede	Melogona scutellare	a millipede	Chordeumatidae
Millipede	Metaiulus pratensis	a millipede	Brachychaeteumi
Millipede	Nanogona polydesmiodes	a millipede	Craspedosomatic

RDB 1	1?	0	0	2	
pRDB 1	1?	0	0	2?	
RDB 2	1	0	1	1	
RDB 3	1	1	1?	1	
pRDB 2	?	?	1?	1	
RDB 2	?	?	0?	1?	
RDB 1	1?	0	0	2	
RDB 2	1?	0	1	1	
RDB 3	0	0	2	1	
RDB 2	?	?	1?	1	
RDB 2	1?	0	0	2	
	1?	0	0	+	
RDB 2	?	?	1?	1	
pRDB 2	?	?	0?	1	
RDB 1	1?	?	-1	2	
RDB 3	?	?	0?	1	
RDB 2	?	?	0	1	
RDB 3	?	?	0?	1	
	2?	3	?	0	
	?	1?	0	2	
	?	?	2	2	
RDB 2	1	0	0	1	
	0	3	?	?	
RDB 1	1	0	2	2	X?
pRDB 2	0	0	0	1	
RDB 1	0	0	0?	2	
RDB 2	?	0	0?	2	
pRDB 1	0	0	0	2	
RDB 2	0?	0	0	1	
RDB 2	1	0	0?	1	
pRDB 1	0	0	0	2	
RDB 2	1	1	0?	1	
pRDB 1	1?	0	0	2	
pRDB 3	0	0	0	1	
RDB 1	1	1	1	2	
RDB 1	?	1	0	1	
pRDB 3	?	?	0?	1	
RDB 2	?	?	1?	+	
RDB 2	?	?	1?	1	
RDB 3	?	?	2?	1	
	?	?	?	1?	
RDB 1	0	0	0	2	
RDB 3	1	0	0	1	
RDB 1	?	?	2	2	
	?	?	1?	+	
	?	?	0?	1?	
RDB 2	0	0	0	2	
pRDB 1	?	?	2	2	
Local	?	2	?	0	
	0	0	0	2	
	?	2	?	+	
	?	2	?	2	
	?	2	?	0	

Millipede	*Polydesmus coriaceus*	a millipede	Polydesmidae
Millipede	*Trachysphaera lobata*	a millipede	Trachysphaerida
Mollusc	*Anisus vorticulus*	a snail	Planorbidae
Mollusc	*Ashfordia granulata*	a gastropod	Helicidae
Mollusc	*Atrina fragilis*	fan mussel	Pinnidae
Mollusc	*Caecum armoricum*	De Folin's lagoon snail	Caecidae
Mollusc	*Catinella arenaria*	sandbowl snail	Succineidae
Mollusc	*Clausillia dubia*	a terrestrial snail	Clausiliidae
Mollusc	*Ena montana*	a terrestrial snail	Enidae
Mollusc	*Gyraulus acronicus*	a snail	Planorbidae
Mollusc	*Helicodonta obvoluta*	a terrestrial snail	Helicidae
Mollusc	*Helix pomatia*	Roman snail: established alien	Helicidae
Mollusc	*Hydrobia neglecta*	a snail	Hydrobiidae
Mollusc	*Hydrobia ventrosa*	a snail	Hydrobiidae
Mollusc	*Lauria sempronii*	a snail	Pupillidae
Mollusc	*Leiostyla anglica*	a snail	Pupillidae
Mollusc	*Limax tenellus*	a slug	Limacidae
Mollusc	*Lymnaea glabra*	a freshwater snail	Lymnaeidae
Mollusc	*Margaritifera margaritifera*	a freshwater pearl mussel	Margaritiferidae
Mollusc	*Modiolus modiolus*	horse mussel	Mytilidae
Mollusc	*Monacha cartusiana*	a snail	Helicidae
Mollusc	*Myxas glutinosa*	glutinous snail	Lymnaeidae
Mollusc	*Nucella lapillus*	dog whelk	Muricidae
Mollusc	*Ostrea edulis*	native oyster	Ostreidae
Mollusc	*Oxyloma sarsi*	a snail	Succineidae
Mollusc	*Paludinella littorina*	a lagoon snail	Assimimeidae
Mollusc	*Pisidium conventus*	a freshwater bivalve	Pisidiidae
Mollusc	*Pisidium pseudosphaerium*	a freshwater bivalve	Sphaeriidae
Mollusc	*Pisidium tenuilineatum*	a freshwater bivalve	Sphaeriidae
Mollusc	*Pseudamnicola confusa*	a brackish water snail	Hydrobiidae
Mollusc	*Pseudanodonta complanata*	a freshwater mussel	Unionidae
Mollusc	*Segmentina nitida*	a freshwater snail	Planorbidae
Mollusc	*Sphaerium solidum*	a freshwater bivalve	Sphaeriidae
Mollusc	*Stelliger bellulus*	sea slug	Stiligeridae
Mollusc	*Succinea oblonga*	a snail	Succineidae
Mollusc	*Tenellia adspersa*	lagoon sea slug	Tergipedidae
Mollusc	*Thyasira gouldi*	northern hatchet-shell	Thyasiridae
Mollusc	*Truncatella subcylindrica*	looping snail	Truncatellidae
Mollusc	*Truncatellina callicratis*	a terrestrial snail	Vertiginidae
Mollusc	*Truncatellina cylindrica*	a snail	Vertiginidae
Mollusc	*Valvata macrostoma*	a freshwater snail	Valvatidae
Mollusc	*Vertigo angustior*	a snail	Vertiginidae
Mollusc	*Vertigo genesii*	a snail	Vertiginidae
Mollusc	*Vertigo geyeri*	a snail	Vertiginidae
Mollusc	*Vertigo lilljeborgi*	a terrestrial snail	Vertiginidae
Mollusc	*Vertigo modesta*	a snail	Vertiginidae
Mollusc	*Vertigo moulinsiana*	a snail	Vertiginidae
Moth	*Acosmetia caliginosa*	reddish buff	Noctuidae
Moth	*Adscita globulariae*	scarce forester	Zygaenidae
Moth	*Adscita statices*	forester	Zygaenidae
Moth	*Agrochola haematidea*	southern chestnut	Noctuidae
Moth	*Agrotera nemoralis*	a small moth	Pyralidae
Moth	*Agrotis cinerea*	light feathered rustic	Noctuidae

	?	2	?	0		
	0	0	0	2		
RDB 2	2?	0	2	I		
	I	2	I	0		
	0?	0?	0/I?	I/+?		
	?	?	0	I/2?		5
RDB I	2	0	0	2		5
	?	?	I?	+		
RDB 3	?	?	0?	I		
RDB 2	I	0	I	I		
RDB 3	?	?	0?	I		
	I	?	0?	+		
	?	?	?	+?		
	?	?	?	+?		
RDB I	?	?	0	I		
	0?	3?	0	0		
	?	?	I?	+		
RDB 2	I	0	I	I		
	2	0	0	2	IIa	5
	0	0	0	0		
RDB 3	0	0	0	I		
RDB I	2	0	0	2		5
	0/I	0/I	0	0		
	I?		I?	0		
RDB 2	I	0	I	I		
	?	?	0?	I		5
	?	?	I?	+		
RDB 3	?	?	0?	I		
RDB 3	2?	0	2	I		
RDB I	I	0	0	2		
	2	0	0	+		
RDB I	I	0	2	2		
RDB I	?	?	0	2		
	?	?	0?	2?		
RDB 3	I	0	0	I		
	?	?	0?	I/2?		5
	0	0?	2?	2?		5
	0	0	0/I?	I?		
RDB 3	?	?	0	I		
RDB 2	I	0	0	I		
RDB 2	I	0	I	I		
RDB I	2	0	0	2	IIa	
RDB I	2	0	0	2	IIa	
RDB I	2	0	0	2	IIa	
RDB 3	?	I?	0?	I		
RDB I	I	0	0	2		
RDB 3	?	?	0	I	IIa	
RDB I	I	0	2	2		5
RDB 3	I	0	0	I		
	0	0	I	+		
	0	0	0	2		
pRDB I	?	?	I?	2		
	I	0	2?	+		

Moth	Anarta cordigera	small dark yellow underwing	Noctuidae
Moth	Anarta melanopa	broad-bordered white underwing	Noctuidae
Moth	Apamea zeta marmorata	the exile	Noctuidae
Moth	Aplasta ononaria	rest harrow	Geometridae
Moth	Apoda limacodes	festoon	Limacodidae
Moth	Archanara algae	rush wainscot	Noctuidae
Moth	Archanara neurica	white-mantled wainscot	Noctuidae
Moth	Aspitates gilvaria gilvaria	straw belle	Geometridae
Moth	Athetis pallustris	marsh	Noctuidae
Moth	Bembecia chrysidiformis	fiery clearwing	Sesiidae
Moth	Brachionycha nubeculosa	Rannoch sprawler	Noctuidae
Moth	Calophasia lunula	toadflax brocade	Noctuidae
Moth	Catocala promissa	light crimson underwing	Noctuidae
Moth	Catocala sponsa	dark crimson underwing	Noctuidae
Moth	Chesias rufata	broom-tip	Geometridae
Moth	Clostera anachoreta	scarce chocolate-tip	Notodontidae
Moth	Coenocalpe lapidata	slender striped rufous	Geometridae
Moth	Coscinia cribraria bivittata	speckled footman	Arctiidae
Moth	Cosmia diffinis	white-spotted pinion	Noctuidae
Moth	Cossus cossus	goat moth	Cossidae
Moth	Cucullia asteris	starwort	Noctuidae
Moth	Cucullia lychnitis	striped lychnis	Noctuidae
Moth	Cyclophora pendularia	dingy mocha	Geometridae
Moth	Deltote bankiana	silver-barred	Noctuidae
Moth	Dicycla oo	heart	Noctuidae
Moth	Dyscia fagaria	grey scalloped bar	Geometridae
Moth	Eilema pygmaeola pallifrons	pigmy footman	Arctiidae
Moth	Eilema pygmaeola pygmaeola	pigmy footman	Arctiidae
Moth	Eilema sericea	northern footman	Arctiidae
Moth	Eilema sororcula	orange footman	Arctiidae
Moth	Endromis versicolora	Kentish glory	Endromidae
Moth	Epione parallelaria	dark bordered beauty	Geometridae
Moth	Epischnia banksiella	a micro moth	Pyralidae
Moth	Eriogaster lanestris	small eggar	Lasiocampidae
Moth	Eriopygodes imbecilla	the Silurian	Noctuidae
Moth	Eugraphe subrosea	rosy marsh	Noctuidae
Moth	Eupithecia egenaria	pauper pug	Geometridae
Moth	Eupithecia extensaria occidua	scarce pug	Geometridae
Moth	Eustroma reticulata	netted carpet	Geometridae
Moth	Gortyna borelii lunata	Fisher's estuarine	Noctuidae
Moth	Hadena albimacula	white spot	Noctuidae
Moth	Hadena caesia mananii	the grey	Noctuidae
Moth	Hadena irregularis	viper's bugloss	Noctuidae
Moth	Heliophobus reticulata	bordered gothic	Noctuidae
Moth	Heliothis maritima warneckeri	shoulder-striped clover	Noctuidae
Moth	Heliothis viriplaca	marbled clover	Noctuidae
Moth	Hemaris fuciformis	broad-bordered bee hawkmoth	Sphingidae
Moth	Hemaris tityus	narrow-bordered bee hawk	Sphingidae
Moth	Herminia tarsicrinalis	shaded fan-foot	Noctuidae
Moth	Heterogenea asella	triangle	Limacodidae
Moth	Hydraecia osseola hucherardi	marsh mallow	Noctuidae
Moth	Hydrelia sylvata	waved carpet	Geometridae
Moth	Hypena obsitalis	Bloxworth snout	Noctuidae

RDB 3	0	0	1	+		
	0	0	1	+		
	0	0	0	1?		
RDB 3	1	0	1	2		
	0	0	1	+		
RDB 3	1	0	1?	1		
RDB 3	1	0	1	2		
	1	0	2	1		
RDB 3	0	0	2	1		
RDB 1	0	0	1?	2		
RDB 3	0	0	1	1		
RDB 3	0	0	2	1		
RDB 3	0	0	2?	1		
RDB 3	0	0	2?	1		
	0	0	1?	+		
RDB 1	0	0	0	1?		
	?	1	1?	2?		
RDB 2	?	?	2	2		
	1	0	2	+		
	0	0	1?	+		
	0	0	2	+		
	0	0	2	1		
RDB 3	1	0	2	1		
RDB 2	0	0	1?	+		
	0	0	2	1		
	1	0	2	+		
RDB 3	0	0	1?	1		
RDB 3	?	?	0?	1		
RDB 3	?	?	1	2		
	0	0	1?	+		
RDB 3	1	0	0	+		
RDB 3	0	0	2?	2		
	1	3	0	+		
RDB 2	1	0	1?	+		
RDB 3	0	0	0	2		
RDB 1	1	1	0	2		
RDB 3	0	0	1?	1		
RDB 3	0	0	1?	1		
RDB 2	1	0	1	1		
RDB 2	1	0	0	2		
RDB 3	0	0	2?	1		
RDB 3	0	0	0	1		
RDB 1	1	0	2	2	5	X
	1	0	2	+		
RDB 3	1	1	1	1		
RDB 3	1	0	1?	+		
	0	0	1?	+		
	1	0	2	+		
RDB 3	0	0	0	1		
RDB 3	0	0	0	1		
RDB 3	1	1	2?	2		
	0	0	2	+		
	0	0	-2	1?		

Moth	Hypena rostralis	buttoned snout	Noctuidae
Moth	Idaea contiguaria	Weaver's wave	Geometridae
Moth	Idaea degeneraria	Portland ribbon wave	Geometridae
Moth	Idaea dilutaria	silky wave	Geometridae
Moth	Idaea ochrata cantiata	bright wave	Geometridae
Moth	Idaea serpentata	ochraceous wave	Geometridae
Moth	Jodia croceago	orange upperwing	Noctuidae
Moth	Leucochlaena oditis	beautiful gothic	Noctuidae
Moth	Lithostege griseata	grey carpet	Geometridae
Moth	Luperina nickerlii gueneei	sandhill rustic	Noctuidae
Moth	Luperina nickerlii leechi	sandhill rustic	Noctuidae
Moth	Lycia zonaria britannica	belted beauty	Geometridae
Moth	Lygephila craccae	scarce blackneck	Noctuidae
Moth	Malacosoma castrensis	ground lackey	Lasiocampidae
Moth	Meganola strigula	small black arches	Nolidae
Moth	Minoa murinata	drab looper	Geometridae
Moth	Moma alpium	scarce Merveille du Jour	Noctuidae
Moth	Mythimnia favicolor	Matthew's wainscot	Noctuidae
Moth	Mythimnia turca	double line	Noctuidae
Moth	Noctua orbona	lunar yellow underwing	Noctuidae
Moth	Orgyia recens	scarce vapourer	Lymantriidae
Moth	Oria musculosa	Brighton wainscot	Noctuidae
Moth	Paracolax derivalis	clay fan-foot	Noctuidae
Moth	Paradiarsia sobrina	cousin German	Noctuidae
Moth	Pareulype berberata	barberry carpet	Geometridae
Moth	Pechipogo strigilata	common fan-foot	Noctuidae
Moth	Pelosia muscerda	dotted footman	Arctiidae
Moth	Pelosia obtusa	small dotted footman	Arctiidae
Moth	Perizoma sagittata	marsh carpet	Geometridae
Moth	Photedes brevilinea	Fenn's wainscot	Noctuidae
Moth	Photedes captiuncula	least minor	Noctuidae
Moth	Photedes extrema	concolorous	Noctuidae
Moth	Phragmataecia castaneae	reed leopard	Cossidae
Moth	Phyllodesma ilicifolia	small lappet	Lasiocampidae
Moth	Pima boisduvaliella	a moth	Pyralidae
Moth	Polia bombycina	pale shining brown	Noctuidae
Moth	Polymixis xanthomista	black-banded	Noctuidae
Moth	Rheumaptera hasta	argent and sable	Geometridae
Moth	Sabra harpagula	scarce hook-tip	Drepanidae
Moth	Schrankia intermedialis	autumnal snout	Noctuidae
Moth	Schrankia taenialis	white-line snout	Noctuidae
Moth	Sciota hostilis	a small moth	Pyralidae
Moth	Scopula nigropunctata	sub-angled wave	Geometridae
Moth	Scopula rubiginata	tawny wave	Geometridae
Moth	Scotopteryx bipunctaria	chalk carpet	Geometridae
Moth	Semiothisa carbonaria	netted mountain	Geometridae
Moth	Siona lineata	black-veined	Geometridae
Moth	Spilosoma urticae	water ermine	Arctiidae
Moth	Synanthedon scoliaeformis	Welsh clearwing	Sesiidae
Moth	Syncopacna vinella	a micro moth	Gelechiidae
Moth	Thalera fimbrialis	Sussex emerald	Geometridae
Moth	Thetidia smaragdaria maritima	Essex emerald	Geometridae
Moth	Trichopteryx polycommata	barred toothed stripe	Geometridae

	0	0	2	+		
	I	I	I?	2?		
RDB 3	0	0	I	2		
RDB 3	0	0	2?	2		
RDB 3	0	0	I?	I		
	0	0	2?	2?		
RDB 3	I	0	2	I		
RDB 3	I	I	I	I		
RDB 3	I	0	I	I		
RDB 2	?	?	I	2		
RDB I	?	?	0?	2		
RDB 3	I	I	I	+		
RDB 3	0	0	2?	2		
RDB 3	0	0	I?	I		
	I	0	I	+		
	0	0	2	+		
RDB 3	0	0	2	I		
	0	I	I?	+		
	I	0	2	+		
	I	0	2	+		
RDB 2	0	0	I	+		
	I	0	2	I		
	0	0	2	I		
	0	0	2	I		
RDB I	I	0	2	I	5	
	0	0	2	+		
RDB 3	I	0	I	+		
RDB I	0	0	0	2		
RDB 2	I	0	0	+		
RDB 3	I	I	I?	I		
RDB 3	I	0	I	I		
RDB 3	I	I	I	I		
RDB 2	0?	0	I	2		
RDB 3	?	?	2	2		
pRDB 3	0	0	I?	I		
	0	0	2	I		
	0	0	2	+		
	0	0	2	+		
RDB 3	0	0	0	I		
	?	?	0	2		
	0	0	2	+		
pRDB I	0	0	0	2		
RDB 2	0	0	I	I		
RDB 3	0	0	I	+		
	I	0	2	+		
RDB 3	0	0	2	I		
RDB I	0	0	2	2	5	
	0	0	I	+		
RDB 3	0	0	I?	I		
pRDB 2	?	0	0	I		
RDB I	0	0	0	2	5	
RDB I	I	0	2	2	5	X(C)
	0	0	2	+		

Moth	*Trisateles emortualis*	olive crescent	Noctuidae
Moth	*Tyta luctuosa*	four-spotted	Noctuidae
Moth	*Xestia alpicola alpina*	northern dart	Noctuidae
Moth	*Xestia ashworthi*	Ashworth's rustic	Noctuidae
Moth	*Xestia rhomboidea*	square-spotted clay	Noctuidae
Moth	*Xylena exsoleta*	sword grass	Noctuidae
Moth	*Zygaena exulans subochracea*	Scotch burnet	Zygaenidae
Moth	*Zygaena loti*	slender burnet	Zygaenidae
Moth	*Zygaena purpuralis caledonensis*	transparent burnet	Zygaenidae
Moth	*Zygaena viciae argyllensis*	New Forest burnet moth	Zygaenidae
Sea Anemone Group	*Aiptasia mutabilis*	trumpet anemone	Aiptasiidae
Sea Anemone Group	*Alcyonium glomeratum*	red sea-finger	Alcyoniidae
Sea Anemone Group	*Amphianthus dohrnii*	sea anemone	Hormathiidae
Sea Anemone Group	*Edwardsia ivelli*	Ivell's sea anemone	Edwardsiidae
Sea Anemone Group	*Eunicella verrucosa*	pink sea-fan	Plexauridae
Sea Anemone Group	*Funiculina quadrangularis*	a sea-pen	Funiculinidae
Sea Anemone Group	*Hoplangia durotrix*	Weymouth carpet coral	Caryophylliidae
Sea Anemone Group	*Leptopsammia pruvoti*	sunset star coral	Dendrophylliidae
Sea Anemone Group	*Nematostella vectensis*	starlet sea anemone	Edwardsiidae
Sea Anemone Group	*Pachycerianthus multiplicatus*	an anemone	Cerianthidae
Sea Anemone Group	*Parazoanthus axinellae*	an anemone	Parazoanthidae
Sea Anemone Group	*Scolanthus callimorphus*	worm anemone	Edwardsiidae
Sea Mat	*Lophopus crystallinus*	a freshwater bryozoan	Lophopodidae
Sea Mat	*Turbicellepora magnicostata*	orange peel bryozoan	Celleporidea
Sea Mat	*Victorella pavida*	trembling sea-mat	Victorellidae
Sea Urchin	*Paracentrotus lividus*	sea urchin	Echinidea
Sea Urchin	*Strongylocentrotus droebachiensis*	northern sea-urchin	Strongylocentrot
Spider Group	*Dendrochernes cyrneus*	a false scorpion	Chernetidae
Spider Group	*Neobisium carpenteri*	a pseudoscorpion	Neobisiidae
Spider Group	*Neobisium maritimum*	a pseudoscorpion	Neobisiidae
Spider	*Agroeca lusatica*	a spider	Liocranidae
Spider	*Alopecosa fabrilis*	a wolf spider	Lycosidae
Spider	*Altella lucida*	a spider	Dictynidae
Spider	*Apostenus fuscus*	a spider	Liocranidae
Spider	*Aulonia albimana*	a spider	Lycosidae
Spider	*Baryphyma gowerense*	a spider	Linyphiidae
Spider	*Callilepis nocturna*	a spider	Gnaphosidae
Spider	*Carorita limnaea*	a spider	Linyphiidae
Spider	*Centromerus albidus*	a spider	Linyphiidae
Spider	*Clubonia rosserae*	a spider	Clubionidae
Spider	*Clubonia subsultans*	a spider	Clubionidae
Spider	*Dipoena coracina*	a spider	Theridiidae
Spider	*Dipoena melanogaster*	a spider	Theridiidae
Spider	*Dipoena torva*	a spider	Theridiidae
Spider	*Dolomedes plantarius*	fen raft spider	Pisauridae
Spider	*Enoplognatha tecta*	a spider	Theridiidae
Spider	*Episinus maculipes*	a spider	Theridiidae
Spider	*Eresus niger*	ladybird spider	Eresidae
Spider	*Ero aphana*	a spider	Mimetidae
Spider	*Euophrys browningi*	a spider	Salticidae
Spider	*Gibbaranea bituberculata*	a spider	Araneidae
Spider	*Hahnia candida*	a spider	Hahniidae
Spider	*Hahnia microphthalma*	a spider	Hahniidae

RDB 3	0	0	2	1		
RDB 2	0	0	2	+		
	?	?	2	1		
	1	1	2	1		
	0	1	2	+		
	1	0	2	+		
RDB 3		3*	0	2		
RDB 3	?	?	0	2		
	?	?	1?	1		
RDB 1	1?	0	2	2	5	
	0?	0?	0?	+?		
	0	0?	0?	+/0?		
	0	?	0/1?	1?		
	2	3?	2	2	5	
	0?	0?	0?	0?	5	
	0?	0?	?	+		
	0	0	0	1		
	0?	0?	?	1?		
RDB 3	2?	?	0?	+	5	
	0?	0?	0	+		
	0?	0	0	+?		
	0	0	0	2		
RDB 3	0	0	1?	1		
	0	0	0	2		
	0?	0?	0?	2?	5	
	0	0	0/1?	+		
	0	0?	0	1/+?		
RDB 3	0	0	0	1		
RDB K	?	2?	0	2?		
	1?	1?	0	1		
RDB 1	1?	0	0	2		
RDB 1	0	0	0	2		
RDB 1	1?	1?	0	2		
RDB 1	0	0	0	2		
RDB 1	0	0	0	2		
	1	2	0	2		
RDB 1	0	0	0	2		
RDB 1	0	0	0	2		
RDB 2	1?	1?	2	1		
RDB 1	1?	1?	0	2		
RDB 2	0	0	0	2		
RDB 1	0	0	0	1		
RDB 2	0	0	2	1		
RDB 2	0	0	0	1		
RDB 1	1	0	-1	2	5	
RDB 1	1	0	0	2		
RDB 3	0	0	0	1		
RDB 1	0	0	0	2	5	
RDB 2	0	0	1?	1		
RDB 3	1?	3*?	0	1		
RDB 1	0	0	0	2		
RDB 2	0	0	0	2		X?
	1?	2*?	0	2		

Spider	*Haplodrassus soerenseni*	a spider	Gnaphosidae
Spider	*Hyptiotes paradoxus*	a spider	Uloboridae
Spider	*Lepthyphantes antroniensis*	a spider	Linyphiidae
Spider	*Lepthyphantes midas*	a spider	Linyphiidae
Spider	*Maro lepidus*	a spider	Linyphiidae
Spider	*Oxyopes heterophthalmus*	a spider	Oxyopidae
Spider	*Pardosa paludicola*	a spider	Lycosidae
Spider	*Pelecopsis elongata*	a spider	Linyphiidae
Spider	*Pellenes tripunctatus*	a jumping spider	Salticidae
Spider	*Pistius truncatus*	a crab spider	Thomisidae
Spider	*Porrhomma rosenhaueri*	a spider	Linyphiidae
Spider	*Robertus insignis*	a spider	Theridiidae
Spider	*Robertus scoticus*	a spider	Theridiidae
Spider	*Tegenaria picta*	a spider	Agelenidae
Spider	*Theridon pinastri*	a spider	Theridiidae
Spider	*Tricca alpigena*	a wolf spider	Lycosidae
Spider	*Tuberta arietina*	a spider	Agelenidae
Spider	*Tuberta macrophthalma*	a spider	Agelenidae
Spider	*Tuberta maerens*	a spider	Agelenidae
Spider	*Uloborus walckenaerius*	a spider	Uloboridae
Spider	*Xysticus luctator*	a crab spider	Thomisidae
Stone Fly	*Isogenus nubecula*	a stonefly	Perlodidae
True Bug	*Aphrodes duffieldi*	a leaf hopper	Cicadellidae
True Bug	*Cicadetta montana*	New Forest cicada	Cicadidae
True Bug	*Hydrometra gracilis*	the lesser water measurer	Hydrometridae
True Bug	*Orthotylus rubidus*	a capsid bug	Miridae
Wasp	*Chrysis pseudobrevitarsis*	a ruby-tailed wasp	Chrysididae
Wasp	*Crossocerus vagabundus*	a digger wasp	Sphecidae
Wasp	*Homonotus sanguinolentus*	a spider wasp	Pompilidae
Wasp	*Miscophus ater*	a digger wasp	Sphecidae
Wasp	*Odynerus simillimus*	a mason wasp	Eumenidae
Wasp	*Pemphredon enslini*	a digger wasp	Sphecidae
Wasp	*Pseudepipona herrichii*	a mason wasp	Eumenidae
Worm	*Alkmaria romijni*	tentacled lagoon-worm	Ampharetidae
Worm	*Armandia cirrhosa*	lagoon sandworm	Opheliidae
Worm	*Hirudo medicinalis*	medicinal leech	Hirudinidae
Worm	*Ophelia bicornis*	an estuarine polychaete	Opheliidae
Worm	*Prostoma jenningsi*	a nemertean	Tetrastemmidae
Worm	*Sabellaria alveolata*	a honeycomb worm	Sabellariidae
Alga	*Anotrichium barbatum*	a red alga	Ceramiacaea
Alga	*Ascophyllum nodosum v. mackii*	a brown alga	Fucaceae
Alga	*Chondria coerulescens*	a red alga	Rhodomelaceae
Alga	*Cruoria cruoriaeformis*	a red alga	Crurociaceae
Alga	*Cryptonemia lomation*	a red alga	Cryptonemiacea
Alga	*Cryptonemia seminervis*	a red alga	Cryptonemiacea
Alga	*Dasya punicea*	a red alga	Dasyaceae
Alga	*Drachiella minuta*	a red alga	Delesseriaceae
Alga	*Gelidiella calicola*	a red alga	Gelidiellaceae
Alga	*Gelidium sesquipedale*	a red alga	Gelidiaceae
Alga	*Gracilaria multipartita*	a red alga	Graciliariaceae
Alga	*Halymenia latifolia*	a red alga	Cryptonemiacea
Alga	*Lithothamnion corallioides*	a red alga	Corallinales
Alga	*Lophosiphonia reptabunda*	a red alga	Rhodomelaceae

RDB 2	0	0	1?	1	
RDB 3	1	0	0?	1	
RDB 1	0	0	0	2	
RDB 2	1?	2?	0?	2	
RDB 3	0?	0?	0	1	
RDB 2	0	0	0	1	
RDB 3	0	0	0	1	
RDB 2	0	0	0?	1	
RDB 1	0	0	0?	2	
RDB 1	0	0	0	2	
RDB 2	0	0	0	2	
RDB 1	1?	1?	0	2	
RDB 1	1?	0	0?	2	
	0	0	0	2	
	0	0	0	2	
RDB 3	0	0	0	1	
RDB 2	0	0	0	1	
RDB 3	1	0	0?	1	
RDB 3	1?	0?	0	1	
RDB 3	0	0	0?	1	
RDB 2	0	0	0?	1	
pRDB 2	?	?	0	1	
	1	3	1?	2?	
pRDB 1	0	0	1	2	5
pRDB 3	1	0	2	1	
pRDB 3	1	1	2	1	
RDB 2	?	?	?	2	
RDB 1	?	?	0	2	
RDB 1	?	?	0?	2	
RDB 2	0	0	0	2	
RDB 1	1?	0?	-2	2	
RDB 3	0?	0?	0	1?	
RDB 1	1	0	0	2	
	0?	0?	0?	1?	5
	2?	?	2?	2?	5
RDB 3	2?	?	0	1	5
	0?	0?	0?	2?	
	2?	3*?	0?	1?	
	0/1?	0?	0?	+?	
	0?	0?	2?	2?	
	?	?3	0	+?	
	?	?	0?	?	
	?	?	0?	+?	
	?	?	0?	2?	
	?	0?	0?	2?	
	0?	0?	0?	1?	
	?	?	?	2?	
	0?	?	?	+	
	0?	0?	?	1?	
	0?	0?	?	1?	
	1?	?	?	1?	
	?	?	?	1?	
	0?	0?	?	2?	

Alga	*Phymatolithon calcareum*	a red alga	Corallinales
Alga	*Polysiphonia ceramiaeformis*	a red alga	Rhodomelaceae
Alga	*Polysiphonia foetidissima*	a red alga	Rhodomelaceae
Alga	*Schmitzia hiscockiana*	a red alga	Calosiphonaceae
Fungus	*Amanita friabilis*	an agaric	Amanitoceae
Fungus	*Armillaria ectypa*	an agaric	Tricholomatacea
Fungus	*Battarraea phalloides*	a phalloid	Talostomataceae
Fungus	*Boletopsis leucomelaena*	a bracket fungus	Boletaceae
Fungus	*Boletus purpureus*	a bolete	Boletaceae
Fungus	*Boletus regius*	the Royal bolete	Boletaceae
Fungus	*Boletus satanas*	Devil's bolete	Boletaceae
Fungus	*Buglossoporus pulvinus*	oak polypore	Polyporaceae
Fungus	*Clavaria zollingeri*	a fairy club	Clavariaceae
Fungus	*Cortinarius praestans*	an agaric	Cortinaniaceae
Fungus	*Geoglossum arenarium*	an earth tongue	Geoglossaceae
Fungus	*Gomphus clavatus*	a club fungus	Gamphaceae
Fungus	*Haploporus odorus*	a bracket fungus	Coriolaceae
Fungus	*Hericeum erinaceum*	hedgehog fungus	Hydnaceae
Fungus	*Hydnellum aurantiacum*	a tooth fungus	Thelepharaceae
Fungus	*Hygrocybe spadicea*	a wax cap	Hygrophoraceae
Fungus	*Hypocreopsis lichenoides*	an ascomycete	Hypocreaceae
Fungus	*Microglossum olivaceum*	an earth tongue	Geoglossaceae
Fungus	*Poronia punctata*	nail fungus	Xylariaceae
Fungus	*Ramariopsis pulchella*	a fairy club	Clavariaceae
Fungus	*Squamanita schreieri*	an agaric	Trichlomataceae
Fungus	*Tricholoma colossus*	an agaric	Trichlomataceae
Fungus	*Tulostoma niveum*	a stalked puffball	Tulustomataceae
Lichen	*Acrocordia cavata*	a lichen	Pyrenulaceae
Lichen	*Alectoria ochroleuca*	alpine sulphur-tresses	Alectoriaceae
Lichen	*Arthothelium dictyosporum*	a lichen	Arthoniaceae
Lichen	*Arthothelium macounii (A. reagens)*	a lichen	Arthoniaceae
Lichen	*Bacidia incompta*	a lichen	Bacidiaceae
Lichen	*Bactrospora dryina*	a lichen	Opegraphaceae
Lichen	*Bellemerea alpina*	a lichen	Porpidiaceae
Lichen	*Belonia calcicola*	a lichen	Gyalectaceae
Lichen	*Bryoria furcellata*	forked hair-lichen	Alectoriaceae
Lichen	*Bryoria smithii*	a lichen	Alectoriaceae
Lichen	*Buellia asterella*	starry Breck-lichen	Physciaceae
Lichen	*Calicium adspersum*	a lichen	Caliciaceae
Lichen	*Calicium corynellum*	a lichen	Caliciaceae
Lichen	*Caloplaca aractina*	a lichen	Teloschistaceae
Lichen	*Caloplaca luteoalba*	orange-fruited elm-lichen	Teloschistaceae
Lichen	*Caloplaca nivalis*	snow caloplaca	Teloschistaceae
Lichen	*Catapyrenium psoromoides*	tree catapyrenium	Verrucaruaceae
Lichen	*Catillaria aphana (Lecidea aphana)*	a lichen	Lecideaceae
Lichen	*Catillaria laureri*	Laurer's catillaria	Catillariaceae
Lichen	*Catillaria subviridis*	a lichen	Catillariaceae
Lichen	*Catolechia wahlenbergii*	goblin lights	Rhizocarpaceae
Lichen	*Chaenotheca phaeocephala*	a lichen	Coniocybaceae
Lichen	*Cladonia botrytes*	a lichen	Cladoniaceae
Lichen	*Cladonia convoluta*	convoluted cladonia	Cladoniaceae
Lichen	*Cladonia fragilissima*	a lichen	Cladoniaceae
Lichen	*Cladonia mediterranea*	a lichen	Cladoniaceae

	1?	?	0?	0?	
	0?	0?	0?	2?	
	?	?	?	2?	
	?	?	0	+	
EN	1	1	0	2	
EN	2?	0	1	2	
EN	2?	2	1	2	
VU	2?	0	1	1	
CR	?	?	?	1	
EN	1	0	2	2	
VU	2	1	1	1	
EN	2	?	?	1	
VU	1	0	1	1	
CR	1	1	0	2	
CR	?	?	?	2	
CR	?	?	?	2	
EN	1	0	1	2	
EN	1	?	?	2	
CR	?	?	?	2	
VU	1	1	1	1	
CR	?	?	?	2	
VU	1	0	1	1	
EN	2	0	0	2	
VU	1	0	1	1	
VU	2?	0	0	1	
EN	1	1	1	2	
CR	2	1	-1	2	
CR	0	0	0?	2	
VU	0	0	1?	2	
	2?	3*?	0	2	
VU	2?	3?	0	1	
VU	2?	0?	2?	0	
CR	0?	0	0	2	
CR	0?	0	0	2	
	2?	3*?	0	2	
VU	1	0	0	2	8
CR	1	0	1?	2	8
CR	1?	0	2?	2	8
CR	0	0	0?	2	
CR	0	0	2	2	
CR	0?	0?	2?	2	
VU	1	1?	2	1?	8
CR	0	0	0	2	8
CR	2?	0?	0	2	8
	2?	3*?	0	2	
VU	1?	0	0	2	8
VU	2?	3*?	0	2	
VU	0	0	0	2	
CR	0	0	2?	2	
CR	0	0	2?	1?	
VU	0	0	0?	2	
LR	2?	2?	0	0?	
CR	0	0	1?	2	

Lichen	Cladonia mitis	a lichen	Cladoniaceae
Lichen	Cladonia peziziformis	a lichen	Cladoniaceae
Lichen	Cladonia stricta	upright mountain-cladonia	Cladoniaceae
Lichen	Collema dichotomum	river jelly lichen	Collemataceae
Lichen	Enterographa elaborata	a lichen	Opegraphaceae
Lichen	Enterographa sorediata	a lichen	Opegraphaceae
Lichen	Fulgensia fulgens	scrambled-egg lichen	Teloschistaceae
Lichen	Graphina pauciloculata	a lichen	Graphidaceae
Lichen	Gyalecta ulmi	Elm's gyalecta	Gyalectaceae
Lichen	Gyalidea roseola	a lichen	Asterothyriaceae
Lichen	Gyalideopsis scotica	a lichen	Gomphillaceae
Lichen	Halecania rhypodiza	a lichen	Catillariaceae
Lichen	Heterodermia isidiophora	a lichen	Physciaceae
Lichen	Heterodermia leucomelos	ciliate strap-lichen	Physciaceae
Lichen	Heterodermia propagulifera	coralloid rosette-lichen	Physciaceae
Lichen	Hypogymnia intestiniformis	a lichen	Parmeliaceae
Lichen	Lecanactis hemisphaerica	churchyard lecanactis	Opegraphaceae
Lichen	Lecanora achariana	tarn lecanora	Lecanoraceae
Lichen	Lecidea inops	copper lecidea	Lecideaceae
Lichen	Lempholemma intricatum	a lichen	Lichinaceae
Lichen	Leptogium burgessii	a lichen	Collemataceae
Lichen	Leptogium cochleatum	a lichen	Collemataceae
Lichen	Leptogium hibernicum	a lichen	Collemataceae
Lichen	Lobaria amplissima	a lichen	Lobariaceae
Lichen	Lobaria virens	a lichen	Lobariaceae
Lichen	Melaspilea interjecta	a lichen	Physciaceae
Lichen	Nephroma arcticum	Arctic kidney-lichen	Nephromataceae
Lichen	Opegrapha fumosa	a lichen	Opegraphaceae
Lichen	Opegrapha paraxanthoides	a lichen	Opegraphaceae
Lichen	Pannaria ignobilis	Caledonian pannaria	Pannariaceae
Lichen	Pannaria sampaiana	a lichen	Pannariaceae
Lichen	Parmelia minarum	New Forest parmelia	Parmeliaceae
Lichen	Parmelia quercina	a lichen	Parmeliaceae
Lichen	Parmelia robusta	a lichen	Parmeliaceae
Lichen	Parmelia subargentifera	pale-edged shield lichen	Parmeliaceae
Lichen	Parmelia taylorensis	a lichen	Parmeliaceae
Lichen	Parmentaria chilensis	oil-stain parmentaria	Trypetheliaceae
Lichen	Peltigera lepidophora	ear-lobed dog-lichen	Peltigeraceae
Lichen	Pertusaria bryontha	Alpine moss pertusaria	Pertusariaceae
Lichen	Physcia clementei	a lichen	Physciaceae
Lichen	Physcia tribacioides	southern grey physcia	Physciaceae
Lichen	Porina guarantica (P. heterospora)	a lichen	Trichotheliacea
Lichen	Pseudocyphellaria aurata	a lichen	Lobariaceae
Lichen	Pseudocyphellaria crocata	a lichen	Lobariaceae
Lichen	Pseudocyphellaria intricata	a lichen	Lobariaceae
Lichen	Pseudocyphellaria lacerata	ragged pseudocyphellaria	Lobariaceae
Lichen	Pseudocyphellaria norvegica	a lichen	Lobariaceae
Lichen	Psora globifera	a lichen	Psoraceae
Lichen	Psora rubiformis	rusty alpine psora	Psoraceae
Lichen	Pyrenula dermatodes	a lichen	Pyrenulaceae
Lichen	Ramalina portuensis	a lichen	Ramalinaceae
Lichen	Schismatomma graphidioides	a lichen	Opegraphaceae
Lichen	Solenopsora liparina	serpentine solenopsora	Bacidiaceae

	0	0	0	1?	
CR	2?	0?	2?	2	
VU	0	0	0	2	8
VU	2	2?	1?	2	8
CR	0	0	0	2	
	2?	3*?	0	2	
	0	0	1?	1?	
VU	2?	3*?	0	2	
EN	1?	0?	2?	1	8
CR	1?	0	0?	2	
	2?	3*?	0	2	
VU	2?	3*?	0	2	
CR	0	0	0?	2	
EN	0	0	2?	1	8
EN	1	0	0?	2	8
CR	0	0	2?	2	
	2?	3?	0	1?	8
CR	?	0?	0	1	8
EN	1	1?	0	2	8
	2?	3?	0	2	
	1	1?	0	+	
	1	0?	0?	1?	
	1	1?	0?	1?	
	1	1?	1?	0?	
	1	1?	0?	0	
	2?	3*?	0	2?	
EN	1	0	0?	2	8
	2?	3*?	0?	1	
	2?	3*?	0?	1?	
VU	0	0	1?	1	8
	1	1?	0?	+	
VU	0	0	0	2	8
VU	0	0	1?	2?	
CR	0	0	0	2	
	0	0	0	2	
LR	1	2?	0	0	
VU	1?	0	0	2	8
CR	0	0	2?	2	8
CR	0	0	2?	2	8
	1	0	1?	1?	
EN	1	0	1?	1?	8
CR	0	0	0	2	
CR	1	0	2	2	
	1	0	0?	+	
	1	0	0	+	
VU	1	1?	0?	2	8
	1	1?	0	+	
CR	0	0	0	2	
VU	0	0	0	2	8
CR	1?	0	0	2	
	1	0?	0?	1?	
VU	2	1?	0?	1	
VU	0?	0	0?	2	8

Lichen	Squamarina lentigera	scaly breck-lichen	Bacidiaceae
Lichen	Teloschistes chrysophthalmus	a lichen	Teloschistaceae
Lichen	Teloschistes flavicans	golden hair-lichen	Teloschistaceae
Lichen	Thelenella modesta	a lichen	Thelenellaceaa
Lichen	Zamenhofia rosei	Francis' blue-green lichen	Trichotheliacea
Liverwort	Acrobolbus wilsonii	a liverwort	Acrobolbaceae
Liverwort	Adelanthus lindenbergianus	Lindenberg's leafy liverwort	Adelanthaceae
Liverwort	Anastrophyllum joergensenii	a liverwort	Lophoziaceae
Liverwort	Cephaloziella nicholsonii	a liverwort	Cephaloziellaceae
Liverwort	Fossombronia crozalsii	a liverwort	Codoniaceae
Liverwort	Fossombronia fimbriata	a liverwort	Codoniaceae
Liverwort	Geocalyx graveolens	turpswort	Geocalycaceae
Liverwort	Gymnomitrion apiculatum	pointed frostwort	Gymnomitriaceae
Liverwort	Gymnomitrion crenulatum	a liverwort	Gymnomitriaceae
Liverwort	Haplomitrium hookeri	Hooker's liverwort	Haplomitriaceae
Liverwort	Herbertus borealis	a liverwort	Herbertaceae
Liverwort	Herbertus stramineus	a liverwort	Herbertaceae
Liverwort	Jamesoniella undulifolia	marsh earwort	Jungermanniaceae
Liverwort	Lejeunea lamacerina	a liverwort	Lejeuneaceae
Liverwort	Lejeunea mandonii	a liverwort	Lejeuneaceae
Liverwort	Lepidozia pearsonii	a liverwort	Lepidoziaceae
Liverwort	Lophozia (Lieocolea) rutheana	Norfolk flapwort	Lophoziaceae
Liverwort	Marsupella profunda	western rustwort	Gymnomitriaceae
Liverwort	Marsupella stableri	a liverwort	Gymnomitriaceae
Liverwort	Pallavicinia lyellii	veilwort	Pallaviciniaceae
Liverwort	Petalophyllum ralfsii	petalwort	Codoniaceae
Liverwort	Plagiochila atlantica	a liverwort	Plagiochilaceae
Liverwort	Plagiochila britannica	a liverwort	Plagiochilaceae
Liverwort	Plagiochila carringtonii	a liverwort	Plagiochilaceae
Liverwort	Plagiochila killarniensis	a liverwort	Plagiochilaceae
Liverwort	Plagiochila punctata	a liverwort	Plagiochilaceae
Liverwort	Plagiochila spinulosa	a liverwort	Plagiochilaceae
Liverwort	Radula voluta	a liverwort	Radulaceae
Liverwort	Riccia bifurca	lizard crystalwort	Ricciaceae
Liverwort	Riccia huebeneriana	violet crystalwort	Ricciaceae
Liverwort	Scapania nimbosa	a liverwort	Scapaniaceae
Liverwort	Southbya nigrella	blackwort	Arnelliaceae
Moss	Acaulon triquetrum	triangular pigmy moss	Pottiaceae
Moss	Andreaea frigida	a moss	Andreaeaceae
Moss	Anoectangium warburgii	a moss	Pottiaceae
Moss	Anomodon longifolius	long-leaved anomodon	Thuidaceae
Moss	Bartramia stricta	rigid apple moss	Bartramiaceae
Moss	Brachydontium trichodes	a moss	Seligeriaceae
Moss	Brachythecium appleyardiae	a moss	Brachytheciaceae
Moss	Bryoerythrophyllum caledonicum	a moss	Pottiaceae
Moss	Bryum calophyllum	a moss	Bryaceae
Moss	Bryum dixonii	a moss	Bryaceae
Moss	Bryum mamillatum	dune thread moss	Bryaceae
Moss	Bryum neodamense	a moss	Bryaceae
Moss	Bryum riparium	a moss	Bryaceae
Moss	Bryum schleicheri	Schleicher's feather-moss	Bryaceae
Moss	Bryum turbinatum	a moss	Bryaceae
Moss	Bryum uliginosum	a moss	Bryaceae

EN	0	0	2	2			8
CR	I	0	2	2			
VU	I	0	I?	+			8
CR	2?	0	2?	2			
VU	2?	2?	0	I			
	2?	2?	0	+			
VU	I	0	0	2			8
	I	2?	0	I			
	2	3*	0?	I			
CR	I	?	2?	2			
	I	3	0	I			
VU	0	0	0	I			8
	0	0	0	2			8
	0	2?	0	0			
	I	I?	0?	+			
VU	2?	3	0	2			
	0	I?	0	0			
EN	2	0?	2	2			8
	0	I?	0	0			
EN	2	I?	0?	2			
	0	3?	0	0			
CR	0	0	2?	2			8
CR	2	I?	2	2	IIb	I	8
	2?	2?	0	+			
VU	I	0	I?	I			
VU	I	I?	I?	+	IIb	I	8
	I	3	0	+			
	0	3	0	+			
	I	3?	0	+			
	0	I?	0	0			
	0	I?	0	0			
	0	2?	0	0			
	I	I?	0	+			
VU	0	0	0?	2			8
VU	I	0?	I?	I			
	I	2?	0	+			
EN	0	0	I?	2			8
EN	0	0	2?	2			8
VU	2?	0?	0?	2			
	I	3	0?	I			
EN	0	0	I?	2			
EN	0	0	2	2			8
	I	0?	I?	+			
	2	3*	0?	2			
	2?	3*	0?	I			
VU	I	0	2?	2			
	I	3*	0	+			
CR	2?	0	2?	2			8
EN	I	0	2?	2			
	I	3?	0?	+			
CR	0	0	I?	2			8
CR	0	0	2?	2			
CR	0?	0	2?	2			

Moss	*Bryum warneum*	a moss	Bryaceae
Moss	*Buxbaumia viridis*	green shield moss	Archidiaceae
Moss	*Campylopus setifolius*	a moss	Dicranaceae
Moss	*Campylopus shawii*	bog gold moss	Dicranaceae
Moss	*Campylostelium saxicola*	a moss	Funariaceae
Moss	*Cryphaea lamyana*	multi-fruited river moss	Cryphaeaceae
Moss	*Cyclodictyon laetevirens*	bright green cave moss	Hookeriaceae
Moss	*Daltonia splachnoides*	a moss	Daltoniaceae
Moss	*Desmatodon cernuus*	a moss	Pottiaceae
Moss	*Dicranodontium subporodictyon*	a moss	Dicranaceae
Moss	*Didymodon (Barbula) glaucus*	glaucous beard-moss	Pottiaceae
Moss	*Didymodon (Barbula) mamillosus*	a moss	Pottiaceae
Moss	*Didymodon (Barbula) tomaculosus*	a moss	Pottiaceae
Moss	*Didymodon cordatus (Barbula cordata)*	cordate beard-moss	Pottiaceae
Moss	*Ditrichum cornubicum*	Cornish path moss	Ditrichaceae
Moss	*Ditrichum plumbicola*	a moss	Ditrichaceae
Moss	*Ephemerum cohaerens*	a moss	Ephemeraceae
Moss	*Ephemerum recurvifolium*	a moss	Ephemeraceae
Moss	*Ephemerum sessile*	a moss	Ephemeraceae
Moss	*Ephemerum stellatum*	a moss	Ephemeraceae
Moss	*Fissidens celticus*	a moss	Fissidentaceae
Moss	*Fissidens exiguus*	a moss	Fissidentaceae
Moss	*Glyphomitrium daviesii*	a moss	Ptychomitriaceae
Moss	*Grimmia retracta*	a moss	Grimmiaceae
Moss	*Hamatocaulis (Drepanocladus) vernicosus*	slender green feather-moss	Amblystegiaceae
Moss	*Hygrohypnum polare*	polar feather-moss	Amblystegiaceae
Moss	*Hymenostelium (Gymnostomum) insigne*	a moss	Pottiaceae
Moss	*Hypnum vaucheri*	Vaucher's feather-moss	Hypnaceae
Moss	*Leptodontium gemmascens*	thatch moss	Pottiaceae
Moss	*Micromitrium tenerum*	millimetre moss	Ephemeraceae
Moss	*Mielichhoferia mielichhoferiana*	Alpine copper moss	Bryaceae
Moss	*Myurium hochstetteri*	a moss	Myuriaceae
Moss	*Orthodontium gracile*	a moss	Bryaceae
Moss	*Orthotrichum gymnostomum*	a moss	Orthotrichaceae
Moss	*Orthotrichum obtusifolium*	blunt-leaved bristle-moss	Orthotrichaceae
Moss	*Orthotrichum pallens*	a moss	Orthotrichaceae
Moss	*Orthotrichum sprucei*	a moss	Orthotrichaceae
Moss	*Oxystegus hibernicus*	a moss	Pottiaceae
Moss	*Philonotis marchica*	a moss	Bartraniaceae
Moss	*Physciomitrium sphaericum*	a moss	Funariaceae
Moss	*Pictus scoticus*	a moss	Amblystegiaceae
Moss	*Plagiothecium piliferum*	hair silk moss	Plagiotheciaceae
Moss	*Pohlia muyldermansii*	a moss	Bryaceae
Moss	*Pohlia scotica*	a moss	Bryaceae
Moss	*Rhynchostegium alopecuroides (R. lusitanicum)*	a moss	Brachytheciaceae
Moss	*Rhynchostegium rotundifolium*	round-leaved feather-moss	Brachytheciaceae
Moss	*Saelania glaucescens*	blue dew moss	Dicranaceae
Moss	*Scorpidium turgescens*	large yellow feather-moss	Amblystegiaceae
Moss	*Seligeria paucifolia*	a moss	Seligeriaceae
Moss	*Sematophyllum demissum*	a moss	Sematophyllaceae
Moss	*Sphagnum balticum*	Baltic bog moss	Sphagnaceae
Moss	*Sphagnum skyense*	a bog moss	Sphagnaceae
Moss	*Tetrodontium repandum*	a moss	Tetraphidaceae

VU	I	0?	2?	2			
CR	I	0	2?	2	IIb	I	8
	2?	3?	0	+			
	I	2?	0	+			
	I	0?	I?	+			
VU	2?	0?	0?	2			8
VU	I	0	I?	2			8
EN	I	0	0?	2			
EN	I	0	2	2			
	I	I?	0	2			
CR	2?	0?	0	2			8
	2?	I?	0?	2			
	2?	3?	0	I			
CR	0	0	0?	2			8
CR	2	3*	0?	2			8
	2?	3	0	2			
CR	I	0	2?	2			
	I	0?	0?	+			
	I	0?	I?	+			
EN	2	I?	2?	2			
	0	3?	0	0			
	2?	2?	0	I			
	I	I?	0?	+			
	I	I?	0?	+			
	I?	0?	?	?	IIb	I	8
VU	0	0	0	2			
	I	2?	0	I			
VU	0	0	0?	2			8
EN	2?	0?	2?	I			
EN	I	0	2?	2			8
VU	I?	0	0?	2			8
	0	I?	0?	+			
EN	I	0	2?	2			
CR	0?	0	2?	2			
CR	0	0	2?	2			8
CR	0	0	2?	2			
	2?	3	0?	+			
	I	2?	0	+			
CR	0	0	I?	2			
	I	0?	I?	I			
	2?	3*	0	2			
EN	0	0	2?	2			8
	0	I?	0	+			
	2	3*	0	I			
	0	2?	0	+			
CR	2?	0?	0	2			8
VU	0	0	0	2			8
EN	0	0	0	2			8
	2?	3	0?	0			
EN	I	0	I?	2			
EN	0	0	I?	2			8
	2?	3*	0?	2			
CR	0	0	2?	2			

Moss	*Thamnobryum angustifolium*	Derbyshire feather-moss	Thamniaceae
Moss	*Thamnobryum cataractarum*	a feather-moss	Thamniaceae
Moss	*Tortula freibergii*	a moss	Pottiaceae
Moss	*Trochobryum carniolicum (Seligeria carniolica)*	a moss	Seligeriaceae
Moss	*Ulota calvescens*	a moss	Orthotrichaceae
Moss	*Weissia multicapsularis*	a moss	Pottiaceae
Moss	*Weissia perssonii*	a moss	Pottiaceae
Moss	*Weissia rostellata*	a moss	Pottiaceae
Moss	*Weissia squarrosa*	a moss	Pottiaceae
Moss	*Weissia sterilis*	a moss	Pottiaceae
Moss	*Zygodon forsteri*	knothole moss	Orthotrichaceae
Moss	*Zygodon gracilis*	Nowell's limestone moss	Orthotrichaceae
Stonewort	*Chara baltica*	Baltic stonewort	Characeae
Stonewort	*Chara canescens*	bearded stonewort	Characeae
Stonewort	*Chara connivens*	convergent stonewort	Characeae
Stonewort	*Chara curta*	lesser bearded stonewort	Characeae
Stonewort	*Chara muscosa*	mossy stonewort	Characeae
Stonewort	*Lamprothamnium papulosum*	foxtail stonewort	Characeae
Stonewort	*Nitella capillaris*	slimy-fruited stonewort	Characeae
Stonewort	*Nitella gracilis*	slender stonewort	Characeae
Stonewort	*Nitella tenuissima*	dwarf stonewort	Characeae
Stonewort	*Nitellopsis obtusa*	starry stonewort	Characeae
Stonewort	*Tolypella intricata*	tassel stonewort	Characeae
Stonewort	*Tolypella nidifica*	bird's nest stonewort	Characeae
Stonewort	*Tolypella prolifera*	great tassel stonewort	Characeae
Vascular Plant	*Adonis annua*	pheasant's-eye	Ranunculaceae
Vascular Plant	*Ajuga chamaepitys*	ground pine	Lamiaceae
Vascular Plant	*Alchemilla minima*	an alchemilla	Rosaceae
Vascular Plant	*Alisma graminea*	ribbon-leaved water-plantain	Alismataceae
Vascular Plant	*Allium sphaerocephalon*	round-headed leek	Liliaceae
Vascular Plant	*Althaea hirsuta*	rough marsh-mallow	Malvaceae
Vascular Plant	*Alyssum alyssoides*	small alison	Brassicaceae
Vascular Plant	*Apium repens*	creeping marshwort	Apiaceae
Vascular Plant	*Arabis alpina*	Alpine rock-cress	Brassicaceae
Vascular Plant	*Arabis glabra*	tower mustard	Brassicaceae
Vascular Plant	*Arabis scabra*	Bristol rock-cress	Brassicaceae
Vascular Plant	*Arenaria norvegica anglica*	English sandwort	Caryophyllaceae
Vascular Plant	*Arenaria norvegica norvegica*	Arctic sandwort	Caryophyllaceae
Vascular Plant	*Artemisia campestris*	field wormwood	Asteraceae
Vascular Plant	*Artemisia norvegica*	Norwegian mugwort	Asteraceae
Vascular Plant	*Aster linosyris*	goldilocks	Asteraceae
Vascular Plant	*Athyrium flexile*	Newman's lady-fern	Woodsiaceae
Vascular Plant	*Atriplex pedunculata*	peduncluate sea-purslane/stalked orache	Chenopodiaceae
Vascular Plant	*Bupleurum baldense*	small hare's-ear	Apiaceae
Vascular Plant	*Bupleurum falcatum*	sickle-leaved hare's-ear	Apiaceae
Vascular Plant	*Buxus sempervirens*	box	Buxaceae
Vascular Plant	*Calamagrostis scotica*	Scottish small-reed	Poaceae
Vascular Plant	*Carex chordorrhiza*	string sedge	Cyperaceae
Vascular Plant	*Carex depauperata*	starved wood-sedge	Cyperaceae
Vascular Plant	*Carex humilis*	dwarf sedge	Cyperaceae
Vascular Plant	*Carex muricata ssp. muricata*	prickly sedge	Cyperaceae
Vascular Plant	*Carex recta*	estuarine sedge	Cyperaceae
Vascular Plant	*Carex vulpina*	true fox-sedge	Cyperaceae

CR	2	3*	1?	2		8	
VU	2	3*	0?	2			
	2?	1?	0	2			
CR	2	0?	2?	2			
	0	1?	0	+			
VU	2?	3	1?	1			
	0	2?	0	+			
	2?	1?	1?	+			
EN	2?	0?	2?	1			
	2?	3	1?	+			
EN	2?	0	0?	2		8	
EN	2?	0?	1?	2		8	
EN	2?	0?	2?	2			
CR	0	0	2	2		8	
EN	1?	?	1?	2			
	2?	1?	1?	1			
	2	2	?	?			
	2?	1?	0?	+		8	
	0	0	0	-			X?
EN	0	0	2?	2			
EN	0?	?	2?	2			
EN	2?	0?	2?	2			
EN	2?	0?	2?	2			
	2?	0?	2?	2			
EN	1?	0?	2?	2			
EN	0	0	1	1			
VU	0	0	1	+		8	
VU	2	3*?	0	2			
CR	1	0	2	2		8	
VU	0	0	0	2		8	
EN	0	0	1	2		8	
CR	0	0	2	2		8	
CR	1	0	2	2	IIb IVb I	8	
VU	0	0	0	2		8	
VU	0	0	2	1?			
VU	0	0	0	2		8	
EN	1	3*	1	2		8	
	1	0	0	1		8	
EN	0	0	0	2		8	
VU	2	0	0	2			
	0	0	0	1			
VU	1	3*	0	2			
CR	1	0	-2	2		8	
EN	0	0	0	2		8	
CR	0	0	0	2		8	
	0	0	0	1			
VU	2	3*	0	2			
VU	1	0	0	2			
CR	1	0	0	2		8	
	0	0	1	+			
	0	0	2	2			
	1	0	0	2			
VU	0	0	2	1			

Vascular Plant	*Carum verticillatum*	whorled caraway	Apiaceae
Vascular Plant	*Centaurea cyanus*	cornflower	Asteraceae
Vascular Plant	*Centaurium tenuiflorum*	slender centaury	Gentianaceae
Vascular Plant	*Cephalanthera longifolia*	sword-leaved helleborine	Orchidaceae
Vascular Plant	*Cephalanthera rubra*	red helleborine	Orchidaceae
Vascular Plant	*Cerastium nigrescens*	Shetland mouse-ear	Caryophyllaceae
Vascular Plant	*Chamaemelum nobile*	wild chamomile	Asteraceae
Vascular Plant	*Chenopodium vulvaria*	stinking goosefoot	Chenopodiaceae
Vascular Plant	*Cicerbita alpina*	Alpine sow-thistle	Asteraceae
Vascular Plant	*Cirsium tubersosum*	tuberous thistle	Asteraceae
Vascular Plant	*Clinopodium menthifolium*	wood calamint	Lamiaceae
Vascular Plant	*Cochlearia micacea*	mountain scurvy-grass	Brassicaceae
Vascular Plant	*Cochlearia scotica*	Scottish scurvy-grass	Brassicaceae
Vascular Plant	*Coincya wrightii*	Lundy cabbage	Brassicaceae
Vascular Plant	*Corrigiola litoralis*	strapwort	Caryophyllaceae
Vascular Plant	*Cotoneaster cambricus*	wild cotoneaster	Rosaceae
Vascular Plant	*Crassula aquatica*	pigmyweed	Crassulaceae
Vascular Plant	*Crepis foetida*	stinking hawk's-beard	Asteraceae
Vascular Plant	*Cynoglossum germanicum*	green hound's-tongue	Boraginaceae
Vascular Plant	*Cyperus fuscus*	brown galingale	Cyperaceae
Vascular Plant	*Cypripedium calceolus*	Lady's-slipper orchid	Orchidaceae
Vascular Plant	*Cystopteris dickieana*	Dickie's bladder fern	Woodsiaceae
Vascular Plant	*Dactylorhiza lapponica*	Lapland marsh orchid	Orchidaceae
Vascular Plant	*Damasonium alisma*	starfruit	Alismataceae
Vascular Plant	*Deschampsia setacea*	bog hair grass	Poaceae
Vascular Plant	*Dianthus armeria*	Deptford pink	Caryophyllaceae
Vascular Plant	*Dianthus gratianopolitanus*	Cheddar pink	Caryophyllaceae
Vascular Plant	*Diapensia lapponica*	diapensia	Diapensiaceae
Vascular Plant	*Diphasiastrum issleri*	Issleri's clubmoss	Lycopodiaceae
Vascular Plant	*Draba aizoides*	yellow whitlow grass	Brassicaceae
Vascular Plant	*Dryopteris aemula*	hay-scented buckler-fern	Dryopteridaceae
Vascular Plant	*Dryopteris cristata*	crested buckler-fern	Dryopteridaceae
Vascular Plant	*Eleocharis parvula*	dwarf spike-rush	Cyperaceae
Vascular Plant	*Epipactis leptochila var. dunensis*	dune helleborine	Orchidaceae
Vascular Plant	*Epipactis youngiana*	Young's helleborine	Orchidaceae
Vascular Plant	*Epipogium aphyllum*	ghost orchid	Orchidaceae
Vascular Plant	*Equisetum ramosissimum*	branched horsetail	Equisetaceae
Vascular Plant	*Erica ciliaris*	Dorset heath	Ericaceae
Vascular Plant	*Erigeron borealis*	Alpine fleabane	Asteraceae
Vascular Plant	*Eriophorum gracile*	slender cottongrass	Cyperaceae
Vascular Plant	*Eryngium campestre*	field eryngo	Apiaceae
Vascular Plant	*Euphorbia platyphyllos*	broad-leaved spurge	Euphorbiaceae
Vascular Plant	*Euphrasia cambrica*	an eyebright	Scrophulariaceae
Vascular Plant	*Euphrasia campbelliae*	an eyebright	Scrophulariaceae
Vascular Plant	*Euphrasia heslop-harrisonii*	an eyebright	Scrophulariaceae
Vascular Plant	*Euphrasia rivularis*	an eyebright	Scrophulariaceae
Vascular Plant	*Euphrasia rotundifolia*	an eyebright	Scrophulariaceae
Vascular Plant	*Euphrasia vigursii*	an eyebright	Scrophulariaceae
Vascular Plant	*Festuca longifolia*	blue fescue	Poaceae
Vascular Plant	*Filago gallica*	narrow-leaved cudweed	Asteraceae
Vascular Plant	*Filago lutescens*	red-tipped cudweed	Asteraceae
Vascular Plant	*Filago pyramidata*	broad-leaved cudweed	Asteraceae
Vascular Plant	*Fumaria occidentalis*	western ramping-fumitory	Fumariaceae

			0		
				0		
EN	0	0	2	2		
VU	0	0	0	2		8
	0	0	-1	1		
EN	0	0	0	2		8
VU	2	3*	0	2		
	0	0	1	+		
VU	0	0	1	2		8
VU	0	0	1	2		8
	1	0	1	1		
VU	0	0	0	2		8
	2	3*	0	1		
	1	3	2	+?		
VU	2	3*	0	2		8
EN	0	0	1	2		8
EN	2?	3*?	0	2		8
VU	1	0	0	2		8
EN	0	0	2	2		8
VU	0	0	1?	1		8
EN	1	0	0	2		8
CR	1	0	0	2	IIb IVb 1	8
VU	0	0	-2	2		8
VU	0	0	0	2		8
EN	1	1	2	2		8
	1	0	1	+		
VU	0	0	2	+		
VU	1	0	1	2		8
VU	0	0	0	2		
VU	0	0	0	2/1		
	0	0	0	2		
	1	1	0	0		
VU	0	0	1	1		
VU	0?	0	0	2		(c)
VU	1	3*?	0	1		
EN	2?	3*	0	2		8
CR	1	0	0	2		8
VU	0	0	0	2		8
	1	0	0	1		
VU	0	0	1?	1		8
VU	1	0	1	1		8
VU	0	0	0	2?/1		8
	0	0	1?	0		
	2	3*	0	1		
	2	3*	0	1		
	2	3*	0	1		
	2	3*	0	1		
VU	2	3*	0	2		
	2	3*	0	+		
	1	0	1	1		
CR	0	0	-2	2		
VU	1	0	2	1		8
EN	0	0	2	2		8
VU	2	3*	0	+		

Vascular Plant	*Fumaria purpurea*	purple ramping-fumitory	Fumariaceae
Vascular Plant	*Fumaria reuterii (martinii)*	Martin's ramping fumitory	Fumariaceae
Vascular Plant	*Gagea bohemica*	early star-of-Bethlehem	Liliaceae
Vascular Plant	*Galeopsis angustifolia*	red hemp-nettle	Lamiaceae
Vascular Plant	*Galium tricornutum*	corn cleavers	Rubiaceae
Vascular Plant	*Genista pilosa*	hairy greenweed	Fabaceae
Vascular Plant	*Gentiana nivalis*	Alpine gentian	Gentianaceae
Vascular Plant	*Gentiana verna*	spring gentian	Gentianaceae
Vascular Plant	*Gentianella anglica*	early gentian	Gentianaceae
Vascular Plant	*Gentianella ciliata*	fringed gentian	Gentianaceae
Vascular Plant	*Gentianella uliginosa*	dune gentian	Gentianaceae
Vascular Plant	*Gladiolus illyricus*	wild gladiolus	Iridaceae
Vascular Plant	*Gnaphalium luteoalbum*	Jersey cudweed	Asteraceae
Vascular Plant	*Gnaphalium sylvaticum*	heath cudweed	Asteraceae
Vascular Plant	*Hammarbya paludosa*	bog orchid	Orchidaceae
Vascular Plant	*Helianthemum appeninum*	white rock rose	Cistaceae
Vascular Plant	*Herniaria glabra*	smooth rupturewort	Caryophyllaceae
Vascular Plant	*Hieracium Sect. Alpestria (13 Shetland spp only)*	hawkweeds	Asteraceae
Vascular Plant	*Himantoglossum hircinum*	lizard orchid	Orchidaceae
Vascular Plant	*Homogyne alpina*	purple colt's-foot	Asteraceae
Vascular Plant	*Hyacinthoides non-scripta*	bluebell	Liliaceae
Vascular Plant	*Hymenophyllum tunbrigense*	Tunbridge filmy-fern	Hymenophyllace
Vascular Plant	*Hymenophyllum wilsonii*	Wilson's filmy-fern	Hymenophyllace
Vascular Plant	*Hypochaeris glabra*	smooth cat's-ear	Asteraceae
Vascular Plant	*Hypochoeris maculata*	spotted car's-ear	Asteraceae
Vascular Plant	*Isoetes hystrix*	land quillwort	Isoetaceae
Vascular Plant	*Juncus pygmaeus*	pygmy rush	Juncaceae
Vascular Plant	*Lactuca saligna*	least lettuce	Asteraceae
Vascular Plant	*Leersia oryzoides*	cut-grass	Poaceae
Vascular Plant	*Limonium (endemic taxa)*	sea lavender	Plumbaginaceae
Vascular Plant	*Limonium bellidifolium*	matted sea lavender	Plumbaginaceae
Vascular Plant	*Limosella australis*	Welsh mudwort	Scrophulariaceae
Vascular Plant	*Linnaea borealis*	twinflower	Caprifoliaceae
Vascular Plant	*Liparis loeselii*	fen orchid	Orchidaceae
Vascular Plant	*Lithospermum arvense*	corn gromwell	Boraginaceae
Vascular Plant	*Lloydia serotina*	Snowdon lily	Liliaceae
Vascular Plant	*Lobelia urens*	heath lobelia	Campanulaceae
Vascular Plant	*Lotus angustissimus*	slender bird's-foot trefoil	Fabaceae
Vascular Plant	*Ludwigia palustris*	Hampshire purslane	Onagraceae
Vascular Plant	*Luronium natans*	floating water plantain	Alismataceae
Vascular Plant	*Lychnis alpina*	Alpine catchfly	Caryophyllaceae
Vascular Plant	*Lychnis viscaria*	sticky catchfly	Caryophyllaceae
Vascular Plant	*Lycopodiella inundata*	marsh clubmoss	Lycopodiaceae
Vascular Plant	*Lythrum hyssopifolia*	grass-poly	Lythraceae
Vascular Plant	*Maianthemum bifolium*	May lily	Liliaceae
Vascular Plant	*Melampyrum arvense*	field cow-wheat	Scrophulariaceae
Vascular Plant	*Melampyrum sylvaticum*	small cow-wheat	Scrophulariaceae
Vascular Plant	*Mentha pulegium*	pennyroyal	Lamiaceae
Vascular Plant	*Minuartia stricta*	Teesdale sandwort	Caryophyllaceae
Vascular Plant	*Moneses uniflora*	one-flowered wintergreen	Pyrolaceae
Vascular Plant	*Myosotis alpestris*	Alpine forget-me-not	Boraginaceae
Vascular Plant	*Najas flexilis*	slender naiad	Najadaceae
Vascular Plant	*Najas marina*	holly-leaved naiad	Najadaceae

	2?	3	0	+			
EN	I	0	I	2			8
VU	0	0	0	2			8
	0	0	2?	I?			
CR	0	0	2	2			
	0	0	0	I			
VU	0	0	0	2			8
	0	0	0	2			8
	I	3*	I	+	IIb IVb	I	8
EN	0	0	0	2			8
EN	I	0	I	2			8
	2?	3*?	0	I			8
CR	0	0	0	2			8
	0	0	I	0			
	I	I	I	+			(c)
	0	0	0	2			
	0	0	0	I			
VU	2	3*	?	2			8 (3 spp)
VU	0?	0	0	I			8
VU	0	0	0	2			8
	0	I	0	0			
	I	I	0	0			
	I	I	0	0			
	0	0	I	+			(c)
VU	0	0	0	I			
VU	I	0	I	2			
EN	0?	?	2	2			
EN	0	0	I?	2			8
EN	0?	0	2	2			
VU	2	3*	0	2			
	0	0	0	2			
	0	0	0	2			8
	0	0	2	+			
EN	I	0	2	2	IIb IVb	I	8
	0	0	I	+?			
VU	0	0	0	2			8
VU	I	0	I	2			
	0	0	0	I			
	I	0	0	I			
	I	I	0	+	IIb IVb	I	8
VU	0	0	0	2			8
VU	0	0	I?	I			
	0	0	2	+			(c)
	0	0	0	2			8
VU	0	0	0	I			
EN	I	0	I	2			8
	0	0	I	+			(c)
VU	0	0	2	I			8
EN	0	0	0	2			8(c)
VU	0	0	I?	I			
	0	0	0	I			
	I	0	0	+	IIb IVb	I	8
VU	I	0	0	2			8

Vascular Plant	*Oenanthe fluviatilis*	river water-dropwort	Apiaceae
Vascular Plant	*Ononis reclinata*	small rest-harrow	Fabaceae
Vascular Plant	*Ophioglossum lusitanicum*	least adder's-tongue	Ophioglossaceae
Vascular Plant	*Ophrys fuciflora*	late spider orchid	Orchidaceae
Vascular Plant	*Ophrys sphegodes*	early spider orchid	Orchidaceae
Vascular Plant	*Orchis militaris*	military orchid	Orchidaceae
Vascular Plant	*Orchis simia*	monkey orchid	Orchidaceae
Vascular Plant	*Orchis ustulata*	burnt-tip orchid	Orchidaceae
Vascular Plant	*Orobanche artemisiae-campestris*	oxtongue broomrape	Orobanchaceae
Vascular Plant	*Orobanche caryophyllacea*	bedstraw broomrape	Orobanchaceae
Vascular Plant	*Orobanche rapum-genistae*	greater broomrape	Orobanchaceae
Vascular Plant	*Orobanche reticulata*	thistle broomrape	Orobanchaceae
Vascular Plant	*Oxytropis halleri*	purple oxytropis	Fabaceae
Vascular Plant	*Petroraghia nanteuilii*	Childing pink	Caryophyllaceae
Vascular Plant	*Petroselinum segetum*	corn parsley	Apiaceae
Vascular Plant	*Phleum phleoides*	purple stem cat's-tail	Poaceae
Vascular Plant	*Phyllodoce caerulea*	blue heath	Ericaceae
Vascular Plant	*Physospermum cornubiense*	bladderseed	Apiaceae
Vascular Plant	*Phyteuma spicatum*	spiked rampion	Campanulaceae
Vascular Plant	*Pilularia globulifera*	pillwort	Mansileaceae
Vascular Plant	*Polemonium caeruleum*	Jacob's ladder	Polemoniaceae
Vascular Plant	*Polygonatum verticillatum*	whorled Solomon's-seal	Liliaceae
Vascular Plant	*Polygonum maritimum*	sea knotgrass	Polygonaceae
Vascular Plant	*Potamogeton compressus*	grass-wrack pondweed	Potamogetonace
Vascular Plant	*Potamogeton rutilus*	Shetland pondweed	Potamogetonace
Vascular Plant	*Potentilla fruticosa*	shrubby cinquefoil	Rosaceae
Vascular Plant	*Potentilla rupestris*	rock cinquefoil	Rosaceae
Vascular Plant	*Primula scotica*	Scottish primrose	Myrsinaceae
Vascular Plant	*Pulicaria vulgaris*	small fleabane	Asteraceae
Vascular Plant	*Pulsatilla vulgaris*	pasqueflower	Ranunculaceae
Vascular Plant	*Pyrus cordata*	Plymouth pear	Rosaceae
Vascular Plant	*Ranunculus arvensis*	corn buttercup	Ranunculaceae
Vascular Plant	*Ranunculus fluitans*	river water-crowfoot	Ranunculaceae
Vascular Plant	*Ranunculus hederaceus*	ivy-leaved water-crowfoot	Ranunculaceae
Vascular Plant	*Ranunculus ophioglossifolius*	adder's-tongue spearwort	Ranunculaceae
Vascular Plant	*Ranunculus penicillatus*	stream water-crowfoot	Ranunculaceae
Vascular Plant	*Ranunculus tripartitus*	three-lobed water-crowfoot	Ranunculaceae
Vascular Plant	*Rhinanthus serotinus*	greater yellow-rattle	Scrophulariaceae
Vascular Plant	*Ribes alpinum*	mountain currant	Grossulariaceae
Vascular Plant	*Romulea columnae*	sand crocus	Iridaceae
Vascular Plant	*Rumex rupestris*	shore dock	Polygonaceae
Vascular Plant	*Sagina boydii*	Boyd's pearlwort	Caryophyllaceae
Vascular Plant	*Sagina saginoides*	alpine pearlwort	Caryophyllaceae
Vascular Plant	*Salix lanata*	woolly willow	Salicaceae
Vascular Plant	*Salvia pratensis*	meadow clary	Lamiaceae
Vascular Plant	*Saxifraga cernua*	drooping saxifrage	Saxifragaceae
Vascular Plant	*Saxifraga cespitosa*	tufted saxifrage	Saxifragaceae
Vascular Plant	*Saxifraga hirculus*	yellow marsh saxifrage	Saxifragaceae
Vascular Plant	*Scandix pecten-veneris*	shepherd's needle	Apiaceae
Vascular Plant	*Scheuchzeria palustris*	Rannoch rush	Scheuchzeriacea
Vascular Plant	*Schoenoplectus pungens*	sharp club-rush	Cyperaceae
Vascular Plant	*Scirpoides holoschoenus*	round-headed club-rush	Cyperaceae
Vascular Plant	*Scirpus triqueter*	triangular club-rush	Cyperaceae

	1	1	1	+		
VU	0	0	0	1		8
VU	0?	0	0	2		8
VU	1	0	0	2		8
	0	0	0	1		8
VU	1?	0	0	2		8
VU	0	0	0	2		8
	0	0	1	+		
EN	0	0	0	2		8
VU	0	0	0	2		8
	0	0	1	+		
	0	0	0	1		8
	0	0	0	1		
EN	0	0	1	2		8
	1	1?	1	0		
	0	0	0	1		
VU	0	0	0	2		8
VU	0	0	0	1		
VU	0	0	1	1		8
	1	1?	0	+		(c)
	0	0	0	1		
EN	0	0	1?	1		8
EN	0?	0	0	2		8
	0	0	2	+		
	1	0	0	1		
	0	0	0	1		
VU	0	0	0	2		8
	1	3*	0	+		
VU	1	0	1	1		8
	1	0	1	+		
EN	1	0	0	2		8
	0	0	1?	+		
	1	1?	1?	0		(c)
	1	1?	1?	0		
EN	0	0	0	2		8
	0	1	0	0		
VU	1	1	2	1		
VU	0	0	0	1		8
	0	0	1	+		
VU	0	0	0	2		8
EN	2	1	2	1	IIb IVb 1	8
EN	2	3*	0	2		X
	0	0	1	+		
EN	0	?	2	1		
VU	0	0	0	1		
VU	0	0	0	2		8
	0	0	0	1		8
	1	0	0	1	IIb IVb 1	8(c)
	0	0	2	+		
VU	1	0	0	2		
EN	0	0	0	2		
VU	0	0	0	2		
CR	0	0	2	2		8

Vascular Plant	Scleranthus perennis ssp. prostratus	prostrate perennial knawel	Caryophyllaceae
Vascular Plant	Scleranthus perennis ssp. perennis	perennial knawel	Caryophyllaceae
Vascular Plant	Scorzonera humilis	viper's-grass	Asteraceae
Vascular Plant	Selinum carvifolia	Cambridge milk-parsley	Apiaceae
Vascular Plant	Senecio cambrensis	Welsh groundsel	Asteraceae
Vascular Plant	Senecio paludosus	fen ragwort	Asteraceae
Vascular Plant	Silene gallica	small-flowered catchfly	Caryophyllaceae
Vascular Plant	Silene otites	a campion	Caryophyllaceae
Vascular Plant	Sium latifolium	greater water-parsnip	Apiaceae
Vascular Plant	Sorbus anglica	a whitebeam	Rosaceae
Vascular Plant	Sorbus domestica	true service tree	Rosaceae
Vascular Plant	Sorbus leyana	a whitebeam	Rosaceae
Vascular Plant	Spergularia bocconei	a greek sea-spurrey	Caryophyllaceae
Vascular Plant	Stachys alpina	limestone woundwort	Lamiaceae
Vascular Plant	Stachys germanica	downy woundwort	Lamiaceae
Vascular Plant	Tephroseris integrifolia ssp. maritima	fleawort	Compositae
Vascular Plant	Teucrium botrys	cut-leaved germander	Lamiaceae
Vascular Plant	Teucrium chamaedrys	wall germander	Lamiaceae
Vascular Plant	Teucrium scordium	water germander	Lamiaceae
Vascular Plant	Thlaspi perfoliatum	perfoliate pennycress	Brassicaceae
Vascular Plant	Thymus serpyllum	Breckland thyme	Lamiaceae
Vascular Plant	Tordylium maximum	hartwort	Umbelliferae
Vascular Plant	Torilis arvensis	spreading hedge-parsley	Apiaceae
Vascular Plant	Trichomanes speciosum	Killarney fern	Hymenophyllace
Vascular Plant	Trinia glauca	honewort	Apiaceae
Vascular Plant	Ulex gallii	western gorse	Fabaceae
Vascular Plant	Ulmus plotii	Plot's elm	Ulmaceae
Vascular Plant	Valerianella dentata	narrow-fruited corn salad	Valerianaceae
Vascular Plant	Valerianella rimosa	broad-fruited corn salad	Valerianaceae
Vascular Plant	Veronica spicata	spiked speedwell	Scrophulariacea
Vascular Plant	Veronica triphyllos	fingered speedwell	Scrophulariacea
Vascular Plant	Viola persicifolia	fen violet	Violaceae
Vascular Plant	Woodsia alpina	Alpine woodsia	Woodsiaceae
Vascular Plant	Woodsia ilvensis	oblong woodsia	Woodsiaceae
Vascular Plant	Zostera marina	seagrass	Zosteraceae

EN	2	3*	0	2		8
EN	?	?	0	2		8
VU	0	0	0	2		8
VU	0	0	0	2		8
	1	3*	-2	1		
CR	0	0	1?	2		8
	0	0	2	+		
	0	0	0	1		
	0	0	1	+		
	1	3*	0	1		
VU	0	0	-2	2		
EN	2	3*	0	2		
CR	0	0	0	2		
EN	0	0	0	2		8
EN	0	0	0	2		8
VU	1	3*	0	2		
VU	0	0	0	2		8
EN	0	0	1?	2		
VU	1	0	1	2		8
VU	0	0	2	1		8
	0	0	0	2		
EN	0	0	1	2		
	0	0	1	+		
VU	2	0	0	1	IIb IVb I	8(c)
	0	0	0	1		
	0	1	0	0		
	1	3*	0	+		
	0	0	1?	0		
EN	?	0	2	3?		
VU	0	0	0	1		8
EN	0	0	0	2		8
EN	1	0	1	2		8(c)
	0	0	1	1		8
EN	0	0	2	1		8
	0	0	1?	+		

LIST OF KEY HABITATS FOR WHICH COSTED PLANS HAVE BEEN PREPARED

Coastal and floodplain grazing marsh
Purple moor grass and rush pasture (*Molinia-Juncus*)
Ancient and/or species rich hedgerows
Reedbeds
Limestone pavements
Lowland heathland
Upland oakwood

Chalk rivers
Saline lagoons
Seagrass beds
Fens
Cereal field margins
Mesotrophic lakes
Native pine wood

LIST OF KEY HABITATS FOR WHICH COSTED PLANS WILL BE PREPARED

Lowland beech
Upland mixed ash woodland
Wet woodlands
Lowland wood pastures and parklands
Lowland hay meadow
Upland hay meadow
Lowland dry acid grassland
Lowland calcareous grassland
Upland calcareous grassland
Raised bog
Eutrophic standing waters
Aquifer fed naturally fluctuating water bodies
Upland heathland
Blanket bog

Maritime cliff and slope
Coastal vegetation shingle structure
Machair
Coastal saltmarsh
Coastal sand dune
Estuaries
Ascophyllum nodosum mackii beds
Maerl beds (inlets and bays)
Deep mud
Maerl beds (open coast)
Chalk coasts (littoral and sublittoral)
[Caves and natural rock exposures to be reviewed for possible inclusion]

LIST OF BROAD HABITAT TYPES FOR WHICH HABITAT STATEMENTS HAVE BEEN PREPARED

Broadleaved and yew woodland
Planted coniferous woodland
Native pine woodland
Lowland wood pastures and parkland
Boundary features
Arable
Improved grassland
Unimproved neutral grassland
Acid grassland
Calcareous grassland
Lowland heathland
Grazing marsh
Fens, carr, marsh, swamp and reedbed
Lowland raised bog
Standing open water
Rivers and streams
Canals
Montane (alpine and subalpine types)
Upland heathland

Blanket bog
Maritime cliff and slope
Shingle above high tide mark
Boulders and rock above the high tide
Coastal strandline
Machair
Saltmarsh
Sand dune
Estuaries
Saline lagoons
Islands and archipelagos
Inlets and enclosed bays (including sea lochs, rias and voes)
Open coast
Open sea water column
Shelf break
Offshore seabed
Limestone pavements
Urban

RELATIONSHIP BETWEEN BIODIVERSITY HABITAT CATEGORIES AND NVC COMMUNITIES.

The classification used here defines habitats as ecologically integrated units at a landscape scale, rather than seeing habitats as simply distinct types of vegetation. As the habitat classification is intended as a framework for the conservation of both flora and fauna, and many animals depend upon the quality of the mosaic of vegetation and not just the vegetation type, this broader form of biotope classification is considered more meaningful.

This table presents an approximation of the relationship between the Habitat Categories used for the Biodiversity Habitat Statements and the communities of the National Vegetation Classification (NVC). However difficulties arise in that these classifications were devised for different purposes and used different principles:

- **Biodiversity Habitat Categories**: this classification is based on a mixture of broad habitat types (e.g. grassland, woodland) and their physical characteristics (e.g. acid/calcareous, lowland/upland/montane). These habitats are often mosaics, rather than stands of individual vegetation communities. This 'biotope complex' approach is similar to that used in the German Biotopes Red Data Book.

- **The National Vegetation Classification**: the foundations of the NVC are the plant communities present on a site, regardless of altitude, soil type and other such physical characteristics of the site. As some NVC communities are found at different altitudes, or are found in an area of transition between some habitat types, it is not always possible to relate an NVC community exclusively to one Biodiversity Habitat Category. For example, while the situation is straightforward for sand dunes, where the NVC sand dune types occur more or less exclusively with the sand dune habitats, some NVC heath communities can occur in the lowland heath, upland heath and montane habitat categories.

  The NVC is of more limited application to rivers and streams due to the dynamic character of these habitats. A broader classification for river systems has therefore been developed and is applied to the selection of SSSIs (and to other contexts)

Consequently there is not always a simple relationship between the NVC and the habitat classification. This table should be used only as a guide to the type of vegetation that is more commonly found in these Habitat Categories, and it is not intended as a cross-reference for use in the numerical analysis of data.

RELATIONSHIP BETWEEN BIODIVERSITY HABITAT CATEGORIES AND NVC COMMUNITIES

1. BROAD-LEAVED AND YEW WOODLAND

W7 *Alnus glutinosa-Fraxinus excelsior-Lysimachia nemorum* woodland

W8 *Fraxinus excelsior-Acer campestre-Mercurialis perennis* woodland

W9 *Fraxinus excelsior-Sorbus aucuparia-Mercurialis perennis* woodland

W10 *Quercus robur-Pteridium aquilinum-Rubus fruticosus* woodland

W11 *Quercus petraea-Betula pubescens-Oxalis acetosella* woodland

W12 *Fagus sylvatica-Mercurialis perennis* woodland

W13 *Taxus baccata* woodland

W14 *Fagus sylvatica-Rubus fruticosus* woodland

W15 *Fagus sylvatica-Deschampsia flexuosa* woodland

W16 *Quercus spp.-Betula spp.-Deschampsia flexuosa* woodland

W17 *Quercus petraea-Betula pubescens-Dicranum majus* woodland

W19 *Juniperus communis ssp. communis-Oxalis acetosella* woodland

2. PLANTED CONIFEROUS WOODLEAF

Dominated by cultivars of *Pinus sylvestris* and non-native conifers. Floristics are often similar to the vegetation present before planting, or support an impoverished woodland flora.

3. NATIVE PINE WOODLAND

W18 *Pinus sylvestris-Hylocomium splendens* woodland

4. LOWLAND WOOD PASTURES AND PARKLAND

W15 *Fagus sylvatica-Deschampsia flexuosa* woodland

W16 *Quercus spp.-Betula spp.-Deschampsia flexuosa* woodland

U1 *Festuca ovina-Agrostis capillaris-Raumex acetosella* grassland

U2 *Deschampsia flexuosa* grassland

U3 *Agrostis curtisii* grassland

U4 *Festuca ovina-Agrostis capillaris-Galium saxatile* grassland

MG6 *Lolium perenne-Cynosurus cristatus* grassland

MG9 *Holcus lanatus-Deschampsia cespitosa* grassland

MG10 *Holcus lanatus-Juncus effusus* rush-pasture

M23 *Juncus effusus/acutiflorus-Galium palustre* rush-pasture

M25 *Molinia caerulea-Potentilla erecta* mire

+ scattered trees

5. BOUNDARY FEATURES

W21 *Crataegus monogyna-Hedera helix* scrub

W22 *Prunus spinosa-Rubus fruticosus* scrub

W23 *Ulex europeaus-Rubus fruticosus* scrub

W24 *Rubus fruticosus-Holcus lanatus* underscrub

W25 *Pteridium aquilinum-Rubus fruticosus* underscrub

U1 *Festuca ovina-Agrostis capillaris-Raumex acetosella* grassland

U4 *Festuca ovina-Agrostis capillaris-Galium saxatile* grassland

MG1 *Arrhenatherum elatius* grassland

6. ARABLE

Relevant NVC comunities yet to be published.

7. IMPROVED GRASSLAND

MG6 *Lolium perenne-Cynosurus cristatus* grassland

MG7 *Lolium perenne* leys and related grassland

8. UNIMPROVED NEUTRAL GRASSLAND

MG1 *Arrhenatherum elatius* grassland

MG2 *Arrhenatherum elatius-Filipendula ulmaria* grassland

MG3 *Anthoxanthum odoratum-Geranium sylvaticum* grassland

MG4 *Alopercus pratensis-Sanguisorba officinalis* grassland

MG5 *Cynosurus cristatus-Centaurea nigra* grassland

MG8 *Cynosurus cristatus-Caltha palustris* grassland

9. ACID GRASSLAND

U1 *Festuca ovina-Agrostis capillaris-Raumex acetosella* grassland

U2 *Deschampsia flexuosa* grassland

U3 *Agrostis curtisii* grassland

U4 *Festuca ovina-Agrostis capillaris-Galium saxatile* grassland

U5 *Nardus stricta-Galium saxatile* grassland

U6 *Juncus squarrosus-Festuca ovina* grassland

10. CALCAREOUS GRASSLAND

CG1 *Festuca-ovina-Carlina vulgaris* grassland

CG2 *Festuca ovina-Avenula pratensis* grassland

CG3 *Bromus erectus* grassland

CG4 *Brachypodium pinnatum* grassland

CG5 *Bromus erectus-Brachypodium pinnatum* grassland

CG6 *Avenula pubescens* grassland

CG7 *Festuca ovina-Hieracium pilosella-Thymus praecox/pulegioides* grassland

CG8 *Sesleria albicans-Scabiosa columbaria* grassland

CG9 *Sesleria albicans-Galium sterneri* grassland

CG10 *Festuca ovina-Agrostis capillaris-Thymus praecox* grassland

CG11 *Festuca ovina-Agrostis capillaris-Alchemilla alpina* grassland

11. LOWLAND HEATHLAND

M15 *Scirpus cespitosus-Erica tetralix* wet heath

M16 *Erica tetralix-Sphagnum compactum* wet heath

H1 *Calluna vulgaris-Festuca ovina* heath

H2 *Calluna vulgaris-Ulex minor* heath

H3 *Ulex minor-Agrostis curtisii* heath

H4 *Ulex gallii-Agrostis curtisii* heath

H5 *Erica vagans-Schoenus nigricans* heath

H6 *Erica vagans-Ulex europaeus* heath

H8 *Calluna vulgaris-Ulex gallii* heath

H9 *Calluna vulgaris-Deschampsia flexuosa* heath

H10 *Calluna vulgaris-Erica cinerea* heath

H12 *Calluna vulgaris-Vaccinium myrtillus* heath

H16 *Calluna vulgaris-Arctostaphylos uva-ursi* heath

12. GRAZING MARSH

MG8 *Cynosurus cristatus-Caltha palustris* grassland

MG9 *Holcus lanatus-Deschampsia cespitosa* grassland

MG10 *Holcus lanatus-Juncus effusus* rush-pasture

MG11 *Festuca rubra-Agrostis stolonifera-Potentilla anserina* grassland

MG12 *Festuca arundinacea* grassland

MG13 *Agrostis stolonifera-Alopecurus geniculatus* grassland

Ditches include NVC aquatic communities A1-A6, A8-A13, A15-A16, A19-A21, and NVC swamp communities S4-S8, S12-S14, S16-S18, S20-S23, S25-S26, S28.

13. FENS, CARR, MARSH, SWAMP AND REEDBED

M4 *Carex rostrata-Sphagnum recurvum* mire

M5 *Carex rostrata-Sphagnum squarrosum* mire

M6 *Carex echinata-Sphagnum recurvum/auriculatum* mire

M7 *Carex curta-Sphagnum russowii* mire

M8 *Carex rostrata-Sphagnum warnstorfii* mire
M9 *Carex rostrata-Calligeron cuspidatum/giganteum* mire
M10 *Carex dioica-Pinguicula vulgaris* mire
M11 *Carex demissa-Saxifraga aizoides* mire
M12 *Carex saxatilis* mire
M13 *Schoenus nigricans-Juncus subnodulosus* mire
M14 *Schoenus nigricans-Narthecium ossifragum* mire
M21 *Narthecium ossifragum-Sphagnum papillosum* valley mire
M22 *Juncus subnodulosus-Cirsium palustre* fen meadow
M24 *Molinia caerulea-Cirsium dissectum* fen-meadow
M26 *Molinia caerulea-Crepis paludosa* mire
M25 *Molinia caerulea-Potentilla erecta* mire
M27 *Filipendula ulmaria-Angelica sylvestris* mire
M28 *Iris pseudacorus-Filipendula ulmaria* mire
M29 *Hypericum elodes-Potamogeton polygonifolius* soakway
M30 Related vegetation of seasonally-innundated habitats
M31 *Anthelia julacea-Sphagnum auriculatum* spring
M32 *Philonotis fontana-Saxifraga stellaris* spring
M33 *Pohlia wahlenbergii var. glacialis* spring
M34 *Carex demissa-Koenigia islandica* flush
M35 *Ranunculus omniophyllus-Montia fontana* rill
M36 Lowland springs and streambanks of shaded situations
M37 *Cratoneuron commutatum-Festuca rubra* spring
M38 *Cratoneuron commutatum-Carex nigra* spring
S1 *Carex elata* sedge-swamp
S2 *Cladium mariscus* sedge-swamp
S3 *Carex paniculata* sedge-swamp
S4 *Phragmites australis* swamp and reed-beds
S5 *Glycera maxima* swamp
S6 *Carex riparia* swamp
S7 *Carex acutiformis* swamp
S8 *Scirpus lacustris* ssp. *lacustris* swamp
S9 *Carex rostrata* swamp
S10 *Equisetum fluviatile* swamp
S11 *Carex vesicaria* swamp
S12 *Typha latifolia* swamp
S13 *Typha angustifolia* swamp
S14 *Sparganium erectum* swamp
S15 *Acorus calamus* swamp
S16 *Sagittaria sagittifolia* swamp
S17 *Carex psuedocyperus* swamp
S18 *Carex otrubae* swamp
S19 *Eleocharis palustris* swamp
S20 *Scirpus lacustris* ssp. *tabernaemontani* swamp
S21 *Scirpus maritimus* swamp
S22 *Glyceria fluitans* swamp
S23 Other water-margin vegetation
S24 *Phragmites australis-Peucedanum palustre* fen
S25 *Phragmites australis-Eupatorium cannabinum* fen
S26 *Phragmites australis-Urtica dioica* fen
S27 *Carex rostrata-Potentilla palustris* fen
S28 *Phalaris arundinacea* fen
W1 *Salix cinerea-Galium palustre* woodland
W2 *Salix cinerea-Betula pubescens-Phragmites australis* woodland
W3 *Salix pentandra-Carex rostrata* woodland
W4 *Betula pubescens-Molinia caerulea* woodland
W5 *Alnus glutinosa-Carex paniculata* woodland
W6 *Alnus glutinosa-Urtica dioica* woodland

14. LOWLAND RAISED BOG

M1 *Sphagnum auriculatum* bog pool community
M2 *Sphagnum cuspidatum/recurvum* bog pool community
M3 *Eriophorum angustifolium* bog pool community

M15 *Scirpus cespitosus-Erica tetralix* wet heath
M16 *Erica tetralix-Sphagnum compactum* wet heath
M17 *Scirpus cespitosus-Eriophorum vaginatum* blanket mire
M18 *Erica tetralix-Sphagnum papillosum* raised and blanket mire
M19 *Calluna vulgaris-Eriophorum vaginatum* blanket mire
M20 *Eriophorum vaginatum* blanket and raised mire

15. STANDING OPEN WATER

A1 *Lemna gibba* community
A2 *Lemna minor* community
A3 *Spirodela polyrhiza-Hydrocharis morsus-ranae* community
A4 *Hydrocharis morsus-ranae-Stratiotes aloides* community
A5 *Ceratophyllum demersum* community
A6 *Ceratophyllum submersum* community
A7 *Nymphaea alba* community
A8 *Nuphar lutea* community
A9 *Potamogeton natans* community
A10 *Polygonum amphibium* community
A11 *Potamogeton pectinatus-Myriophyllum spicatum* community
A12 *Potamogeton pectinatus* community
A13 *Potamogeton perfoliatus-Myriophyllum alterniflorum* community
A14 *Myriophyllum alterniflorum* community
A15 *Elodea canadensis* community
A16 *Callitriche stagnalis* community
A19 *Ranunculus aquatilis* community
A20 *Ranunculus peltatus* community
A21 *Ranunculus baudotii* community
A22 *Littorella uniflora-Lobelia dortmanna* community
A23 *Isoetes lacustris/setacea* community
A24 *Juncus bulbosus* community

16. RIVERS AND STREAMS

A2 *Lemna minor* community
A8 *Nuphar lutea* community
A9 *Potamogeton natans* community
A11 *Potamogeton pectinatus-Myriophyllum spicatum* community
A12 *Potamogeton pectinatus* community
A13 *Potamogeton perfoliatus-Myriophyllum alterniflorum* community
A14 *Myriophyllum alterniflorum* community
A15 *Elodea canadensis* community
A16 *Callitriche stagnalis* community
A17 *Ranunculus penicillatus* ssp. *pseudofluitans* community
A18 *Ranunculus fluitans* community
A19 *Ranunculus aquatilis* community
A20 *Ranunculus peltatus* community

17. CANALS

A1 *Lemna gibba* community
A2 *Lemna minor* community
A3 *Spirodela polyrhiza-Hydrocharis morsus-ranae* community
A5 *Ceratophyllum demersum* community
A7 *Nymphaea alba* community
A8 *Nuphar lutea* community
A9 *Potamogeton natans* community
A10 *Polygonum amphibium* community
A11 *Potamogeton pectinatus-Myriophyllum spicatum* community
A12 *Potamogeton pectinatus* community
A13 *Potamogeton perfoliatus-Myriophyllum alterniflorum* community
A15 *Elodea canadensis* community

A16 *Callitriche stagnalis* community
A19 *Ranunculus aquatilis* community
A20 *Ranunculus peltatus* community
Canals may also support the NVC swamp communities S4-S8,
S12, S14-S18, S20, S22-S23, S25-S26, S28.

18. MONTANE (ALPINE AND SUB-ALPINE TYPES)

H12 *Calluna vulgaris-Vaccinium myrtillus* heath
H13 *Calluna vulgaris-Cladonia arbuscula* heath
H14 *Calluna vulgaris-Racomitrium lanuginosum* heath
H15 *Calluna vulgaris-Juniperus communis* ssp. nana heath
H16 *Calluna vulgaris-Arctostaphylos uva-ursi* heath
H17 *Calluna vulgaris-Arctostaphylos alpinus* heath
H18 *Vaccinium myrtillus-Deschampsia flexuosa* heath
H19 *Vaccinium myrtillus-Cladonia arbuscula* heath
H20 *Vaccinium myrtillus-Racomitrium lanuginosum* heath
H21 *Calluna vulgaris-Vaccinium myrtillus-Sphagnum capillifolium*
heath
H22 *Vaccinium myrtillus-Rubus chamaemorus* heath
U7 *Nardus stricta-Carex bigelowii* grass heath0
U8 *Carex bigelowii-Polytrichum alpinum* sedge heath
U9 *Juncus trifidus-Racomitrium lanuginosum* rush-heath
U10 *Carex bigelowii-Racomitrium lanuginosum* moss heath
U11 *Polytrichum sexangulare-Kiaeria starkei* snow-bed
U12 *Salix herbacea-Racomitrium heterostichum* snow-bed
U13 *Deschampsia cespitosa-Galium saxatile* grassland
U14 *Alchemilla alpina-Sibbaldia procumbens* dwarf-herb
community
U15 *Saxifraga aizoides-Alchemilla glabra* banks
CG12 *Festuca ovina-Alchemilla alpina-Silene acualis* dwarf-herb
heath
CG13 *Dryas octopetala-Carex flacca* heath
CG14 *Dryas octopetala-Silene acualis* ledge community
W20 *Salix lapponum-Luzula sylvatica* scrub

19. UPLAND HEATHLAND

M15 *Scirpus cespitosus-Erica tetralix* wet heath
M16 *Erica tetralix-Sphagnum compactum* wet heath
H4 *Ulex gallii-Agrostis curtisii* heath
H8 *Calluna vulgaris-Ulex gallii* heath
H9 *Calluna vulgaris-Deschampsia flexuosa* heath
H10 *Calluna vulgaris-Erica cinerea* heath
H12 *Calluna vulgaris-Vaccinium myrtillus* heath
H16 *Calluna vulgaris-Arctostaphylos uva-ursi* heath
H18 *Vaccinium myrtillus-Deschampsia flexuosa* heath
H21 *Calluna vulgaris-Vaccinium myrtillus-Sphagnum capillifolium*
heath

20. BLANKET BOG

M1 *Sphagnum auriculatum* bog pool community
M2 *Sphagnum cuspidatum/recurvum* bog pool community
M3 *Eriophorum angustifolium* bog pool community
M15 *Scirpus cespitosus-Erica tetralix* wet heath
M16 *Erica tetralix-Sphagnum compactum* wet heath
M17 *Scirpus cespitosus-Eriophorum vaginatum* blanket mire
M18 *Erica tetralix-Sphagnum papillosum* raised and blanket mire
M19 *Calluna vulgaris-Eriophorum vaginatum* blanket mire
M20 *Eriophorum vaginatum* blanket and raised mire
M25 *Molinia caerulea-Potentilla erecta* mire
A number of other NVC communities associated with
soligenous soils may be found on blanket bogs.

21. MARITIME CLIFF AND SLOPE

MC1 *Crithmum maritimum-Spergularia rupicola* maritime rock-
crevice community
MC2 *Armeria maritima-Lingusticum scoticum* maritime rock-
crevice community
MC3 *Rhodiola rosea-Aremeria maritima* maritime cliff-ledge
community
MC4 *Brassica oleracea* maritime cliff-ledge community
MC5 *Armeria maritima-Cerastium diffusum* ssp. *diffusum*
maritime therophyte community
MC6 *Atriplex hastata-Beta vulgaris* ssp. *maritima* seabird cliff
community
MC7 *Stellaria media-Rumex acetosa* seabird cliff community
MC8 *Festuca rubra-Armeria maritima* maritime grassland
MC9 *Festuca rubra-Holcus lanatus* maritime grassland
MC10 *Festuca rubra-Plantago* spp. maritime grassland
MC11 *Festuca rubra-Daucus carota* ssp. *gummifer* maritime
grassland
MC12 *Festuca rubra-Hyacinthoides non-scripta* maritime
grassland
H6 *Erica vagans- Ulex europaeus* heath
H7 *Calluna vulgaris-Scilla verna* heath
H8 *Calluna vulgaris-Ulex gallii* heath
+ other non-NVC vegetation of soft rock cliffs.

22. SHINGLE ABOVE HIGH TIDE MARK

SD1 *Rumex crispus-Glaucium flavum* shingle beach community
A large number of other NVC communities may occur on
shingle.

23. BOULDERS AND ROCK ABOVE THE HIGH TIDE

24. COASTAL STRANDLINE

SD2 *Honkenya peploides-Cakile maritima* strandline community
SD3 *Matricaria maritima-Galium aparine* shingle beach
community

25. MACHAIR

SD6 *Ammophila arenaria* mobile dune community
SD7 *Ammophila arenaria-Festuca rubra* semi-fixed dune
community
SD8 *Festuca rubra-Galium verum* fixed dune grassland
MG8 *Cynosurus cristatus-Caltha palustris* grassland
MG10 *Holcus lanatus-Juncus effusus* rush-pasture
MG11 *Festuca rubra-Agrostis stolonifera-Potentilla anserina*
grassland
+ a wide range of other associated swamp and aquatic
communities.

26. SALTMARSH

SM2 *Ruppia maritima* saltmarsh
SM3 *Eleocharis parvula* saltmarsh
SM4 *Spartina maritima* saltmarsh
SM5 *Spartina alterniflora* saltmarsh
SM6 *Spartina anglica* saltmarsh
SM7 *Arthrocnemum perenne* stands
SM8 Annual *Salicornia* saltmarsh
SM9 *Suaeda maritima* saltmarsh
SM10 Transitional low-marsh vegetation
SM11 *Aster tripolium* var. *discoideus* saltmarsh
SM12 Rayed *Aster tripolium* saltmarsh
SM13 *Puccinellia maritima* saltmarsh

SM14 *Halimione portulacoides* saltmarsh
SM15 *Juncus maritimus-Triglochin maritima* saltmarsh
SM16 *Festuca rubra* saltmarsh
SM17 *Artemisia maritima*
SM18 *Juncus maritimus* commuNity
SM19 *Blysmus rufus* saltmarsh
SM20 *Eleocharis uniglumis* community
SM21 *Suaeda vera-Limonium binervosum* saltmarsh
SM22 *Halimione portulacoides-Frankenia laevis* saltmarsh
SM23 *Spergularia marina-Puccinellia distans* saltmarsh
SM24 *Elymus pycnanthus* saltmarsh
SM25 *Suaeda vera* saltmarsh
SM26 *Inula crithmoides* on saltmarshes
SM27 Ephemeral saltmarsh vegetation with *Sagina maritima*
SM28 *Elymus repens* saltmarsh

27. SAND DUNE

SD2 *Honkenya peploides-Cakile maritima* strandline community
SD3 *Matricaria maritima-Galium aparine* shingle beach community
SD4 *Elymus farctus* spp. *boreali-atlanticus* foredune community
SD5 *Leymus arenarius* mobile dune community
SD6 *Ammophila arenaria* mobile dune community
SD7 *Ammophila arenaria-Festuca rubra* semi-fixed dune community
SD8 *Festuca rubra-Galium verum* fixed dune grassland
SD9 *Ammophila arenaria-Arrhenatherum elatius* grassland
SD10 *Carex arenaria* dune community
SD11 *Carex arenaria-Cornicularia aculeata* dune community
SD12 *Carex arenaria-Festuca ovina-Agrostis capillaris* grassland
SD13 *Salix-repens-Bryum pseudotriquetrum* dune slack community
SD14 *Salix repens-Campylium stellatum* dune slack community
SD15 *Salix repens-Calliergon cuspidatum* dune slack community
SD16 *Salix repens-Holcus lanatus* dune slack community
SD17 *Potentilla anserina-Carex nigra* dune slack community
SD18 *Hippophae rhamnoides* dune scrub
H11 *Calluna vulgaris-Carex arenaria* heath
H1 *Calluna vulgaris-Festuca ovina* heath (*Carex arenaria* subcommunity)
H10 *Calluna vulgaris-Erica cinerea* heath
M15 *Scirpus cespitosus-Erica tetralix* wet heath
M16 *Erica tetralix-Sphagnum compactum* wet heath

28. ESTUARIES

SM1 *Zostera* communities
The MNCR classification (currently incomplete) provides biotopes for these areas.
N.B. Saltmarshes, an integral component of estuarine systems, are considered separately.

29. SALINE LAGOONS

SM1 *Zostera* communities
The MNCR classification (currently incomplete) provides biotopes for these areas.

30. ISLANDS AND ARCHIPELAGOS

SM1 *Zostera* communities
The MNCR classification (currently incomplete) provides biotopes for these areas.

31. INLETS AND ENCLOSED BAYS (INCLUDING SEA LOCHS, RIAS AND VOES)

SM1 *Zostera* communities
The MNCR classification (currently incomplete) provides biotopes for these areas.

32. OPEN COAST

SM1 *Zostera* communities
The MNCR classification (currently incomplete) provides biotopes for these areas.

33. OPEN SEA WATER COLUMN

MNCR biotopes classification currently unavailable for these areas.

34. SHELF BREAK

MNCR biotopes classification currently unavailable for these areas.

35. OFFSHORE SEABED

MNCR biotopes classification currently unavailable for these areas.

36. LIMESTONE PAVEMENTS

CG2 *Festuca ovina-Avenula pratensis* grassland
CG9 *Seslaria albicans-Galium sterneri* grassland
W8 *Fraxinus excelsior-Acer campestre-Mercurialis perennis* woodland
W9 *Fraxinus excelsior-Sorbus aucuparia-Mercurialis perennis* woodland
W21 *Crataegus monogyna-Hedera helix* scrub
U22 *Asplenium trichomanes-Asplenium ruta-muraria* community
U23 *Asplenium viridis-Cystopteris fragilis*
U24 *Arrenatherum elatius-Geranium robertianum* community
H8 *Calluna vulgaris-Ulex gallii* heath (*Sanguisorba minor* sub-community)

37. URBAN

ANNEX G
SPECIES ACTION PLANS, HABITAT ACTION PLANS AND HABITAT STATEMENTS

ANNEX G: THE ACTION PLANS

INTRODUCTION

This volume of the Biodiversity Steering Group report contains 116 key species action plans and 14 plans for the conservation of our most threatened habitats. It also contains 37 statements for the broad habitat types which make up the land surface of the UK and the surrounding sea to the edge of the continental shelf in the Atlantic Ocean. These identify the main issues which need to be addressed to conserve each habitat type and allow it to retain its value to biodiversity.

SPECIES ACTION PLANS

During preparation of the species action plans, a number of issues and actions were identified which were common to most, or all of the plans. These are summarised in the following paragraphs. When a detailed action plan is prepared for any species, these generic issues should, where relevant, be incorporated into the plan.

Responsibility for actions

Statutory agencies are tasked with taking forward most of the actions in section 5 of the plans. The action lists do not include non-governmental organisations, but it should be emphasised that the success of many plans requires effective collaboration between the statutory, voluntary and other sectors.

Rationale for targets

In some cases specific details of why the target was chosen have been included. There are, however, a number of reasons for target selection which apply generally.

Some species have been selected for priority action as a result of a decline in their range or distribution. Consequently, many plans identify the need to restore species to their former range through translocation or re-establishment of viable populations. Implementation of a translocation or re-introduction programme should begin only after the reasons for each species' decline have been identified, and research has been undertaken into habitat restoration and the most appropriate translocation methods.

Research and survey is an important objective for many species, particularly where the factors leading to a species' decline or rarity are not known. In some cases there may be unknown colonies still waiting to be discovered. Site management targets are needed where the needs of a species are not being met by current management practices, and where neglect is leading to ecological change making sites less suitable.

Where it is recommended to increase the total number of colonies of a very rare species, a minimum of five is sometimes chosen as this will reduce the risk of chance events leading to extinction. In other cases the target aims to maintain existing populations or colonies in the core areas of a species distribution.

Proposed translocations or re-introduction programmes should conform to the IUCN translocation guidelines.

Legislative protection

The UK offers legislative protection to many species of plants and animals under Schedules 5 and 8 of the Wildlife and Countryside Act 1981 and the Nature Conservation and Amenity Lands (Northern Ireland) Order 1985. Provision exists for a review of the Schedules every five years. This process should be used to add new species to the Schedules, where this is thought necessary or beneficial for their conservation, and to review the effectiveness of continuing protection for species which are already listed.

Site Protection

The Wildlife and Countryside Act 1981 and the Nature Conservation and Amenity Lands (Northern Ireland) Order 1985 are the statutory foundation of nature conservation in this country. Species and habitats are protected through a network of some 6,000 SSSIs and ASSIs covering almost two million hectares. These will continue to be used as the basis for securing the conservation and enhancement of the best sites for wildlife.

Government policy is to encourage voluntary co-operation in managing sites to achieve favourable conservation status for key species. In many cases this will prove effective. For some of the species in the action plans further statutory site protection is required. We have therefore specifically recommended site notification where this offers a clear and immediate benefit.

Monitoring

An essential part of the conservation action for species is to measure the changes in their conservation status against targets in the plans. The plans are written on the assumption that existing schemes for monitoring species' distribution, abundance and population trends are continued and refined as necessary, and that where required, new schemes are established to inform future action.

Action plan review

The detailed plans should be reviewed on a five-yearly basis to ensure that they reflect up-to-date knowledge. For those species listed on the Wildlife and Countryside Act 1981, the action plan review should be timed to correspond with the five-yearly review of the Schedules. Information obtained from the action plan reviews should be used to inform the six-yearly reporting requirement for those species listed under the Habitats Directive (with the initial report scheduled for the year 2000).

International co-operation

International co-operation and the exchange of information are fundamental aspects of the Convention on Biological Diversity. Many species were selected for priority action in the UK on the basis of their international conservation status. The provision and exchange of information should be undertaken at both European and worldwide levels where this can support the species and inform action either within the UK or in other countries.

Air quality and climate change

A significant threat to species and habitat conservation is the effects of changes in air quality. In addition, climate change as a consequence of global warming may become a significant factor in the long term. Such widespread effects are difficult to quantify and cannot usually be addressed through individual species action plans. Consequently, relevant actions are only specified where local implementation offers direct benefit to the species concerned.

Development

Many species need conservation action because of the loss or fragmentation of suitable habitat due to development of land. Those species and others remain vulnerable to further loss and development planning needs to take this into account.

HABITAT ACTION PLANS AND STATEMENTS

Without mankind's intervention, the natural terrestrial habitat over much of the UK would be forest. Human influence has, however, shaped our surroundings over thousands of years, starting with the first tilling of the soil and building of a permanent homestead by ancient man. Through natural selection, flora and fauna have taken advantage of the opportunities offered to them by these developments and have adapted to fill niches in nature caused by human progress.

In seeking to conserve habitats we should, therefore, recognise that it would be not only impractical but undesirable to turn back the clock and try to recreate a Garden of Eden. Such action would now threaten the survival of many of the species to be found in our islands. For that reason, each habitat type we have in the UK is regarded sympathetically, and its unique contribution to biodiversity is recognised through its own conservation statement.

Definition of "habitat"

In the past the conservation of habitats has been undertaken because they are home to certain rare and endangered species, rather than for their own sake. In this report we have considered each habitat to be an assemblage of plants and animals found together, as well as the geographical area and features on which they exist.

Principal threats

One of the principal threats identified in many of the species conservation action plans is that posed by habitat fragmentation. Apart from the population limits imposed by decreasing geographical boundaries, isolated communities of plants and animals are more at risk of eradication from disease, loss of genetic vigour because of in-breeding, and other natural or man-made threats.

A key conservation aim for many species is, therefore, to create conditions that allow particularly fragmented habitats to expand or, in the case of animal species, to retain or create wildlife corridors allowing natural migration, escape from danger and inter-breeding. By concentrating action for implementing the targets on prime biodiversity areas (where concentrations of high priority habitats occur) as recommended in Annex C of this Report (Developing Local Biodiversity Action Plans), these conditions will be achieved in the most cost effective way.

Several other threats are identified in the action plans and conservation statements. Inappropriate management of woodlands, moors and other farmed habitats was seen to be a major problem. This included over-grazing in upland woods and moors, under-grazing of semi-natural lowland habitats, and unsympathetic felling rates or species planting in forests and woodlands. The Steering Group felt that in many cases these threats could be effectively countered by provision of advice to land managers, though often this would need to be bolstered by other action.

Excessive ground water and surface water abstraction leading to a lowering of water levels are also identified as threats, as is the interruption of natural coastal processes through the building of sea defences, and dredging activities affecting sediment supply. Airborne pollution by sulphur, nitrogen oxides and other emissions, and marine pollution and contamination by oil, nutrients and persistent, bio-accumulating chemicals are identified as a danger to both terrestrial and marine habitats.

A thorough analysis of the main issues and themes arising from species action plans, habitat action plans and habitat statements was carried out as part of the process of preparing this Report. These issues and the appropriate conservation measures that would benefit species and habitats are discussed more fully in Chapter 5.

Rationale for conservation targets

Because of the particular problem that habitat fragmentation presents, the targets in relevant action plans have been designed to help towards the reversal of fragmentation through re-creation in appropriate areas. Another consideration is that each habitat needs to be managed so it can support the full range of dependent species: targets for restoration address the problem of deterioration in the quality through neglect or mis-management of some habitats. *Biodiversity: The UK Action Plan* contains the objective to conserve the natural range of species. Where appropriate, habitat action plan targets are designed to secure this end.

Habitat Statements

These habitat statements, covering the whole of the UK, provide a context for the preparation of the costed Action Plans for Species and Habitats.

Each contains a description of the current status of the habitat, the factors affecting it, current action in hand and a conservation direction, drawing on the threats to the habitat. The statements include the Group's preliminary findings on the measures which need to be addressed to conserve UK biodiversity.

The Table of Issues (see Volume One, Chapter 5) takes account of this work, which will also inform the action plans still to be completed. The statements are also intended to assist all concerned at the national and local level in taking forward and focusing work to conserve UK biodiversity.

MAMMALS

WATER VOLE (ARVICOLA TERRESTRIS)

1. CURRENT STATUS

1.1 The water vole is found throughout Britain but is confined mainly to lowland areas near water. Once common and widespread, this species has suffered a significant decline in numbers and distribution. A national survey in 1989-90 failed to find signs of voles in 67% of sites where they were previously recorded and it is estimated that this will rise to 94% by the turn of the century. A recent population estimate based on the number of latrines found suggested a total GB pre-breeding population of 1,200,000 animals.

1.2 As the lower reaches of rivers become unsuitable for habitation, the distribution of water voles becomes discontinuous and existing sites become isolated and vulnerable. There are few data available on the ecology or conservation requirements of this species as its former common status means that it has attracted little study.

1.3 The water vole is being considered for addition to parts of Schedule 9 of the WCA 1981.

2. CURRENT FACTORS CAUSING LOSS OR DECLINE

2.1 Loss and fragmentation of habitats.

2.2 Disturbance of riparian habitats.

2.3 Predation by mink.

2.4 Pollution of watercourses and poisoning by rodenticides.

3. CURRENT ACTION

3.1 A national survey for water vole was conducted by the Vincent Wildlife Trust in 1989-90.

3.2 Research, funded by Oxford University and the NRA, is now underway on the relationship between mink and water voles, on movements and on winter activity.

4. ACTION PLAN OBJECTIVES AND TARGETS

4.1 Maintain the current distribution and abundance of the species in the UK.

4.2 Ensure that water voles are present throughout their 1970s range by the year 2010, considering habitat management and possible translocation of populations to areas from where they have been lost.

5. PROPOSED ACTIONS AND LEAD AGENCIES

5.1 Policy and legislation

5.1.1 Following further research to identify the ecological requirements of this species, seek to ensure that these are taken into account when setting water quality objectives for occupied standing and running waters. (ACTION: NRA, SEPA)

5.1.2 Promote favourable management of riparian habitats to favour the water vole. (ACTION: NRA, SEPA)

5.2 Site safeguard and management

5.2.1 Seek to include the needs of water voles in management of SSSIs or Wildlife Sites. (ACTION: CCW, EN, SNH)

5.2.2 Seek to avoid the use of rodenticides and herbicides, particularly Paraquat, in riparian habitat where water voles would be at risk. (ACTION: LAs, MAFF, NRA, SEPA, SOAEFD, WOAD)

5.2.3 Seek to develop and implement catchment management plans for all catchments supporting water vole populations, initially targeting priority areas and completing the process by 2005. (ACTION: NRA, SEPA)

5.3 Species management and protection

5.3.1 Discourage the illegal use of rodenticides in areas supporting water voles and ensure all offenders are prosecuted. (ACTION: MAFF, SOAEFD, WOAD)

5.3.2 Following further investigation on the effects of mink predation and, if deemed to be appropriate, encourage control of mink in the existing water vole range. (ACTION: MAFF, SOAEFD, WOAD)

5.3.3 Identify potential sites for water vole habitation and seek to secure agreements with landowners to control mink if these should pose a threat to any population likely to establish. (ACTION: LAs, MAFF, SOAEFD, WOAD)

5.4 Advisory

5.4.1 Ensure the provision of advice to relevant authorities and riparian owners on the conservation problems of the species. (ACTION: CCW, EN, NRA, SEPA, SNH)

5.5 Future research and monitoring

5.5.1 Promote research to quantify the effects of mink predation on water voles, and assess the logistics and efficacy of mink control. (ACTION: CCW, EN, JNCC, SNH)

5.5.2 Undertake research to identify the causes of decline and appropriate measures to arrest it, including interactions with mink, effects of habitat fragmentation, and the effect of rodenticides and herbicides in riparian habitats. (ACTION: CCW, EN, JNCC, NRA, SEPA, SNH)

5.5.3 Seek to establish a National Water Vole Monitoring Scheme based on indices and regular survey of key sites in all counties. (ACTION: CCW, EN, JNCC, SNH)

5.5.4 Survey to determine the distribution of the water voles throughout Britain, identifying key populations in all counties and regions. (ACTION: CCW, EN, JNCC, SNH)

5.5.5 Promote research to evaluate the use of translocation programmes in restoring populations where they have been lost. (ACTION: CCW, EN, JNCC, SNH)

5.5.6 Pass information gathered during survey and monitoring of this species to JNCC or BRC so that it can be incorporated in a national database and contribute to the maintenance of an up-to-date Red List. (ACTION: CCW, EN, SNH)

5.6 Communications and publicity

5.6.1 Raise awareness and improve understanding of the water vole as an indicator species of the quality of riparian habitats. (ACTION: CCW, EN, NRA, SNH)

BROWN HARE (*LEPUS EUROPAEUS*)

1. CURRENT STATUS

1.1 The brown hare is a common and conspicuous farmland species in Britain, probably introduced by the Romans in ancient times. It is widespread, but is absent from the north-west and western Highlands, where is it replaced by the mountain hare (*Lepus timidus*). The brown hare is present in Northern Ireland as a relatively recent introduction, where it competes with the indigenous mountain hare. Because of this, further action to support the population in Northern Ireland is discouraged, and this action plan is relevant only to the British mainland.

1.2 Formerly considered abundant, the brown hare appears to have undergone a substantial decline in numbers since the early 1960s, with population estimates now varying between 817,500 and 1,250,000. Information from shooting estates suggests that hare numbers have remained stable for the past ten years, although other evidence of this is unclear. Similar patterns of population change appear to have occurred throughout much of Europe.

2. CURRENT FACTORS CAUSING LOSS OR DECLINE

2.1 Conversion of grassland to arable.

2.2 Loss of habitat diversity in the agricultural landscape.

2.3 Changes in planting and cropping regimes, such as a move from hay to silage, and autumn planting of cereals.

3. CURRENT ACTION

3.1 Various aspects of hare ecology have been studied in Britain at The Game Conservancy Trust, Bristol University and Oxford University.

3.2 Populations are currently monitored through numbers of hares seen or shot during hunting, or numbers counted in spring.

3.3 JNCC commissioned a survey from Bristol University which provides a baseline against which conservation policies and action may be assessed.

3.4 Experimental work in Denmark suggests that simplified farming systems lead to reduced breeding performance. This appears to account for the link between hare numbers and farming pattern.

4. ACTION PLAN OBJECTIVES AND TARGETS

4.1 Maintain and expand existing populations, doubling spring numbers in Britain by 2010.

5. PROPOSED ACTION WITH LEAD AGENCIES

5.1 Policy and legislation

5.1.1 Take account of the requirements of the brown hare when reviewing or developing agri-environmental schemes. (ACTION: CC, MAFF, SOAEFD, WO)

5.1.2 Consider the requirements of this species in any negotiations on changes to, or reform of, agricultural support, seeking to enhance the integration of livestock with arable farming. (ACTION: CC, MAFF, SOAEFD, WO)

5.1.3 Encourage the uptake of the new flexible set-aside scheme instead of rotational set aside, thereby allowing it to be left in place for two years and providing greater benefit to this species. (ACTION: ADAS, MAFF, SOAEFD, WOAD)

5.1.4 Review the use of legislation pertaining to shooting and selling of hares in the light of research findings on the seasonality of reproduction. (ACTION: CCW, DOE, EN, JNCC, SNH, SOAEFD, WO)

5.2 Site safeguard and management

5.2.1 No action proposed.

5.3 Species management and protection

5.3.1 Seek to develop a strategy for the conservation and monitoring of the brown hare (possibly as part of a wider mammals strategy). (ACTION: CCW, EN, SNH, JNCC)

5.3.2 Review legislation pertaining to the shooting and selling of the hare in the light of new research findings on the seasonality of hare productivity. (ACTION: DoE, JNCC)

5.4 Advisory

5.4.1 Prepare and distribute a management advisory booklet for hares. (ACTION: JNCC)

5.5 Future research and monitoring

5.5.1 Promote further research to assess the effects of different agricultural practices (e.g. crops planted, cutting dates and cutting methods) on brown hare populations. (ACTION: EN, SNH)

5.5.2 Investigate the relative economic importance of hares as either a game species or a pest, to assist farmers make informed choices in hare management. (ACTION: MAFF, SOAEFD, WOAD)

5.5.3 Repeat the National Hare Survey at appropriate intervals. (ACTION: JNCC)

5.5.4 Pass information gathered during survey and monitoring of this species to JNCC in order that it can be incorporated in a national database and contribute to the maintenance of an up-to-date Red List. (ACTION: CCW, EN, SNH)

5.6 Communications and publicity

5.6.1 Use the popularity of brown hares to highlight the impact on biodiversity of modern agricultural practices and loss of mixed farms. (ACTION: CCW, EN, JNCC, SNH)

OTTER (LUTRA LUTRA)

1. CURRENT STATUS

1.1 Formerly widespread throughout the UK, the otter underwent a rapid decline in numbers from the 1950s to 1970s and was effectively lost from midland and south-eastern counties of England by the 1980s. Populations remain in Wales, south-west England and much of Scotland, where sea loch and coastal colonies comprise one of the largest populations in Europe. There is also a significant population of otters in Northern Ireland. The decline now appears to have halted and sightings are being reported in former habitats.

1.2 The otter is listed on Appendix I of CITES, Appendix II of the Bern Convention and Annexes II and IV of the Habitats Directive. It is protected under Schedule 5 of the WCA 1981 and Schedule 2 of the Conservation (Natural Habitats, etc.) Regulations, 1994 (Regulation 38). The European sub-species is also listed as globally threatened on the IUCN/WCMC RDL.

2. CURRENT FACTORS CAUSING LOSS OR DECLINE

2.1 Pollution of watercourses, especially by PCBs.

2.2 Insufficient prey associated with poor water quality.

2.3 Impoverished bankside habitat features needed for breeding and resting.

2.4 Incidental mortality, primarily by road deaths and drowning in eel traps.

3. CURRENT ACTION

3.1 The JNCC has prepared a *Framework for Otter Conservation in the UK 1995-2000*.

3.2 National surveys have been conducted every five to seven years. Local surveys by Wildlife Trusts and other organisations have established the present distribution and potential for future spread in many areas.

3.3 Research is in progress on the implications of heavy metal and PCB contamination in fish and ecosystems.

3.4 Conservation management (for example creating log piles and artificial holts, and designation of "otter havens") has proved successful in many river catchments.

3.5 The Habitat Scheme Water Fringe Option administered by MAFF is being used to manage waterside habitat in six pilot areas. MAFF also provides advice on creating otter havens on set-aside.

3.6 FA and FE promote sensitive woodland management and expansion to favour otters, through preparation and implementation of their Forest and Water Guidelines, e.g. managing riparian areas with deciduous trees and shrubs mixed with open grassland and wetland habitat, and the prevention of sediments and other pollution.

3.7 Two SACs have been proposed for this species under the EC Habitats Directive.

4. ACTION PLAN OBJECTIVES AND TARGETS

4.1 Maintain and expand existing otter populations.

4.2 By 2010, restore breeding otters all catchments and coastal areas where they have been recorded since 1960.

5. PROPOSED ACTION WITH LEAD AGENCIES

5.1 Policy and legislation

5.1.1 Seek to secure agreement on the UK Framework for Otter Conservation. (ACTION: JNCC)

5.1.2 Seek to ensure management agreements and incentive schemes (e.g.: ESAs, Countryside Stewardship and Tir Cymen) take account of the requirements of otters in occupied areas. (ACTION: DANI, MAFF, SOAEFD, WOAD)

5.1.3 Seek to determine by 2000 Statutory Water Quality Objectives for standing and running waters in Britain which will sustain otters. (ACTION: DoE, NRA, OFWAT, SEPA, SOAEFD, Water Services Association, WO)

5.1.4 Review the protection afforded to otters by current legislation and investigate the usefulness and appropriateness of licensing to control release of otters. (ACTION: CCW, DoE, EN, JNCC, SNH)

5.1.5 Identify and resolve problems with existing legislation. Seek to clarify the definition of "trap" in the WCA 1981 and resolve inconsistencies over the use of otter guards on fishtraps. (ACTION: CCW, DoE, EN, JNCC, SNH)

5.2 Site safeguard and management

5.2.1 Seek to include action for otters in Catchment Management Plans for all rivers containing otter populations by 2005, including "otter havens" in relevant areas. (ACTION: DANI, NRA, SEPA, MAFF, WOAD)

5.2.2 Continue to secure appropriate management of riparian habitats and catchments in woodlands to maintain or enhance otter populations. (ACTION: FA)

5.3 Species management and protection

5.3.1 Seek to establish an "Otter Forum" to co-ordinate conservation, information exchange, publicity and research. (ACTION: JNCC)

5.3.2 Ensure otter releases are carried out only under the guidelines set out in the Framework for Otter Conservation. (ACTION: CCW, DoE(NI), EN, SNH, JNCC)

5.3.3 Attempt to limit accidental killing or injury (for example by provision of road underpasses and dyke net guards), particularly on key catchments. (ACTION: DoE(NI), DOT, LAs, NRA, SEPA)

5.4 Advisory

5.4.1 Ensure the provision of information on otter requirements and conservation to key groups, to include land owners, through the publication of posters and guidelines. (ACTION: CCW, DoE(NI), EN, FA, SNH)

5.5 Future research and monitoring

5.5.1 Collate information on prey productivity, biomass and pollution in occupied and likely re-colonisation areas. (ACTION: DANI, DoE(NI), ITE, JNCC, NRA, SEPA, SOAEFD, WOAD)

5.5.2 Develop a standard methodology to analyse the level of pollution accumulation in otters. (ACTION: DANI, DoE(NI), JNCC, NRA, SEPA, SOAEFD, WOAD)

5.5.3 Investigate the effects of disturbance on otter populations. (ACTION: DoE(NI), JNCC, NRA, SEPA)

5.5.4 Develop and implement methods to estimate otter numbers and permit population modelling. (ACTION: DoE(NI), JNCC, NRA, SEPA)

5.5.5 Monitor populations and distribution of otters throughout the UK, including local survey to monitor the expansion of fringe populations. (ACTION: JNCC)

5.5.6 Pass information gathered during survey and monitoring of this species to JNCC in order that it can be incorporated in a national database and contribute to the maintenance of an up-to-date Red List. (ACTION: CCW, DoE(NI), EN, SNH)

5.6 Communications and publicity

5.6.1 Use this popular species to publicise the importance of water quality and riparian habitats to biodiversity. (ACTION: CCW, DoE(NI), EN, FA, JNCC, SNH, NRA, SEPA)

DORMOUSE (MUSCARDINUS AVELLANARIUS)

I. CURRENT STATUS

1.1 The dormouse does not occur in Scotland or Northern Ireland. In Wales, there are few known populations and in England it has become extinct in up to 7 counties (comprising half its former range) in the past 100 years. It is absent from the north, except for small populations in Cumbria and Northumberland, and although dormice are still widespread in southern counties (Devon to Kent), they are patchily distributed. Population densities everywhere are less than 10 adults per hectare, even in good habitats.

1.2 The dormouse is listed on Appendix 3 of the Bonn Convention and Annex IVa of the EC Habitats Directive. It is protected under Schedule 2 of the Conservation (Natural Habitats. etc.) Regulations, 1994 (Regulation 38) and Schedule 5 of the WCA 1981

2. CURRENT FACTORS CAUSING LOSS OR DECLINE

2.1 Changes in woodland management practice, notably cessation of hazel coppicing and stock incursion into woodland.

2.2 Fragmentation of woodland, leaving isolated, non-viable populations. (Short distances, possibly as little as 100m, form absolute barriers to dispersal, unless arboreal routes are available).

3. CURRENT ACTION

3.1 Ecological research has led to practical proposals for conservation management. A nestbox scheme has been established, aimed at collating data on breeding and population density from sites throughout the present range.

3.2 *A Practical Guide to Dormouse Conservation* was published by the Mammal Society in 1989, and EN are preparing manual of dormouse conservation management.

3.3 In 1992 the dormouse was added to English Nature's Species Recovery Programme, with the aim of protecting and consolidating the species at selected sites where it still occurs, and developing methods to re-establish dormice in counties from which they have been lost. Trial re-introductions have been undertaken in Cambridgeshire and Nottinghamshire.

3.4 A major public participation exercise - the Great Nut Hunt of 1993 - aroused considerable interest and prompted many local surveys which improved knowledge of dormouse conservation status.

3.5 Developments which fragment habitats and break up natural features which link wildlife sites (notably road building) have a significant impact on dormouse populations. The importance of retaining and managing natural features linking wildlife sites was emphasised in DoE's Planning Policy Guidance Note on Nature Conservation (PPG9), published in October 1994, which covers England.

4. ACTION PLAN OBJECTIVES AND TARGETS

4.1 Maintain and enhance dormouse populations in all the counties where they still occur.

4.2 Re-establish self-sustaining populations in at least 5 counties where they have been lost.

5. PROPOSED ACTION WITH LEAD AGENCIES

5.1 Policy and legislation

5.1.1 Seek to ensure that PPG9 guidance issued by DoE and the WO is taken into account by Highway Authorities and LAs. (ACTION: DoT, LAs, WO)

5.2 Site safeguard and management

5.2.1 Sites supporting dormice should be identified and advice provided to land managers on appropriate management. (ACTION: CCW, EN)

5.2.2 Grant-aid and incentive schemes (such as the Woodland Grant Scheme) should be used to encourage owners to manage suitable habitat sensitively. (ACTION: FA)

5.2.3 Manage woodlands and hedgerows to maintain current populations and prevent further habitat fragmentation. (ACTION: FA, MAFF)

5.3 Species management and protection

5.3.1 Continue the programme to re-introduce dormice in 5 counties (Cambridgeshire, Nottinghamshire and 3 others yet to be selected) where they are currently absent. Reinforce populations in at least 3 other counties where they are scattered (e.g.: Bedfordshire, Northamptonshire and Berkshire). (ACTION: EN)

5.3.2 Establish by 1996 a co-ordinated programme of captive breeding to support the re-introduction programme, including research into the long term survival of captive bred individuals. (ACTION: EN)

5.4 Advisory

5.4.1 A new manual on dormouse conservation will be published in 1995. (ACTION: EN)

5.4.2 Support training in conservation of dormice both for land managers and advisers. (ACTION: MAFF, FA, WOAD, CCW, EN)

5.5 Future research and monitoring

5.5.1 Continue research into dormouse ecology, with particular emphasis on the ecology of dormice in hedgerows or conifer sites, the analysis of existing population data, hibernation requirements, and the effects on populations of isolation. (ACTION: EN)

5.5.2 Promote research on methods of conserving dormice which are consistent with various silviculture systems. (ACTION: EN, FA)

5.5.3 The National Dormouse Monitoring Scheme should be maintained and extended to 25 counties. Methods of survey or monitoring should be further developed and standardised to obtain sufficient long-term data on which to assess the effects of site management and successional development. (ACTION: CCW, EN)

5.5.4 Surveys of sites identified in the Great Nut Hunt of 1993 should be repeated at 5-10 year intervals to provide data on changes in distribution and abundance. (ACTION: EN)

5.5.5 Carry out a survey of dormice in Wales to assess the range and habitat use and identify necessary conservation measures. (ACTION: CCW)

5.5.6 Encourage research on the ecology and conservation of this species in an international context. (ACTION: CCW, EN, JNCC)

5.5.7 Pass information gathered during survey and monitoring of this species to JNCC in order that it can be incorporated in a national database and contribute to the maintenance of an up-to-date Red List. (ACTION: CCW, EN)

5.6 Communications and publicity

5.6.1 Ensure that landowners, agencies and local authorities are aware of the requirements of the dormouse, especially the impact woodland and hedgerow management may have, and the effects of habitat fragmentation. (ACTION: CCW, EN)

5.6.2 Ensure continued public awareness of this species as a key indicator of desirable woodland and hedge conditions. (ACTION: CCW, EN, FA, MAFF, WOAD)

GREATER MOUSE-EARED BAT (*MYOTIS MYOTIS*)

I. CURRENT STATUS

I.I Small populations of the greater mouse-eared bat once existed in Dorset and Sussex, but these were lost due largely to collection and roost destruction. It has been extinct in the UK since 1990.

I.2 A globally threatened species, this bat is listed on Appendix II of the Bonn Convention (and is included in the Convention's Agreement on the Conservation of Bats in Europe), Annex II of the Bern Convention and Annex II and IV of the EC Habitats Directive. It is protected under Schedule 2 of the Conservation (Natural Habitats, etc.) Regulations, 1994 (Regulation 38) and Schedule 5 of the WCA 1981.

2. CURRENT FACTORS CAUSING LOSS OR DECLINE

2.1 Not applicable.

3. CURRENT ACTION

3.1 None known.

4. ACTION PLAN OBJECTIVES AND TARGETS

4.1 Maintain and enhance any extant populations discovered in the UK.

4.2 Ensure maximum conservation effort should the species re-establish.

5. PROPOSED ACTION WITH LEAD AGENCIES

5.1 Policy and legislation

5.1.1 No action proposed.

5.2 Site safeguard and management

5.2.1 Ensure continued protection of known formerly occupied key sites. No further action would be appropriate unless the species re-colonises. (ACTION: EN)

5.3 Species management and protection

5.3.1 Prepare to launch major conservation initiative should the species re-colonise naturally or be rediscovered. (ACTION: EN)

5.4 Advisory

5.4.1 No action proposed.

5.5 Future research and monitoring

5.5.1 Check recently occupied sites annually in case re-colonisation takes place. (ACTION: EN)

5.5.2 Pass information gathered during survey and monitoring of this species to JNCC in order that it can be incorporated in a national database and contribute to the maintenance of an up-to-date Red List. (ACTION: EN)

5.6 Communication and publicity

5.6.1 No action proposed.

PIPISTRELLE BAT (*PIPISTRELLUS PIPISTRELLUS*)

1. CURRENT STATUS

1.1 Although it remains the most abundant and widespread bat species in the UK, the pipistrelle is thought to have undergone a significant decline in numbers this century. Estimates from the National Bat Colony Survey suggest a population decline of approximately 70% between 1978 and 1993. The current pre-breeding population estimate for the UK stands at approximately 2,000,000. The problems of estimating populations trends have been compounded by the recent discovery that there may be two distinct species of pipistrelle bat in the UK.

1.2 The pipistrelle is listed on Appendix III of the Bern Convention, Annex IV of the EC Habitats Directive and ; Appendix II of the Bonn Convention (and is included under the Agreement on the Conservation of Bats in Europe). It is protected under Schedule 2 of the Conservation (Natural Habitats, etc.) Regulations, 1994 (Regulation 38) and Schedules 5 and 6 of the WCA 1981 and Schedules 5 and 6 of the Wildlife (Northern Ireland) Order 1985.

2. CURRENT FACTORS CAUSING LOSS OR DECLINE

2.1 Reduction in insect prey abundance, due to high intensity farming practice and inappropriate riparian management.

2.2 Loss of insect-rich feeding habitats and flyways, due to loss of wetlands, hedgerows and other suitable prey habitats.

2.2 Loss of winter roosting sites in buildings and old trees.

2.3 Disturbance and destruction of roosts, including the loss of maternity roosts due to the use of toxic timber treatment chemicals.

3. CURRENT ACTION

3.1 The JNCC recently commissioned a National Bat Habitat Survey, which provided much information on habitat preference and distribution.

3.2 The DoE is to commission a National Bat Monitoring programme which will include the pipistrelle.

3.3 The National Bat Colony Survey has monitored many pipistrelle roosts since 1978 on the basis of annual summer roost counts.

3.4 A large amount of research is underway, investigating reproductive physiology, mating strategies, field activity, and the morphology and ecology of two taxa by investigation of echolocation calls and mitochondrial DNA.

3.5 SNH have developed design briefs for the conservation of pipistrelle roosts in houses.

4. ACTION PLAN OBJECTIVES AND TARGETS

4.1 Maintain existing populations and range of pipistrelles.

4.2 Restore populations to pre-1970 numbers.

5. PROPOSED ACTION WITH LEAD AGENCIES

5.1 Policy and legislation

5.1.1 Encourage water quality levels which will help support populations of aquatic insects on which pipistrelles feed. (ACTION: NRA, SEPA)

5.1.2 Ensure the needs of this species are considered in incentive schemes designed to encourage the management of habitat suitable for this species. (ACTION: FA, MAFF, SOAEFD, WOAD)

5.2 Site safeguard and management

5.2.1 Encourage favourable management of land adjacent to known roost sites to support foraging by juvenile pipistrelles. (ACTION: CCW, DoE(NI), EN, FA, SNH)

5.3 Species management and protection

5.3.1 Maintain current licensing procedures and training schemes as appropriate. Assess the effect of current management and protection policies and amend as necessary to ensure maintenance of healthy populations. (ACTION: CCW, DoE(NI), EN, SNH)

5.4 Advisory

5.4.1 Ensure landowners are aware of the presence and legal status of pipistrelle bats, and that advice is available on appropriate methods of management for conservation of their roosts and foraging habitats. (ACTION: CCW, DoE(NI), EN, FA, SNH)

5.5 Future research and monitoring

5.5.1 Undertake research to clarify the taxonomic status of pipistrelle bats in the UK. (ACTION: JNCC)

5.5.2 Continue to research the habitat requirements and ecology of the species to help develop appropriate management advice. (ACTION: CCW, DoE(NI), EN, SNH, JNCC)

5.5.3 Develop and implement a systematic survey technique to clarify the conservation status of the species in the UK. This should include monitoring of summer maternity roosts and the extent and effect of reproductive isolation of summer colonies used for monitoring. (ACTION: CCW, DoE(NI), EN, SNH, JNCC)

5.5.4 Encourage research on the ecology and conservation of pipistrelles on an international level. (ACTION: CCW, DoE(NI), EN, JNCC, SNH)

5.5.5 Pass information gathered during survey and monitoring of this species to JNCC in order that it can be incorporated in a national database and contribute to the maintenance of an up-to-date Red List. (ACTION: CCW, DoE(NI), EN, SNH)

5.6 Communications and publicity

5.6.1 Maintain programmes of carefully supervised roost visiting, general education and publicity. (ACTION: CCW, DoE(NI), EN, SNH)

GREATER HORSESHOE BAT (*RHINOLOPHUS FERRUMEQUINUM*)

1. CURRENT STATUS

1.1 During this century the greater horseshoe bat has declined significantly throughout northern Europe. In the UK, this species is restricted to south-west England and south Wales, although vagrants may be recorded elsewhere. There are currently 35 recognised maternity and all-year roosts and 369 hibernation sites. Current estimates range between 4,000 and 6,600 individuals.

1.2 This bat is listed on Appendix II of the Bonn Convention (and is included in the Convention's Agreement on the Conservation of Bats in Europe), Appendix II of the Bern Convention (and Recommendation 36 on the Conservation of Underground Habitats) and Annex II of the EC Habitats Directive. It is protected under Schedule 2 of the Conservation (Natural Habitats, etc.) Regulations, 1994 (Regulation 38) and Schedule 5 of the WCA 1981.

2. CURRENT FACTORS CAUSING LOSS OR DECLINE

2.1 Reductions in insect prey abundance, especially loss of old pasture due to high intensity agricultural systems.

2.2 Loss, destruction and disturbance of roosting and hibernation sites.

2.3 Loss of insect-rich feeding habitats and flyways, due to loss of wetlands and hedgerows and the conversion of permanent pasture to other arable.

3. CURRENT ACTION

3.1 Approximately 10 maternity roosts and 27 hibernation sites are designated as SSSIs. Five sites have been proposed as SACs for this species under the EC Habitats Directive.

3.2 Research continues on at least seven maternity roosts and at many hibernation sites. Recent research has investigated the home range, preferred habitat and feeding requirements of this species. Research into habitat re-instatement is currently being considered.

3.3 The greater horseshoe bat is the subject of an EN Species Recovery Programme, concentrating on feeding requirements.

3.4 Five greater horseshoe sites have been proposed for designation as SAC under the Habitats Directive, which will increase protection for foraging habitats.

3.5 The Advisory Committee to the Agreement on the Conservation of Bats in Europe will consider how selected hibernation sites should be monitored, and data collected and analysed to detect population trends at national and international level.

3.6 The Co-ordinating Panel for the Conservation of Bats in Europe will maintain liaison between involved parties.

4. ACTION PLAN OBJECTIVES AND TARGETS

4.1 Maintain all existing maternity roosts and associated hibernation sites.

4.2 Increase current population by 25% by 2010.

5. PROPOSED ACTION WITH LEAD AGENCIES

5.1 Policy and legislation

5.1.1 Consider the obligations of the Habitats Directive and Agreement on the Conservation of Bats in Europe, and seek to develop appropriate policies on wider habitat conservation for bats. (ACTION: CCW, DOE, EN, FA, JNCC, WO)

5.2 Site safeguard and management

5.2.1 Consider statutory protection for roost sites not already covered, and seek to ensure that consideration is given to key areas, or population centres, in respect of planning and land-use strategies. (ACTION: CCW, EN, LAs)

5.2.2 Following further research to identify the ecological requirements of this species more precisely, encourage favourable habitat management (aiming for up to 4 km around each roost), seeking to implement these through voluntary or informal agreements. (ACTION: CCW, EN)

5.3 Species management and protection

5.3.1 No action proposed.

5.4 Advisory

5.4.1 Continue to implement the current advisory mechanisms for roost sites. (ACTION: CCW, EN)

5.4.2 Prepare and distribute advice on the management of foraging areas by the year 2000. (ACTION: CCW, EN)

5.5 Future research and monitoring

5.5.1 Seek to maintain the current level of research into the ecology and conservation requirements of this species, identifying further areas of research as necessary. This should include studies on the population genetics and feeding requirements of the species. (ACTION: CCW, EN)

5.5.2 Promote research to assess the importance of sites used by small numbers of bats and develop and implement a strategy for their conservation. Investigate the rate of loss of minor sites and their importance to the population structure. (ACTION: CCW, EN)

5.5.3 Identify key areas or population centres for this species. (ACTION: CCW, EN)

5.5.4 Develop and implement a systematic recording scheme to standardise population estimates between sites and between years. (ACTION: CCW, EN, JNCC)

5.5.5 Pass information gathered during survey and monitoring of this species to JNCC in order that it can be incorporated in a national database and contribute to the maintenance of an up-to-date Red List. (ACTION: CCW, EN)

5.6 Communications and publicity

5.6.1 No action proposed.

RED SQUIRREL (SCIURUS VULGARIS)

1. CURRENT STATUS

1.1 Populations of red squirrel in the UK have suffered markedly over the last 50 years with the introduced grey squirrel (*Sciurus carolinensis*) replacing the species throughout most of England and Wales. The distribution is now largely confined to Scotland and Ireland, although isolated populations persist in southern England, on three islands in Poole Harbour in Dorset, at Cannock Chase in Staffordshire, on the Isle of Wight and at Thetford in Norfolk. At the current rate of decline, it is estimated that the population will probably disappear from Staffordshire by the year 2000. In Wales only a few thousand red squirrels remain, confined to scattered localities and in northern England it is found only where greys have not yet established themselves. The species remains widespread and locally common in Scotland, where they have shown a modest expansion in range and number. The species is also widespread in Northern Ireland.

1.2 Reds are usually displaced within 15 years of the arrival of greys, appearing to suffer competitive exclusion by a species better adapted to conditions in the now fragmented British woodland, where acorns are often the principal food. The current population is estimated to be 160,000.

1.3 The red squirrel is listed on Appendix III of the Bern Convention and is protected by Schedules 5 and 6 of the WCA and Schedules 5 and 6 of the Wildlife (Northern Ireland) Order 1985.

2. CURRENT FACTORS CAUSING LOSS OR DECLINE

2.1 Spread of grey squirrels.

2.2 Habitat fragmentation making some areas less suitable for red squirrels, increasing their vulnerability to displacement by grey squirrels.

2.3 Disease.

3. CURRENT ACTION

3.1 JNCC is drafting a UK strategy for Red Squirrel Conservation.

3.2 The species is the subject of a Species Recovery Programme run by EN. A major campaign "Red Alert" has been initiated to raise public awareness and co-ordinate conservation projects, and a Squirrel Forum has been established.

3.3 The Forestry Commission is currently researching a new hopper designed to be selective in poisoning grey but not red squirrels. Permission to trial the hopper live is being sought from MAFF at present. If the trials are successful, this will be a major advance in controlling greys.

3.4 Habitat manipulation studies are in progress. Forest management studies are being carried out with FA funding, while FE have identified at least three large forest areas where red squirrel conservation management is a priority.

3.5 Experimental translocations to Thetford have identified protocols, but await genetic studies before translocation takes place. Planning for a full-scale translocation is in progress.

4. ACTION PLAN OBJECTIVES AND TARGETS

4.1 Maintain and enhance current populations of red squirrel, where appropriate, through good management.

4.2 Re-establish red squirrel populations, where appropriate.

5. PROPOSED ACTION AND LEAD AGENCIES

5.1 Policy and legislation

5.1.1 Achieve agreement on the UK Red Squirrel Strategy and develop regional guidelines for management of red and grey squirrel populations within the national framework. (ACTION: FA, JNCC, LAs)

5.1.2 Review geographical restrictions on use of Warfarin. (ACTION: FA, DANI, MAFF, SOAEFD, WOAD)

5.1.3 Seek to ensure that the needs of the red squirrels are taken into account when reviewing or preparing Indicative Forestry Strategies. (ACTION: FA, LAs)

5.2 Site safeguard and management

5.2.1 Prepare and implement site management plans for all sites with viable populations. This should be phased, with plans for all marginal sites by the year 2000 and all other sites by 2005. (ACTION: CCW, EN, DoE(NI), FA, FE, LAs, SNH,)

5.2.2 Attempt to create or maintain 2,000 ha of conifer reserves in Wales to provide a suitable habitat for the red squirrel. (ACTION: CCW, FA, FE, WOAD)

5.3 Species management and protection

5.3.1 Develop strategies, within the national framework, to guide and co-ordinate work. (ACTION: CCW, DoE(NI), EN, FC, JNCC, SNH)

5.3.2 Assess experimental translocation projects for wider use. (ACTION: CCW, EN, FA, FE)

5.3.3 Attempt to prevent expansion of grey squirrel range to key areas currently occupied by reds. (ACTION: FA, FE,)

5.4 Advisory

5.4.1 Advise land managers on the relationship between reds and greys, and appropriate management. (ACTION: CCW, DoE(NI), EN, FA, SNH)

5.4.2 Develop guidance on forestry design to benefit red squirrels. (ACTION: DANI, FA, MAFF, SOAEFD, WOAD,)

5.5 Future research and monitoring

5.5.1 Continue research on feeding ecology, bait hoppers, supplementary feeding, red/grey interactions, methods of control and eradication (e.g. immunosterilants), translocation, population reinforcement, habitat manipulation (including nestbox provision), and phylogenetic studies. (ACTION: CCW, EN, FC, DoE(NI), JNCC, SNH,)

5.5.2 Establish a survey method and Squirrel Monitoring Scheme to ascertain population levels, identify key sites and monitor range and population of greys. (ACTION: FC, JNCC).

5.5.3 Pass information gathered during survey and

monitoring of this species to JNCC in order that it can be incorporated in a national database and contribute to the maintenance of an up-to-date Red List. (ACTION: CCW, EN, SNH)

5.6 Communications and publicity

5.6.1 The balance between red and grey squirrel populations is an emotive issue. Clear information explaining the relationship between reds and greys should be made available to the public and landowners. (ACTION: CCW, EN, DoE(NI), FA, SNH)

HARBOUR PORPOISE (PHOCOENA PHOCOENA)

1. CURRENT STATUS

1.1 There is some evidence of a decline in numbers of harbour porpoise in UK waters since the 1940s, especially in the southern North Sea and English Channel. The conservation status of the species around the whole UK coast is unknown, but the recent "SCANS" survey of small cetaceans in the North Sea, Channel and Celtic Sea indicated the population in those waters was approximately 350,000.

1.2 The harbour porpoise is listed on Appendix II of CITES, Appendix II of the Bern Convention and Annexes II and IV of the EC Habitats Directive. It is also on Appendix 2 of the Bonn Convention and is covered by the terms of the Agreement on the Conservation of Small Cetaceans of the Baltic and North Seas (ASCOBANS), a regional agreement under the Bonn Convention. It is protected under Schedule 5 of the WCA 1981.

2. CURRENT FACTORS CAUSING LOSS OR DECLINE

2.1 The current factors affecting this species are not clear but may include:

2.1.1 Incidental capture and drowning in fishing nets.

2.1.2 Environmental contaminants (toxic substances at sea, marine debris, disease, noise disturbance).

2.1.3 Environmental change (effects of fishing and possibly climate change).

3. CURRENT ACTION

3.1 Distribution studies have been undertaken by JNCC since 1980. The Sea Mammal Research Unit co-ordinated the international "SCANS" survey in 1994.

3.2 Studies of the scale and effects of by-catch by SMRU and other will take place during 1995-1998.

3.3 Experiments to increase the acoustic detectability of fishing nets have been undertaken to reduce by-catch.

3.4 Guidelines to minimise the effects of acoustic disturbance from seismic surveys have been agreed with the oil and gas industry and published by DOE.

3.5 Post mortem and tissue studies of stranded corpses are carried out on stranded specimens to establish the cause of death and condition of the animals at the time of death.

3.6 Conservation, management and research action is being undertaken and planned under ASCOBANS.

4. ACTION PLAN OBJECTIVES AND TARGETS

4.1 Maintain the current range and abundance, with a longer term aim of ensuring that no anthopogenic factors inhibit a return to waters that previously held the harbour porpoise.

5. PROPOSED ACTION WITH LEAD AGENCIES

5.1 Policy and legislation

5.1.1 Extend the ASCOBANS boundary to include the Western Approaches and the Irish Sea through a bilateral treaty with the Republic of Ireland and agreement of ASCOBANS Parties. (ACTION: DoE, DoE(NI))

5.1.2 Seek to improve coastal water quality by reducing the discharge of substances which are toxic, persistent and liable to bioaccumulate, giving priority to phasing out identifiable PCBs, and reducing discharges of organohalogens to safe levels. (ACTION: DANI, MAFF, NRA, SEPA, SOAEFD)

5.1.3 Continue the duty on sea fisheries regulators to take account of potential wider impacts on wildlife and habitats (in addition to target species) when deciding fishery management measures. (ACTION: DANI, DoE, MAFF, SOAEFD)

5.1.4 Consider, in the light of research at 3.2, the possible need to monitor and control gill nets and other set net fisheries. (ACTION: DANI, MAFF, SOAEFD, WOAD)

5.1.5 Continue to introduce agreed codes of conduct to reduce disturbance from acoustic sources and physical pressures. (ACTION: CCW, EN, DoE(NI), JNCC, SNH)

5.2 Site safeguard and management

5.2.1 Review existing UK marine site protection to determine how it might be improved. If appropriate, introduce additional protection and emergency designation to benefit the species. (ACTION: DoE, DoE(NI), JNCC, SOAEFD)

5.3 Species management and protection

5.3.1 Work with fishers with the aim of reducing and avoiding by-catches in active and passive gear, and to dispose of discarded gear safely. (ACTION: DANI, MAFF, SOAEFD, WOAD)

5.3.2 Introduce codes of practice to reduce disturbance from whale-watching. (ACTION: CCW, DoE(NI), EN, JNCC, SNH)

5.4 Advisory

5.4.1 None proposed.

5.5 Future research and monitoring

5.5.1 Expand research on the areas frequented by harbour porpoise to identify waters which may qualify for further protection as SACs or Marine Nature Reserves. (ACTION: DoE(NI), JNCC)

5.5.2 Establish long-term research on population and conservation needs of all small cetaceans in UK waters, co-ordinated through ASCOBANS. (ACTION: DoE, DOE(NI), JNCC)

5.5.3 Subject to the results of the research at 3.2, consider monitoring of UK population and reporting of by-catches of small cetaceans (including observers on vessels, where feasible). (ACTION: DANI, JNCC, MAFF, SOAEFD)

5.5.4 Seek to minimise the by-catch of small cetaceans by promoting research into fishing gear and other possible mechanisms. (ACTION: DANI, MAFF, SOAEFD)

5.5.5 Promote research into the causes of death of the harbour porpoise within UK waters to determine the context and need for future conservation action. (ACTION: CCW, DANI, DoE(NI), EN, JNCC, MAFF, SNH, SOAEFD, WOAD)

5.5.6 Pass information gathered during survey and monitoring of this species to JNCC or BRC in order that it can be incorporated in a national database and contribute to the maintenance of an up-to-date Red List. (ACTION: CCW, DoE(NI), EN, SNH)

5.6 Communication and publicity

5.6.1 Subject to the results of research at 3.2, consider the need to encourage fishermen to report sightings and by-catches through an awareness programme. (ACTION: DANI, DoE, MAFF, SOAEFD)

5.6.2 Encourage international exchange of information to assess and, if appropriate, reduce by-catches. (ACTION: DANI, DoE, JNCC, MAFF, SOAEFD)

5.6.3 Continue to publicise reporting schemes for strandings and live-sightings. (ACTION: CCW, DoE(NI), EN, SNH, SOAEFD)

BIRDS

AQUATIC WARBLER (ACROCEPHALUS PALUDICOLA)

1. CURRENT STATUS

1.1 The aquatic warbler is a regular autumn migrant to sites in southern Britain, particularly to wetlands along the south coast from Kent to Cornwall. Although there is no accurate record of numbers, it is estimated that hundreds of individuals pass through Britain each year, comprising between 1% and 25% of the world population of this globally threatened species.

1.2 The aquatic warbler is listed on Annex I of the EC Birds Directive and Appendix II of the Bern Convention.

2. CURRENT FACTORS CAUSING LOSS OR DECLINE

2.1 Wetland habitat deterioration in a number of important sites where the aquatic warbler regularly occurs. During migration through Britain it has a very localised distribution and is therefore very susceptible to factors affecting even a small number of sites.

3. CURRENT ACTION

3.1 Known key passage sites are designated as nature reserves or SSSIs.

3.2 RSPB is currently assessing historic records to confirm all likely key sites.

3.3 EN promote habitat management for this species through action plans for reedbed birds.

4. ACTION PLAN OBJECTIVES AND TARGETS

4.1 This is a globally threatened species which passes through the UK on migration in autumn *en route* between eastern Europe and Africa. We do not know what proportion of the world population passes through the UK but it may be significant (>10%). Further research is needed to assess the importance of the UK for this species but in the meantime its parlous global status means that the UK should ensure that the few sites known to be used (mostly reedbeds) are protected and appropriately managed.

4.2 Ensure all key passage sites are, and remain, protected.

4.3 Develop monitoring methodology to assess and monitor numbers and distribution of birds in the UK.

4.4 Undertake research to identify habitat requirements.

5. PROPOSED ACTIONS WITH LEAD AGENCIES

5.1 Policy and legislation

5.1.1 Encourage the uptake of schemes such as ESA and Countryside Stewardship to manage wetlands and watersides for the species. (ACTION: MAFF, WOAD)

5.1.2 Support initiatives, where appropriate and identified in the international Action Plan, which safeguard and enhance populations in other countries. (ACTION: DoE, JNCC)

5.2 Site safeguard and management

5.2.1 Seek to designate any sites regularly supporting qualifying numbers of warbler as SPAs. (ACTION: CCW, WO)

5.2.2 Seek to oppose any development proposal which would adversely affect key sites for this migrant species. (ACTION: CCW, EN)

5.2.3 Following further research to identify the ecological requirements of this species, ensure that the needs of this species are taken into account in management plans for any SSSI used regularly by this species. (ACTION: CCW, EN)

5.3 Species management and protection

5.3.1 Consider this species for protection under international legislation. (ACTION: CCW, DoE. EN, JNCC)

5.4 Advisory

5.4.1 Ensure land owners and managers with regularly occurring migratory populations are aware of the importance of their land to the species, and appropriate methods of habitat management, when known. (ACTION: CCW, EN)

5.5 Future research and monitoring

5.5.1 Identify and implement a method for monitoring aquatic warbler numbers on passage through the UK. (ACTION: CCW, EN, JNCC)

5.5.2 Survey to identify sites which regularly hold significant numbers of aquatic warbler. (ACTION: EN)

5.5.3 Research habitat use and ecology of species to provide habitat management advice for regularly used sites. (ACTION: EN)

5.5.4 Pass information gathered during survey and monitoring of this species to JNCC or BRC so that it can be incorporated in national databases. (ACTION: CCW, EN)

5.5.5 Provide information annually to Birdlife International on the UK status of the species to contribute to maintenance of an up-to-date global red lists. (ACTION: JNCC)

5.6 Communications and publicity

5.6.1 No action proposed.

SKYLARK (ALAUDA ARVENSIS)

1. CURRENT STATUS

1.1 One of the most widespread birds of the British Isles, with over 2 million breeding pairs, the resident population is joined in winter by a significant proportion of the northern European population - possibly up to 25 million individuals. Nonetheless, the UK breeding population of skylark on lowland farmland declined by 54% between 1969 and 1991. The population has also declined substantially in many other European countries.

1.2 The causes of decline are poorly understood because population trends in habitats other than farmland are largely unknown. It is thought that autumn-sown cereals may make an unsuitable nesting habitat compared with spring-sown varieties, and dense, tall fertilised grass is also unsuitable.

1.3 The skylark is protected under the EC Birds Directive. It is also protected under the WCA 1981 and the Wildlife (Northern Ireland) Order 1985.

2. CURRENT FACTORS CAUSING LOSS OR DECLINE

2.1 Intensive management of arable fields has reduced ephemeral weeds and insect prey through the use of agrochemicals. An increased trend to autumn-sown cereals has reduced the number of essential winter stubble fields and may provide unsuitable habitat in comparison with spring-sown varieties.

2.2 Conversion of lowland grassland to arable.

2.3 Intensive management of grasslands.

2.4 Early silage cutting, which destroys nests and exposes skylarks to predators.

3. CURRENT ACTION

3.1 Little action has been taken to help the skylark, as BTO census work has only recently highlighted its decline. Survey and research is now commencing to identify the causes of the decline, particularly the effects of habitat change.

3.2 A Species Action Plan has been prepared and agreed by RSPB and the country agencies.

4. ACTION PLAN OBJECTIVES AND TARGETS

4.1 This is a rapidly declining species whose numbers on farmland have fallen by over 50% in the last 25 years. The plan aims to stabilise the population and to prevent further declines. This is a species whose fate is intimately bound up with the management of lowland agriculture.

4.2 Maintain present breeding numbers, wintering numbers and distribution throughout the UK.

4.3 Reverse the population decline on lowland farmland and other habitats where found to be declining.

4.4 Protect the skylark's habitat, particularly during the breeding season.

5. PROPOSED ACTIONS WITH LEAD AGENCIES

5.1 Policy and legislation

5.1.1 In the light of the outcome of action re 5.5.2, consider the need for incentives for maintaining and re-establishing permanent pasture, reducing pesticide use, retaining field margin features and introducing winter stubbles. (ACTION: DANI, MAFF, SOAEFD, WOAD)

5.1.2 Consider the requirements of the skylark in any negotiations on changes to, or reform of, agricultural support. (ACTION: DANI, MAFF, SOAEFD, WOAD)

5.1.3 Consider further improvements to the set aside regulations to reduce the harmful effects of cutting and wide-spectrum pesticide use. (ACTION: DANI, MAFF, SOAEFD, WOAD)

5.1.4 Review procedures for testing, introduction and replacement of pesticides and other agricultural chemicals to assess indirect effects on non-target species before approval for use is given. (ACTION: DANI, MAFF, SOAEFD, WOAD)

5.1.5 Encourage a more cautious and targeted use of pesticides on farmland. (ACTION: DANI, MAFF, SOAEFD, WOAD)

5.2 Site safeguard and management

5.2.1 Encourage sympathetic management of rotational set aside. (ACTION: CCW, DoE(NI), EN, SNH)

5.3 Species management and protection

5.3.1 No actions proposed.

5.4 Advisory

5.4.1 Disseminate information on skylark conservation to farmers and farm advisory services. (ACTION: DANI, MAFF, SOAEFD, WOAD)

5.5 Future research and monitoring

5.5.1 Survey habitat use to determine the distribution of farmland skylarks in relation to crop types. (ACTION: CCW, DoE(NI), EN, JNCC, SNH)

5.5.2 Undertake a detailed ecological study on skylarks on lowland farmland, to determine the reasons for decline, including examination of crop preferences, breeding success, diet and food supply. (ACTION: CCW, DoE(NI), EN, JNCC, SNH)

5.5.3 Ensure annual monitoring of breeding skylarks through the BTO/ JNCC/ RSPB Breeding Bird Survey. (ACTION: CCW, DoE(NI), EN, JNCC, SNH)

5.5.4 Assess the wintering population of skylarks to put the UK population into a European context. (ACTION: JNCC)

5.5.5 Pass information gathered during survey and monitoring of this species to JNCC or BRC so that it can be incorporated in national databases. (ACTION: CCW, DoE(NI), EN, SNH)

5.5.6 Provide information annually to Birdlife International on the UK status of the species to contribute to maintenance of an up-to-date global red lists. (ACTION: JNCC)

5.6 Communications and publicity

5.6.1 Ensure that the problem of the decline of farmland birds has a high profile, using the skylark as an illustration. (ACTION: CCW, DoE(NI), EN, SNH)

BITTERN (*BOTAURUS STELLARIS*)

1. CURRENT STATUS

1.1 The bittern is a declining, localised and rare breeding species. It is confined almost entirely to lowland marshes in Norfolk, Suffolk and Lancashire dominated by the common reed *Phragmites australis*, where it feeds principally on fish and amphibians. The UK population had declined to fifteen or sixteen booming males in 1994 from a peak of 70 pairs in the late 1960s, when it bred in eight counties. Numbers are boosted in winter by continental immigrants (usually less than 100).

1.2 The bittern is listed on Annex I of the EC Birds Directive and Appendix III of the Bern Convention. It is protected in the UK under Schedule 1 of the WCA 1981 and Schedule 1 of the Wildlife (Northern Ireland) Order 1985.

2. CURRENT FACTORS CAUSING LOSS OR DECLINE

2.1 Loss of suitable large reedbeds through seral succession, inappropriate management (particularly drainage and water abstraction) and fragmentation.

2.2 Degradation of habitat through water pollution, pesticide and heavy metal pollution.

2.3 Food availability, especially of eels, affected by inappropriate habitat management and pollution.

2.4 Salt water intrusion into coastal reedbeds.

2.5 Problems due to small population size.

3. CURRENT ACTION

3.1 A high proportion of remaining bittern sites are protected as nature reserves.

3.2 Detailed studies on bittern ecology have been carried out by the RSPB, leading to a greater understanding of habitat requirements.

3.3 Management work has been carried out by statutory agencies and NGOs to restore and re-create suitable reedbed habitat for bitterns.

3.4 English Nature launched its Bittern Recovery Project, with funding available to landowners and NGOs for reedbed management and restoration.

3.5 Improved monitoring of populations has been achieved through voice pattern analysis.

4. ACTION PLAN OBJECTIVES AND TARGETS

4.1 The bittern has declined by over 50% in the past 25 years. The objectives of the plan are modest, and represent an aim of increasing the population level to a more sustainable level over the next 25 years in stages. This appears to be relatively easily achievable by restoring a small proportion of existing reedbeds and by creating new reedbeds (thus linking with the reedbed habitat plan).

4.2 To arrest the decline of the bittern, maintaining at least 20 booming birds over the present range, and start to increase the population and range before the year 2000.

4.3 Increase the population to about 50 booming males by 2010, by ensuring appropriate management of the existing 22 large reedbeds where bittern once occurred.

4.4 Initiate work to secure the long-term future of bitterns in the UK by providing suitable habitat for a population of not less than 100 booming males by 2020.

4.5 Encourage the creation of at least 1,200 hectares of reedbed in blocks of greater than 20 hectares at existing former and new areas in England and Wales.

5. PROPOSED ACTION WITH LEAD AGENCIES

5.1 Policy and legislation

5.1.1 Implement initiatives for the creation and management of large scale reedbeds on agricultural land. (ACTION: EN)

5.1.2 Implement water abstraction policies which give priority to nature conservation sites. (ACTION: NRA, IDBs)

5.1.3 Protect freshwater sites of high conservation importance from seawater incursion. (ACTION: NRA)

5.1.4 Promote, in development plans, appropriate conditions of after-use for sand and gravel extraction sites which would favour reedbed development. (ACTION: LAs, DoE)

5.1.5 Consider developing environmental land management schemes to include prescriptions and incentives for reedbed restoration and management. (ACTION: CC, CCW, EN, MAFF)

5.1.6 Promote the development and enhancement of suitable bittern habitats in relevant catchment management plans and water level management plans. (ACTION: NRA, IDBs)

5.2 Site safeguard and management

5.2.1 Protect any sites which are important for bitterns, having regard to the significance of formal and informal site designations when considering any proposed developments. (ACTION: LAs, DoE, EN, NRA)

5.2.2 Facilitate reedbed restoration through collaborative projects and appropriate wetland strategies, to maintain wet conditions and prevent scrub encroachment in existing reedbeds. (ACTION: CCW, EN, NRA)

5.2.3 Seek to ensure appropriate management for this species, of reedbeds currently within designated areas. (ACTION: CCW, EN)

5.2.4 Promote the creation of new reedbeds on suitable sites such as surplus agricultural land, mineral extraction sites, etc. (ACTION: DoE, LAs)

5.3 Species management and protection

5.3.1 Consider supplementary feeding in severe winters. (ACTION: CCW, EN)

5.3.2 Determine current food supply on key sites and manage accordingly. (ACTION: CCW, EN)

5.4 Advisory

5.4.1 Advise reedbed owners and managers of bittern requirements in order to promote appropriate management for this species. (ACTION: EN)

5.5 Future research and monitoring

5.5.1 Monitor the UK population annually. (ACTION: EN)

5.5.2 Monitor reedbed habitats and food availability at key bittern sites, in conjunction with NGOs. (ACTION: CCW, EN)

5.5.3 Ensure that any bittern corpses or addled eggs are analysed for heavy metals and pesticides. (ACTION: CCW, EN)

5.5.4 In conjunction with NGOs, produce assessments of the suitability and management of key reedbeds for bitterns, to identify the main features of each site and the principal actions required to improve or maintain them. (ACTION: CCW, EN)

5.5.5 Promote further research into habitat use, suitability and the requirements of this species in the UK. (ACTION: CCW, EN)

5.5.6 Pass information gathered during survey and monitoring of this species to JNCC or BRC so that it can be incorporated in national databases. (ACTION: CCW, EN)

5.5.7 Provide information annually to Birdlife International on the UK status of the species to contribute to maintenance of an up-to-date global red lists. (ACTION: JNCC)

5.6 Communications and publicity

5.6.1 Use this species to promote the importance of reedbeds and their conservation. (ACTION: CCW, EN)

STONE CURLEW (BURHINUS OEDICNEMUS)

1. CURRENT STATUS

1.1 The stone curlew is a rare and declining species, numbers of which have fallen by 85% in the past 50 years, and more than 50% since 1960. It is now largely restricted to two areas of the country, Breckland and Wessex. The current UK population is estimated at 150-160 pairs.

1.2 The stone curlew is listed on Annex I of the EC Birds Directive and Appendix II of the Bern Convention. It is also protected under Schedule 1 of the WCA 1981.

2. CURRENT FACTORS CAUSING LOSS OR DECLINE

2.1 Loss of semi-natural grasslands to arable farming, and reduced grazing by livestock and rabbits on the remaining grasslands.

2.2 Nest destruction in arable crops due to farming operations, such as mechanical hoeing.

2.3 Predation by foxes in semi-natural habitats.

2.4 Changes in agricultural practices resulting in fewer crops retaining an open structure until June or July.

2.5 Egg collecting.

2.6 Collisions with utility lines and fences.

2.7 Shooting in European countries while on migration.

3. CURRENT ACTION

3.1 Protection schemes, have been run by RSPB since the mid 1980s, to protect nest and young on arable land. This work is now included in a joint RSPB/EN Stone Curlew Recovery Project.

3.2 Most semi-natural grassland nest sites are SSSIs or military areas, but few are managed specifically for the species. NNRs supporting stone curlews are managed for them, i.e. Carenham, Martin Down.

3.3 The Brecklands and part of South Wessex Downs are designated ESAs. Rotation and non-rotational set-aside with some modifications may have helped the species.

4. ACTION PLAN OBJECTIVES AND TARGETS

4.1 The stone curlew was once a widespread and familiar farmland bird over much of southern England, but has decreased by over 50% in numbers over the past 25 years. The plan aims to halt the decline and restore some of the lost population. A high proportion of the remaining vulnerable population is only maintained because of intensive nest protection work by NGOs, so the plan aims to encourage stone curlews to return to semi-natural grassland where their future would be less dependent on costly protection measures.

4.2 Increase the breeding population in the present UK range to 200 pairs by the year 2000, and 300 pairs by 2010.

4.3 Encourage re-colonisation of the past breeding range in the UK.

4.4 Increase the population breeding on semi-natural grassland to 120 pairs by the year 2000.

5. PROPOSED ACTION WITH LEAD AGENCIES

5.1 Policy and legislation

5.1.1 Consider the requirements of the stone curlew when establishing and reviewing agri-environmental schemes. (ACTION: MAFF)

5.1.2 Seek to ensure that the Breckland and South Wessex Downs ESAs, and Countryside Stewardship, take into account the requirements of the species, in particular grazing, heath and downland prescriptions, to reverse fragmentation. (ACTION: CC, EN, MAFF)

5.1.3 Encourage the uptake of schemes supporting the reversion of arable to heathland in ESA and Countryside Stewardship schemes within set aside to benefit stone curlew. (ACTION: MAFF)

5.1.4 Persuade the European Commission and Council of Europe to ban or discourage hunting of this species in any European country where it is traditionally shot. (ACTION: DoE, FCO)

5.2 Site safeguard and management

5.2.1 Encourage favourable management plans on all land in the former and current range of the species, including land currently held by the MoD and FE. (ACTION: EN, MoD)

5.2.2 Consider designating a SPA within Breckland. (ACTION: EN)

5.3 Species management and protection

5.3.1 Seek to protect nests and chicks on arable land. (ACTION: EN)

5.3.2 Monitor the effects of fox predation on nesting, and control if necessary. (ACTION: EN)

5.3.3 Discourage illegal egg collecting and seek to ensure offenders are prosecuted. (ACTION: DoE, EN, Police Forces)

5.4 Advisory

5.4.1 Provide training in stone curlew conservation for relevant conservation advisors, including ADAS, ESA, Countryside Stewardship and FWAG staff. (ACTION: EN, MAFF)

5.4.2 Ensure landowners and managers are aware of the presence, legal status and conservation requirements of this species, and appropriate methods of habitat management. (ACTION: EN)

5.5 Future research and monitoring

5.5.1 Investigate survival data on birds on arable sites compared with semi-natural sites. (ACTION: DoE, EN)

5.5.2 Monitor the UK stone curlew breeding population regularly to assess whether the action plan is attaining its objectives. (ACTION: EN)

5.5.3 Pass information gathered during survey and monitoring of this species to JNCC or BRC so that it can be incorporated in national databases. (ACTION: EN)

5.5.4 Provide information annually to Birdlife International on the UK status of the species to contribute to maintenance of an up-to-date global red lists. (ACTION: JNCC)

5.6 Communications and publicity

5.6.1 Encourage birdwatchers to visit the Norfolk Wildlife Trust Reserve at Weeting Heath in Breckland to view stone curlews to highlight the decline and importance of the species and minimise the disturbance elsewhere. (ACTION: EN)

CORNCRAKE (CREX CREX)

1. CURRENT STATUS

1.1 Over the past 100 years the corncrake has shown a sustained decline in numbers in the UK and a contraction in range. By the early 1970s there were only 3,250 calling males, falling to 478 in 1993. Over 90% of calling males are located in the Hebrides, with the remainder mainly in Orkney. There are very few in England and Wales and, in recent years, few calling males in Northern Ireland.

1.2 The corncrake is a globally threatened species. It is listed on Appendix II of the Bern Convention and Annex I of the EC Birds Directive. In the UK it is protected under Schedule I of the WCA 1981 and the Wildlife (Northern Ireland) Order 1985.

2. CURRENT FACTORS CAUSING LOSS OR DECLINE

2.1 Loss of traditional grassland habitat mosaics, especially tall vegetation throughout the breeding season.

2.2 Changes in grass management and cutting techniques (e.g. earlier cutting).

2.3 Predation and disturbance may be contributing to the decline in some localities.

3. CURRENT ACTION

3.1 Approximately 10% of the British corncrake population is protected on RSPB reserves.

3.2 Corncrake grant schemes, funded by DoE(NI), RSPB, SNH and Scottish Crofters' Union under their joint Corncrake Initiative, provide incentives for corncrake-friendly grass cutting and management to protect corncrakes, but it is hoped to supersede this approach by improved ESA prescriptions with advice to land managers.

4. ACTION PLAN OBJECTIVES AND TARGETS

4.1 The corncrake is a globally threatened species which was once found throughout the UK, but is now mostly restricted to north and west Scotland. The reasons for decline of this species have been elucidated by an excellent programme of research, and the means of reversing the decline and providing an increase in numbers are now known. This species responds rapidly to favourable management of meadows and an increase in numbers and range is perfectly feasible. The UK can lead the global recovery of this species.

4.2 Halt the decline in UK corncrake population and range.

4.3 Maintain the numbers of corncrakes in the UK at or above the 1993 level (478 singing males).

4.4 Maintain the range of corncrakes in the UK at or above the 1993 level (82 occupied 10km squares).

4.5 By 1998, increase the range of the corncrake in Britain to at least the same number of 10km squares occupied in 1988 (90 squares).

4.6 In the longer-term, re-establish corncrakes in parts of its former range in the UK.

5. PROPOSED ACTION WITH LEAD AGENCIES

5.1 Policy and legislation

5.1.1 Support and promote the uptake of corncrake grant schemes for this species in Scotland and Northern Ireland. (ACTION: DoE(NI), SOAEFD)

5.1.2 Support and promote the uptake of ESA agreements and review the effectiveness of existing ESAs for this species in Scotland, i.e. the Outer Hebrides machair, Argyll Islands and Shetland. Seek to improve where necessary. (ACTION: SNH, SOAEFD)

5.1.3 If existing ESAs are effective as conservation measures, consider designating remaining core corncrake areas in the Western Isles, Inner Hebrides and Orkney as ESAs, to encourage continued hay production and sympathetic management. (ACTION: SOAEFD)

5.1.4 Develop and promote measures for traditional crofting land management in areas supporting this species. (ACTION: SOAEFD)

5.2 Site safeguard and management

5.2.1 Seek to secure favourable management on all suitable land within designated sites, and in all non-designated areas supporting populations of corncrake. (ACTION: DANI, DoE(NI), SNH, SOAEFD)

5.2.2 Consider designating sites of particular importance as SSSI. (ACTION: SNH)

5.3 Species management and protection

5.3.1 Seek to reduce damage to nests and mortality of adults and young from mowing operations by wardening and promoting corncrake-friendly techniques. (ACTION: DANI, DoE(NI), SNH, SOAEFD)

5.3.2 Ensure crofters and small farmers are advised of risks to species from predation by domestic cats, and support local mink and ferret control, preventing their spread to new areas. (ACTION: DANI, DoE(NI), SNH, SOAEFD)

5.4 Advisory

5.4.1 Provide advice to agricultural advisors, and to all those managing corncrake areas on corncrake-friendly cutting methods and other beneficial management practices. (ACTION: DANI, SOAEFD)

5.4.2 Provide advice on corncrake-friendly management techniques to agricultural colleges to aid their inclusion in land management courses. (ACTION: DoE(NI), SNH)

5.5 Future research and monitoring

5.5.1 Conduct a full survey of the breeding population of corncrake in Britain and Northern Ireland every three years. (ACTION: DoE(NI), SNH)

5.5.2 Study economic, technical and agronomic aspects of modifying grassland management in key corncrake areas to benefit the species. (ACTION: DANI, DoE(NI), SNH)

5.5.3 Investigate the responses of corncrakes to approaching mowing machinery, and conduct "after mowing" surveys to assess the density of nests and broods, and the mortality rate. Seek to identify the least damaging time for mowing. (ACTION: DoE(NI), SNH)

5.5.4 Investigate levels of mortality due to cat, mink and feral ferret predation and assess the possibility of reducing mortality. (ACTION: DoE(NI), SNH)

5.5.5 Encourage annual monitoring of breeding numbers and periodic surveys of habitat at key sites. (ACTION: DoE(NI), SNH)

5.5.6 Review the factors affecting corncrake migration and wintering grounds. (ACTION: DoE(NI), JNCC, SNH)

5.5.7 Pass information gathered during survey and monitoring of this species to JNCC or BRC so that it can be incorporated in national databases. (ACTION: DoE(NI), SNH)

5.5.8 Provide information annually to Birdlife International on the UK status of the species to contribute to maintenance of an up-to-date global red lists. (ACTION: JNCC)

5.6 Communication and publicity

5.6.1 Consider projects to develop controlled "green tourism" based on the species. (ACTION: SNH, Tourist Authorities)

5.6.2 Consider publishing a Code of Practice for birdwatching, to reduce the pressure on this species from birdwatchers in sensitive areas. (ACTION: DoE(NI), SNH)

SCOTTISH CROSSBILL (*LOXIA SCOTICA*)

1. CURRENT STATUS

1.1 The Scottish crossbill is the UK's only endemic bird species. However, the specific status of this bird is unclear due to taxonomic confusion and difficulty in distinguishing between this species and the common and parrot crossbills.

1.2 As far as can be ascertained, Scottish crossbills are largely confined to the remaining fragments of Caledonian pine forest, or planted woods dating from the middle of the last century. Little is known of population trends, although it is thought likely that numbers and ranges have contracted in response to the loss and decline in availability of the preferred habitat. The most recent estimates indicate a population of approximately 1,500 adults in the UK.

1.3 The Scottish crossbill is listed as data deficient in the European RDL due to doubts over taxonomic status. It is listed in Annex I of the EC Birds Directive and Appendix II of the Bern Convention. It is protected under Schedule 1 of the WCA 1981.

2. CURRENT FACTORS CAUSING LOSS OR DECLINE

2.1 None known.

3. CURRENT ACTION

3.1 RSPB is funding DNA analysis to clarify taxonomic status.

3.2 The FA grant-aid native pinewood establishment and restoration. A FA management guide promotes the management of native pinewoods for dead trees and for structural diversity which is likely to favour this bird.

3.3 FE is expanding its native pinewood areas by 3,000 hectares by the year 2000.

4. ACTION PLAN OBJECTIVES AND TARGETS

4.1 This bird resembles another, much commoner, species and whether there really are two species is not yet fully established. If it is a true species, it is the UK's only endemic bird, and stands as a flagship for all others dependent on the relict native Caledonian pinewoods. The precautionary principle requires that we give the species the benefit of the doubt while carrying out further research to establish its taxonomic status.

4.2 Clarify the taxonomy of the species to confirm endemic status.

4.3 Maintain current range and population.

5. PROPOSED ACTION WITH LEAD AGENCIES

5.1 Policy and legislation

5.1.1 Promote the protection, creation and management of native pinewoods. (ACTION: FA, FE, SOAEFD, Scottish Office)

5.2 Site safeguard and management

5.2.1 Consider additional protection for remaining native pinewoods which hold important populations of crossbills, and review the boundaries of existing protected areas. (ACTION: SNH)

5.2.2 Seek to minimise the impact of any development proposals that would damage native pinewood SSSIs. (ACTION: SNH, Highland RC, Grampian RC)

5.2.3 Consider proposals for aerial insecticide spraying on a case-by-case basis to ensure local populations of Scottish crossbill are not affected. (ACTION: FA, FE)

5.2.4 Enhance and manage native pinewood and plantations of Scots pine to the benefit of the crossbill, ensuring as far as possible the continuity of existing, isolated woodland within the range of this species and review boundaries of existing protected areas. (ACTION: SOAEFD, SNH, FA, FE)

5.3 Species management and protection

5.3.1 No action required.

5.4 Advisory

5.4.1 Provide advice to managers of native pinewood and Scots pine plantations on appropriate methods of management to benefit this species. (ACTION: FA, SNH)

5.5 Future research and monitoring

5.5.1 Improve methods for identification of Scottish crossbills in the field. (ACTION: SNH)

5.5.2 Clarify the taxonomic status of Scottish crossbill in relation to common and parrot crossbills. (ACTION: SNH)

5.5.3 Research the effects of different pinewood characteristics and management on the species. (ACTION: FA, SNH)

5.5.4 Research distribution, population, habitat, food requirements, effects of predation, and the need for breeding populations to be inter-connected. (ACTION: SNH)

5.5.5 Encourage regular monitoring of known sites. (ACTION: SNH)

5.5.6 Pass information gathered during survey and monitoring of this species to JNCC or BRC so that it can be incorporated in national databases. (ACTION: SNH)

5.5.7 Provide information annually to Birdlife International on the UK status of the species to contribute to maintenance of an up-to-date global red lists. (ACTION: JNCC)

5.6 Communication and publicity

5.6.1 Emphasise the importance of native Caledonian pinewood for the species. (ACTION: SNH)

GREY PARTRIDGE (*PERDIX PERDIX*)

1. CURRENT STATUS

1.1 The UK population of grey partridge declined by over 50% between 1969-1990 to a current estimated 150,000 pairs. Populations in some mixed farming areas seem stable, especially in the north, but in areas of historical low abundance such as intensive grasslands in the west, declines have sometimes exceeded 95%. The species is almost extinct in Northern Ireland.

1.2 Grey partridge is protected in Britain under the Game Acts and in Northern Ireland by the Game Preservation (Partridge and Hen Pheasant) Order (Northern Ireland) 1967. It is listed as endangered in the Irish Vertebrate Red Data Book. It is also listed on Annex III/I of the EC Birds Directive and Appendix III of the Bern Convention.

2. CURRENT FACTORS CAUSING LOSS OR DECLINE

2.1 Loss of nest sites (such as hedge bottoms) to farm intensification.

2.2 Reduced food supplies and sources for chick food through the use of pesticides and herbicides, as well as the loss of winter stubble feeding grounds for overwintering birds.

2.3 Vulnerability of nests to predators in farmland with poor cover.

2.4 Nest destruction caused by early mowing and other farm operations.

3. CURRENT ACTION

3.1 The Game Conservancy Trust (GCT) encourages land managers to create suitable conditions for grey partridge, including suitable nest sites and cover, summer and winter feeding areas (e.g.: conservation headlands and winter stubbles), and control of predators and shooting.

3.2 A Species Action Plan has been prepared for this species by the RSPB, the country agencies and the GCT.

4. ACTION PLAN OBJECTIVES AND TARGETS

4.1 Despite still being numerous and widespread, the grey partridge has declined dramatically on farmland in the UK throughout this century. Without action, this species could repeat the trends demonstrated by the corncrake, declining throughout its range and becoming globally threatened due to agricultural intensification. The reasons for decline are well known and have been the subject of intensive study by NGOs. The grey partridge will respond quickly to favourable management, and the plan aims to restore a proportion of the population to its previous level.

4.2 Halt the decline by 2005.

4.3 Ensure the population is above 150,000 pairs by 2010.

4.4 Maintain, and where possible enhance, the current range of this species.

5. PROPOSED ACTION WITH LEAD AGENCIES

5.1 Policy and Legislation

5.1.1 Consider the requirements of the grey partridge when establishing and reviewing agri-environment schemes. (ACTION: DANI, MAFF, SOAEFD, WOAD)

5.1.2 Consider the requirements of the grey partridge in any negotiations on changes to, or reform of, agricultural support. (ACTION: DANI, MAFF, SOAEFD, WOAD)

5.1.3 Encourage targeted use of pesticides on farmland. (ACTION: DANI, MAFF, SOAEFD, WOAD)

5.2 Site safeguard and management

5.2.1 No actions proposed.

5.3 Species management and protection

5.3.1 No action proposed.

5.4 Advisory

5.4.1 Continue to provide information and management advice to land managers through GCT, FWAG and other advisors. (ACTION: CCW, DoE(NI), EN, SNH)

5.4.2 Promote field margins as wildlife habitat. (ACTION: DANI, MAFF, SOAEFD, WOAD)

5.5 Future research and monitoring

5.5.1 Continue to investigate the ecological requirements of the grey partridge to help develop management advice. (ACTION: CCW, DoE(NI), EN, SNH, JNCC)

5.5.2 Investigate the impact of different management regimes on grey partridge populations, using selected farms with experimental schemes or ESA prescriptions. (ACTION: CCW, DANI, DoE(NI), EN, MAFF, SNH, SOAEFD, WOAD)

5.5.3 Encourage regular monitoring of the UK population through census work and bag returns. (ACTION: CCW, DoE(NI), EN, JNCC, SNH)

5.5.4 Promote further research into the indirect effects of agrochemical use on the grey partridge. (ACTION: CCW, DoE(NI), EN, JNCC, SNH)

5.5.5 Pass information gathered during survey and monitoring of this species to JNCC or BRC so that it can be incorporated in national databases. (ACTION: CCW, DoE(NI), EN, SNH)

5.5.6 Provide information annually to Birdlife International on the UK status of the species to contribute to maintenance of an up-to-date global red lists. (ACTION: JNCC)

5.6 Communications and publicity

5.6.1 Use grey partridge in agriculture courses to illustrate the impact farm management may have on wildlife. (ACTION: DANI, MAFF, SOAEFD, WOAD)

REPTILES AND AMPHIBIANS

SAND LIZARD (*LACERTA AGILIS*)

I. CURRENT STATUS

1.1 The sand lizard is under threat throughout its palearctic range and beyond. In the UK, natural populations have disappeared over much of its former range, including coastal dunes and the Wealden heaths, and were lost from the New Forest and from Wales. Surviving colonies are mostly confined heathland habitats within coniferous forests, dry heaths of south Dorset, with only a few populations remaining in heathlands of south-west Surrey and the Merseyside sand dunes and one long established, introduced colony in Scotland on the Isle of Coll. The species is absent from Northern Ireland. Sand lizards have recently been re-introduced to sites in the New Forest, the Weald and Wales.

1.2 Populations are declining in Belgium, Denmark, northern France, northern Germany, Luxembourg, the Netherlands and Sweden. It is listed on Annex IV of the Habitats Directive and Annex II (and Recommendation 26) of the Bern Convention. It is protected under Schedule 2 of the Conservation (Natural Habitats, etc.) Regulations, 1994 (Regulation 38) and Schedule 5 of the WCA 1981.

2. CURRENT FACTORS CAUSING LOSS OR DECLINE

2.1 Loss, deterioration and fragmentation of heathland and dune habitat to a wide range of competing uses and pressures, for example development, forestry, mineral extraction, etc.

2.2 Birch, pine, bracken and other scrub (for example *Gaultheria shallon*) encroachment of dune and heathland habitats.

2.3 Uncontrolled fires.

2.4 Shortage of suitable breeding sand on heathland sites.

3. CURRENT ACTION

3.1 Populations have been successfully re-introduced to some heaths in south-east England, Dorset and Wales. An introduction to the Inner Hebrides has survived for 25 years.

3.2 Research on distribution, status and habitat resulted in a programme of habitat management led by the British Herpetological Society (BHS), grant-aided by the World-Wide Fund for Nature (WWF) and the statutory agencies. This has recently been expanded by the Herpetofauna Conservation Trust (HCT). A programme of translocations to former sites is continuing work begun by BHS in the 1970s.

3.3 This species is the subject of a 3-year Species Recovery Programme, initiated in 1994 by CCW, EN, HCT and WWF.

4. ACTION PLAN OBJECTIVES AND TARGETS

4.1 Re-establishment of 10 populations seems to be both achievable and feasible. The current Species Recovery Programme, now in its second year, achieved four translocations in the first year and one further site was included in 1995. Eleven sites have been identified for further consideration (although it is unlikely that all will be suitable). A target of 10 is achievable, and hopefully could be exceeded by the year 2000. A longer target would be unwise.

4.2 Re-establish 10 populations to restore the range and distribution in suitable habitat within its former range by the year 2000.

4.3 Maintain all breeding populations at current levels, and enhance where possible.

4.4 Reverse the fragmentation of sites by habitat re-creation and management.

5. PROPOSED ACTION WITH LEAD AGENCIES

5.1 Policy and legislation

5.1.1 Encourage the development and uptake of management schemes and incentive payments for heathland management and restoration in southern England, and ensure these include provision to assist sand lizard conservation. (ACTION: MAFF)

5.1.2 Consider removal of limited areas of woodland on former heathland to allow linkages of fragmented heathland populations and expand populations within forests. (ACTION: FA, FE)

5.1.3 Seek to ensure that dune management policies are consistent with sand lizard needs in occupied areas. (ACTION: LAs)

5.2 Site safeguard and management

5.2.1 Review SSSI coverage of sand lizard sites in Wales and seek to ensure all significant populations are designated. (ACTION: CCW)

5.2.2 Identify all sites with sand lizards to LAs for identification in Development Plans. (ACTION: CCW, EN, LAs)

5.2.3 Consider habitat re-creation on suitable heathland and dune vegetation to consolidate and expand the current range. (ACTION: CCW, EN, FA, FE, LAs, MAFF)

5.3 Species management and protection

5.3.1 Ensure sand lizard needs are catered for in programmes of cutting, burning or grazing management on sites supporting populations, or likely to do so. (ACTION: CCW, EN, SNH)

5.3.2 Maintain all breeding populations at current levels, and enhance where possible. (ACTION: CCW, EN)

5.3.3 Where feasible, and following the identification of suitable sites, consider 10 translocations to re-establish the former range and distribution of the species in suitable habitats (for example coastal sand dunes). (ACTION: CCW, EN)

5.4 Advisory

5.4.1 Ensure that relevant LAs and landowners and managers of sites containing sand lizard are aware of its needs, legal status and importance of conserving the species and that advice on management is available. (ACTION: CCW, EN, FA, SNH)

5.5 Research and monitoring

5.5.1 Investigate and refine methods for permanently controlling and redressing habitat degradation by bracken and *Gaultheria*. (ACTION: CCW, EN, JNCC, MAFF)

5.5.2 Evaluate the genetic differences between the Merseyside, Weald and Dorset populations. (ACTION: EN, JNCC)

5.5.3 Encourage the regular monitoring of known populations. (ACTION: CCW, EN, JNCC)

5.5.4 Pass information gathered during survey and monitoring of this species to JNCC or BRC in order that it can be incorporated in a national database and contribute to the maintenance of an up-to-date Red List. (ACTION: CCW, EN, SNH)

5.6 Communication and publicity

5.6.1 Publicise the importance, rarity and conservation needs of sand lizard through the use of interpretative materials and the involvement of the media, zoos and other captive collections. (ACTION: CCW, EN)

GREAT CRESTED NEWT (*TRITURUS CRISTATUS*)

1. CURRENT STATUS

1.1 The great crested newt is still quite widespread in Britain. It is widespread but local in Scotland, where there are fewer than 1000 individuals. The species may be numerous locally in parts of lowland England and Wales but is absent or rare in Cornwall and Devon. It is absent from Northern Ireland.

1.2 The species has suffered a decline in recent years with studies in the 1980s indicating a national rate of colony loss of approximately 2% over five years. It is estimated that there are a total of 18,000 ponds within Britain, although only 3,000 of these have been identified. The British population is amongst the largest in Europe, where it is threatened in several countries.

1.3 The great crested newt is listed on Annexes II and IV of the EC Habitats Directive and Appendix II of the Bern Convention. It is protected under Schedule 2 of the Conservation (Natural Habitats, etc.) Regulations, 1994, (Regulation 38) and Schedule 5 of the WCA 1981.

2. CURRENT FACTORS CAUSING LOSS OR DECLINE

2.1 Loss of suitable breeding ponds caused by water table reduction, in-filling for development, farming, waste disposal, neglect or fish stocking and the degradation, loss and fragmentation of terrestrial habitats.

2.2 Pollution and toxic effects of agrochemicals.

3. CURRENT ACTION

3.1 JNCC have published a five-year framework (1994 - 1999) for the conservation of amphibians and reptiles in the UK, in collaboration with the statutory nature conservation agencies and voluntary bodies.

3.2 SNH commissioned a study on the distribution and status of this species in Scotland in 1994 and followed up with site surveys in 1995.

3.3 CCW, EN and SNH support a post within the NGOs to develop further local Amphibian and Reptile Groups, and support surveys and conservation initiatives. EN recently published the results of a symposium on the species, and leaflets have been published by EN and CCW, and by British Coal.

4. ACTION PLAN OBJECTIVES AND TARGETS

4.1 Work in the early 1980s documented a 2% decline in the number of ponds every five years. A more recent report suggests that 42% of great crested newt populations in the London area have been lost in 20 years. Assuming a 0.4-2% annual loss of ponds, and assuming 18,000 populations, then between 72-360 populations are being lost each year. A target of 100 re-colonisations will offset these losses. This represents new ponds required to offset losses due to neglect and should be in addition to preventing site loss through development.

4.2 Where feasible, restore populations to 100 unoccupied sites each year for the next five years, creating new ponds and managing habitat where necessary.

4.3 Maintain the range, distribution and viability of existing great crested newt populations.

5. PROPOSED ACTIONS WITH LEAD AGENCIES

5.1 Policy and legislation

5.1.1 Seek to ensure all ponds known to hold viable populations are identified in Local plans or Part II of unitary development plans, and that the protection and enhancement of the ponds is taken into account in accordance with paragraph 24 of DOE's Planning Policy Guidance note: PPG9. (ACTION: CCW, DoE, EN, LAs, SNH)

5.1.2 Consider expanding incentives for pond creation and management on farmland under the Countryside Stewardship and agri-environment schemes.(ACTION: MAFF, SOAEFD, WOAD)

5.1.3 Seek to create new pond protection measures to prevent deterioration and loss of great crested newt habitats. (ACTION: DoE, SOAEFD, WO)

5.2 Site safeguard and management

5.2.1 Seek to ensure that key sites for the great crested newt in Wales are safeguarded, considering SSSI notification where necessary to secure appropriate management. (ACTION: CCW)

5.2.2 Promote favourable management on all key sites where this species is known to occur. (ACTION: CCW, EN, FA, FE, LAs, SNH)

5.2.3 Seek to maintain the number and distribution of occupied sites through habitat restoration or creation of sufficient new sites near existing ones to compensate for local losses. (ACTION: CCW, EN, FA, FE, LAs, SNH)

5.3 Species management and protection

5.3.1 Encourage the natural dispersal of the species to new sites through habitat management and re-creation and, if necessary, consider establishing a translocation or re-introduction programme to restore populations to previously occupied or appropriate new sites. (ACTION: CCW, EN, SNH)

5.4 Advisory

5.4.1 Publish guidance for LAs, developers, land managers and others on legal obligations for the species, local management and, where appropriate, translocation techniques for the species. (ACTION: CCW, EN, JNCC, NRA, RPBs, SNH)

5.4.2 Promote training of professional and volunteer surveyors and those involved in the management and conservation of the great crested newt. (ACTION: CCW, EN, SNH)

5.5 Future research and monitoring

5.5.1 Develop further survey methods, recording, updating and data retrieval systems and surveillance systems to monitor the changes in status and the means of disseminating information. (ACTION: BRC, JNCC)

5.5.2 Encourage further surveys to identify important breeding sites. (ACTION: BRC, CCW, EN, JNCC, SNH)

5.5.3 Support research on habitat requirements, habitat use, population dynamics and species genetics to determine the favourable conservation status and underpin management advice. (ACTION: JNCC)

5.5.4 Expand the National Recording Scheme to ensure regular monitoring of known and potential sites. (ACTION: BRC, JNCC)

5.5.5 Pass information gathered during survey and monitoring of this species to JNCC or BRC in order that it can be incorporated in a national database and contribute to the maintenance of an up-to-date Red List. (ACTION: CCW, EN, SNH)

5.6 Communications and publicity

5.6.1 Further develop communications between statutory authorities and local conservation groups. (ACTION: CCW, EN, SNH)

5.6.2 Promote, through publicity and media opportunities, a wider and more sympathetic understanding of amphibian conservation. (ACTION: CCW, EN, SNH)

NATTERJACK TOAD (BUFO CALAMITA)

1. CURRENT STATUS

1.1 The natterjack toad has suffered a substantial decline in numbers and range during the 20th century due to reductions in its habitat (heathland, sand dune and upper saltmarsh). Excluding translocation sites where populations have been recently re-established, the species can be found at four natural sites in Scotland and 35 in England, but had become extinct in Wales. It has now been introduced to 13 sites, including one in Wales.

1.2 The species is listed on Appendix II of the Bern Convention and Annex IVa of the EC Habitats Directive. It is protected by Schedule 2 of the Conservation (Natural Habitats, etc.) Regulations, 1994, and Schedule 5 of the WCA 1981.

2. CURRENT FACTORS CAUSING LOSS OR DECLINE

2.1 Loss of habitat due to housing and industrial development, agriculture and reduced grazing on heathlands

2.2 Fixation of dune systems and prevention of tidal inundation through the creation of sea defence mechanisms.

2.3 Habitat fragmentation, leading to genetic isolation of populations.

2.4 Acidification and loss of breeding pools.

3. CURRENT ACTION

3.1 This species has been the subject of conservation action by both statutory and voluntary organisations (notably the British Herpetological Society) for over twenty years. A Species Recovery Programme, funded by EN and CCW, was completed in June 1995. This included habitat management, research, and translocation to 13 formerly occupied and other suitable sites. This work has now been taken on by the Herpetological Conservation Trust.

3.2 The British Herpetological Society maintain a register of all sites in the UK, which is updated annually.

4. ACTION PLAN OBJECTIVES AND TARGETS

4.1 Sustain all existing populations and, where appropriate, restore each population to its size in the 1970s. (The 1970s level was chosen as a date when baseline information was available, and represents a recent historic date for which the targets should be both achievable and measurable).

4.2 Expand the number of populations within their former range by carrying out at least five further translocations by 2005. (A target of five sites was selected since this represents an approximate increase of 10%, and it is an achievable target. There may be difficulties selecting more than five sites over the next five years; more may divert conservation attention away from the need to enhance existing populations).

5. PROPOSED ACTION WITH LEAD AGENCIES

5.1 Policy and legislation

5.1.1 No action proposed.

5.2 Site safeguard and management

5.2.1 Notify owners of all sites of the presence of natterjack toads and their protected status. (ACTION: CCW, EN, SNH)

5.2.2 Review opportunities for purchasing sites to consolidate NNRs important for natterjack toads. (ACTION: CCW, EN, SNH)

5.2.3 Produce management plans for all sites and begin implementation by 2000. (ACTION: EN, SNH)

5.3 Species management and protection

5.3.1 Review the suitability of other sites where the species has become extinct, and undertake five translocations where appropriate by 2005. (ACTION: CCW, EN, SNH)

5.4 Advisory

5.4.1 Ensure a conservation handbook is produced as part of the Species Recovery Programme to support landowners, local authorities, statutory agencies NGOs. (ACTION: EN)

5.4.2 Ensure that landowners and local authorities are aware of the legal status and appropriate methods of habitat management for this species. (ACTION: CCW, EN, SNH)

5.5 Future research and monitoring

5.5.1 Encourage regular monitoring of known populations. Maintain and develop a network of recorders and ensure the continued production of the natterjack site register. (ACTION: JNCC)

5.5.2 Research the impact of grazing, colonisation of new ponds, breeding success in large fish-stocked ponds and the significance of competition between tadpoles. (ACTION: CCW, EN, SNH)

5.5.3 Pass information gathered during survey and monitoring of this species to JNCC or BRC in order that it can be incorporated in a national database and contribute to the maintenance of an up-to-date Red List. (ACTION: CCW, EN, SNH)

5.6 Communications and publicity

5.6.1 Develop opportunities to raise public awareness, including a slide pack and a leaflet on toad conservation. Progress reports on achievements of the strategy will be needed every 2-3 years. (ACTION: CCW, EN, JNCC, SNH)

FISH

ALLIS SHAD (ALOSA ALOSA)

I. CURRENT STATUS

1.1 The allis shad is found along the coasts of western Europe, from southern Norway to Spain, and in the Mediterranean eastwards to northern Italy. It occurs mainly in shallow coastal waters and estuaries, but in the breeding season may penetrate large rivers to spawn. The population of this fish has declined significantly throughout Europe. In the UK adult fish occur in small numbers round the coast in most years. Although it may breed in the Solway Firth, there is no definite evidence of spawning stocks at present. It may now only breed in a few French rivers.

1.2 Allis shad is listed on Appendix II of the Bern Convention and Annexes II and V of the Habitats Directive. It is protected under Schedule 5 of the WCA 1981.

2. CURRENT FACTORS CAUSING LOSS OR DECLINE

2.1 Pollution.

2.2 Overfishing.

2.3 Habitat destruction.

2.4 Artificial river obstructions.

3. CURRENT ACTION

3.1 SNH fund research in the Solway Firth where mature fish are found each summer.

3.2 An action plan for this species in England and Wales is being prepared jointly by the NRA, CCW and EN, which will lead to a programme of work to identify key rivers and spawning sites by 1996.

4. ACTION PLAN OBJECTIVES AND TARGETS

4.1 Confirm the status of the allis shad as a breeding fish in UK waters.

4.2 Protect the allis shad in UK waters and ensure the continued survival of stocks.

5. PROPOSED ACTION WITH LEAD AGENCIES

5.1 Policy and legislation

5.1.1 Consider providing fishery and conservation powers equivalent to those of the NRA in England and Wales to an appropriate Scottish body. (ACTION: SOAEFD)

5.2 Site safeguard and management

5.2.1 Seek to protection of shad habitat and access routes to spawning grounds (if confirmed) by the notification as SSSIs/ASSIs of areas if this is necessary to secure appropriate management. (ACTION: CCW, DoE(NI), EN, NRA, RPBs, SNH)

5.2.2 Seek to secure and implement favourable management plans for key rivers in which this species occurs by 2004. (ACTION: NRA, RPBs)

5.2.3 Seek to secure favourable actions in management plans covering any confirmed spawning sites within one year of discovery. (ACTION: CCW, DoE(NI), EN, NRA, RPBs, SNH)

5.3 Species management and protection

5.3.1 If the fish is confirmed as breeding in the UK, investigate the reasons for its limited breeding distribution and seek to extend and re-create these at other sites, with a view to expanding the breeding distribution within the UK. (ACTION: DoE(NI), EN, NRA, RPBs, SNH)

5.4 Advisory

5.4.1 No action proposed.

5.5 Future research and monitoring

5.5.1 Complete research to confirm spawning grounds of mature fish in the Solway. (ACTION: SNH)

5.5.2 Consider establishment of a monitoring scheme to record incidental catches by anglers and commercial fisheries. (ACTION: DANI, JNCC, MAFF, NRA, SOAEFD, WOAD).

5.5.3 Promote genetic research to examine the speciation between the two species of shad. (ACTION: CCW, DoE(NI), EN, JNCC, NRA, RPBs, SNH)

5.5.4 Support a pan-European study of the shad to determine the status, genetics, biology and conservation needs of the shad across Europe. (ACTION: CCW, DoE(NI), EN, JNCC, SNH)

5.5.5 Pass information gathered during survey and monitoring of this species to JNCC or BRC in order that it can be incorporated in a national database and contribute to the maintenance of an up-to-date Red List. (ACTION: CCW, DoE(NI), EN, MAFF, SNH)

5.6 Communications and publicity

5.6.1 Prepare and distribute guidance to all coastal fishermen and angling centres in appropriate areas explaining the threat to the shad in the UK, reminding them of the legal protection afforded to allis shad and, if a monitoring scheme is established, explaining the need to record all catches and notify the appropriate body. (ACTION: DANI, JNCC, MAFF, SOAEFD, WOAD)

TWAITE SHAD (ALOSA FALLAX)

1. CURRENT STATUS

1.1 The twaite shad occurs along the west coast of Europe, the eastern Mediterranean, and in the lower reaches of a few large rivers along these coasts. It has declined in many parts of Europe: in the UK it is now virtually absent in several rivers where it is believed previously to have spawned. Rivers which still have spawning stocks include the Wye, Usk, Severn and Tywi. It may also spawn in river mouths around the Solway Firth, the only known area around Scotland where mature fish are found each summer.

1.2 The species is listed on Appendix III of the Bern Convention and Annexes II and V of the EC Habitats Directive.

2. CURRENT FACTORS CAUSING LOSS OR DECLINE

2.1 Pollution.

2.2 River and estuary barriers.

2.3 Overfishing.

2.4 Habitat destruction.

3. CURRENT ACTION

3.1 An action plan for this species in England and Wales is being prepared jointly by the NRA, CCW, and EN which will lead to a programme of work to identify key rivers and spawning sites by 1996.

3.2 Research has been conducted into the biology of this fish in the Severn and Wye.

3.3 SNH fund research in the Solway Firth.

3.4 Records of fish caught at sea are held by MAFF, SOAEFD and the Marine Biological Association.

4. ACTION PLAN OBJECTIVES AND TARGETS

4.1 Ensure the continued survival of twaite shad around the UK.

5. PROPOSED ACTION WITH LEAD AGENCIES

5.1 Policy and legislation

5.1.1 Consider providing fishery and conservation powers equivalent to those of the NRA in England and Wales to an appropriate Scottish body. (ACTION: SOAEFD)

5.2 Site safeguard and management

5.2.1 Consider the protection of shad habitat and access to spawning grounds (particularly where barriers impede access) by designating appropriate parts of the Rivers Usk, Wye, Severn and Tywi catchments as SSSIs. (ACTION: CCW, EN)

5.2.2 Seek to secure and implement favourable management plans for these rivers by 2000. (ACTION: CCW, EN, NRA)

5.2.3 Seek to secure favourable actions in catchment management plans covering any new spawning sites within one year of discovery. (ACTION: CCW, DoE(NI), EN, NRA, RPBs, SNH)

5.3 Species management and protection

5.3.1 Encourage anglers and commercial fishermen to record and release the twaite shad they catch. (ACTION: EN, CCW, DANI, DoE(NI), MAFF, NRA, SNH, SOAEFD)

5.3.2 Investigate the reasons for its declined and limited breeding distribution and seek to extend and re-create these at other sites, with a view to expanding the breeding distribution within the UK. (ACTION: DoE(NI), EN, NRA, RPBs, SNH)

5.4 Advisory

5.4.1 No action proposed.

5.5 Future research and monitoring

5.5.1 Continue research to identify the precise location of the spawning grounds in the Solway area, with a view to protecting this habitat, if appropriate. (ACTION: EN, SNH)

5.5.2 Survey former sites to establish the current status of the species in the UK and identify suitable rivers for re-establishing breeding populations. (ACTION: CCW, DoE(NI), EN, SNH)

5.5.3 Identify all spawning rivers and migration routes and provide them with protection, where appropriate. (ACTION: CCW, DoE(NI), EN, SNH)

5.5.4 Promote genetic research to examine the speciation between the two species of shad. (ACTION: CCW, EN, NRA, RPBs, SNH)

5.5.5 Consider establishing a monitoring scheme to record catches by anglers and commercial fisheries. (ACTION: DANI, JNCC, MAFF, NRA, RPBs, SOAEFD, WOAD)

5.5.6 Support a pan-European study of the shad to determine the status, genetics, biology and conservation needs of the shad across Europe. (ACTION: JNCC)

5.5.7 Pass information gathered during survey and monitoring of this species to JNCC or BRC in order that it can be incorporated in a national database and contribute to the maintenance of an up-to-date Red List. (ACTION: CCW, DoE(NI), EN, MAFF, SNH)

5.6 Communications and publicity

5.6.1 Prepare and distribute guidance to all coastal fishermen and angling centres in appropriate areas explaining the threat to shad in the UK encouraging them to release twaite shad and, if a monitoring scheme is established, explaining the need to record all catches and notify the appropriate body. (ACTION: DANI, JNCC, MAFF, SOAEFD, WOAD)

POLLAN (COREGONUS AUTUMNALIS POLLAN)

1. CURRENT STATUS

1.1 In the UK, the pollan occurs only in Lough Neagh and Lower Lough Erne in Northern Ireland. It could also be found in Upper Lough Erne, but there are no recent records of that population which must now be considered extinct. The species has declined in Lower Lough Erne over the past two decades to such an extent that is not easy to find specimens. In 1994, DANI surveys found 12 fish representing 6 year classes, an improvement on the 1992 situation where only two fish of a single ageing year class were found. The Lough Neagh population still supports a local commercial fishery.

1.2 Elsewhere, populations may be found in Loughs Ree and Derg, and on the Shannon system in the Irish Republic. Little is known about the status or abundance trends of these populations. Genetically similar species occur in Russia (known as *Omul*), and in Arctic Canada and Alaska (known as *Arctic Cisco*).

2. CURRENT FACTORS CAUSING LOSS OR DECLINE

2.1 Eutrophication of lake habitats.

2.2 Competition with introduced roach (*Rutilus rutilus*).

2.3 Commercial exploitation.

3. CURRENT ACTION

3.1 DANI, as fishery owners in Upper and Lower Lough Erne, has ceased to issue licences for commercial pollan fishing. The few licence holders were no longer able to capture many pollan. Commercial fishing will not be renewed on Lower Lough Erne until surveys reveal an exploitable stock. Regular further surveys are planned to assess pollan numbers.

3.2 Fishing in Lough Neagh is regulated by legislation, including close-seasons, restrictions on fishing methods, and mesh size limits preventing capture of immature fish.

3.3 A water quality management strategy is currently being prepared as a joint initiative between DoE(NI) and the Department of the Environment for the Republic of Ireland (DoE-RoI), with the involvement of County Councils in the Republic (CCs-RoI). This is part-funded under the EU INTERREG initiative. The key objective of the strategy will be to ensure a sufficiently high water quality standard to satisfy the requirements of the various uses.

3.4 DoE(NI)'s Environment Service aims to set up a Technical Working Group for Lough Neagh by December 1995, and should be in a position to let the appropriate contracts for the development of Water Quality Management Standards for the Lough Neagh system by December 1996.

3.5 Nutrient levels in both Lough Neagh and Lower Lough Erne are monitored on a routine basis, and phosphorus removal is carried out at the larger Sewage Treatment Works.

4. ACTION PLAN OBJECTIVES AND TARGETS

4.1 Maintain the population in Lough Neagh at a level that can be sustainably harvested.

4.2 Maintain viable populations of pollan in Lower Lough Erne.

4.3 Restore the population to Upper Lough Erne by 2005.

5. PROPOSED ACTIONS WITH LEAD AGENCIES

5.1 Policy and legislation

5.1.1 Seek to achieve and enforce an appropriate level of fishery protection in areas occupied by this species. (ACTION: DANI, Fisheries Conservancy Board)

5.1.2 Co-operate with the relevant authorities in the Republic of Ireland to ensure that the cross-border water quality management strategy addresses the requirements of the pollan. (ACTION: DANI, DoE(NI))

5.2 Site safeguard and management

5.2.1 Seek to reduce the trophic status of Lough Neagh and the Lower Erne system. (ACTION: DANI, DoE(NI))

5.2.2 Consider the protection of pollan habitat on Lower Lough Erne through ASSI notification. (ACTION: DoE(NI))

5.3 Species management and protection

5.3.1 Seek the co-operation of Lough Neagh Fishermen's Co-operative Society in monitoring the population changes through commercial fishery data. (ACTION: DANI, Fisheries Conservancy Board)

5.3.2 Consider the potential for culturing and re-introducing pollan to Upper Lough Erne. (ACTION: DANI)

5.4 Advisory

5.4.1 Publicise information on the pollan and its conservation requirements to generate public interest. (ACTION: DANI, DoE(NI))

5.5 Future research and monitoring

5.5.1 Survey to identify the spawning grounds of the remaining pollan in Lower Lough Erne and to provide more quantitative assessments of the Lough Erne stock. Integrate these findings with the current investigations, including those on sonar-based counts. (ACTION: DANI)

5.5.2 Pass information gathered during survey and monitoring to JNCC or BRC so that it can be incorporated in a national database and contribute to the maintenance of an up-to-date Red List. (ACTION: DoE(NI))

5.6 Communication and publicity

5.6.1 No action proposed.

VENDACE (COREGONUS ALBULA)

I. CURRENT STATUS

1.1 In the UK, the vendace has only been known to occur in four lakes: two in Scotland and two in England. The Scottish populations were formerly described as a distinct species, however, one population has not been recorded since shortly after a local sewage works was opened in 1911, and the species has not been recorded at the other site for over a decade, so that population may also be regarded as extinct.

1.2 In 1966, vendace were found to be common in Bassenthwaite Lake and Derwentwater in Cumbria. Since then further specimens have been taken under licence for research.

1.3 The vendace is listed on Appendix III of the Bern Convention and Annex V of the EC Habitats Directive. It is protected under Schedule 5 of the Wildlife and Countryside Act 1981.

2. CURRENT FACTORS CAUSING LOSS OR DECLINE

2.1 Pollution, in particular eutrophication caused by nutrient enrichment.

2.2 Habitat destruction.

3. CURRENT ACTION

3.1 Bassenthwaite Lake is an NNR owned by the National Trust, and has a management plan in which vendace is highlighted. Derwentwater is to be notified as an SSSI in the next by 1999.

3.2 NRA-funded ecological research is being carried out in Cumbria, and the NRA and water companies are acting to reduce nutrients entering Bassenthwaite Lake by phosphate stripping at Keswick sewage works. Emergency procedures for accidental spillages from lorries on the nearby A66 are in place. Water level management for the lake, by modifying local drainage, is under consideration.

3.3 The species is included in SNH's Species Action Programme, and a detailed plan for the species in England has been prepared by EN.

4. ACTION PLAN OBJECTIVES AND TARGETS

4.1 Ensure the continued survival of the species in Bassenthwaite and Derwentwater.

4.2 Re-introduce a self-sustaining population to one of the Scottish lochs by 2005, and subsequently to the second loch if the first re-introduction is successful and cost-effective.

5. PROPOSED ACTION WITH LEAD AGENCIES

5.1 Policy and legislation

5.1.1 None proposed.

5.2 Site safeguard and management

5.2.1 Ensure that management plans are operational for Bassenthwaite Lake and Derwentwater by 1998, protecting water quality, physical habitat of spawning grounds, and native fish from invading alien species. (ACTION: EN, NRA).

5.2.2 Seek to restore the Scottish lochs, so they are ecologically suitable for the vendace. (ACTION: SEPA, SNH)

5.3 Species management and protection

5.3.1 Consider how local byelaws can prevent use of livebait and associated translocation of alien coarse fish into the Bassenthwaite and Derwentwater catchments. (ACTION: EN, LAs, National Park Authority, NRA).

5.4 Advisory

5.4.1 No action proposed.

5.5 Future research and monitoring

5.5.1 Continue current research at Bassenthwaite Lake and Derwentwater. (ACTION: EN, NRA, water companies).

5.5.2 Survey former and likely sites to identify a suitable site for re-introduction in Scotland and to assess the feasibility of re-introducing self-sustaining populations to other lakes in Cumbria. (ACTION: SNH)

5.5.3 Encourage regular monitoring of known populations. (ACTION: EN)

5.5.4 Pass information gathered during survey and monitoring to JNCC or BRC so that it can be incorporated in a national database and contribute to the maintenance of an up-to-date Red List. (ACTION: EN, SNH)

5.6 Communications and publicity

5.6.1 Prepare and distribute a poster or leaflet on vendace to interested groups in catchments of existing populations or lochs where it is proposed to re-introduce the species. (ACTION: EN, JNCC, SNH)

INSECTS

HIGH BROWN FRITILLARY (ARGYNNIS ADIPPE)

I. CURRENT STATUS

I.I The high brown fritillary was formerly widespread and locally abundant across much of England and Wales. It has, however, declined very rapidly in the last 50 years and is now extinct over 94% of its former range. In 1994, only 53 definite colonies of the butterfly were known, many of these being very small and possibly not viable in isolation. The main centres of distribution are the limestone outcrops of Morecombe Bay and bracken slopes in Herefordshire, Exmoor and Dartmoor. The butterfly is still widespread across much of Europe although it may have experienced local declines.

I.2 The high brown fritillary is listed as vulnerable on the GB Red List and is protected by Schedule 5 of the WCA 1981.

2. CURRENT FACTORS CAUSING LOSS OR DECLINE

2.1 Reduction of coppicing.

2.2 Agricultural improvement.

2.3 Cessation of grazing and traditional forms of bracken management.

3. CURRENT ACTION

3.1 A full species action plan is being prepared by Butterfly Conservation.

3.2 Ecological research by Butterfly Conservation has been commissioned by EN and several reports have been received.

3.3 Recent surveys by Butterfly Conservation, National Trust and the Dartmoor National Park Authority have been carried out over most of its current range.

3.4 Conservation management has been undertaken on sites on Dartmoor, Exmoor, Herefordshire and Lancashire.

4. ACTION PLAN OBJECTIVES AND TARGETS

4.1 Halt the current decline and maintain at least 50 self-sustaining populations.

4.2 Restore suitable habitat within its former range and encourage spread to 10 additional sites by 2005, using re-introductions if necessary.

4.3 Ensure that a minimum number of colonies are protected within SSSIs.

5. PROPOSED ACTION WITH LEAD AGENCIES

5.1 Policy and legislation

5.1.1 Following further survey and research to identify the ecological requirements of this species, encourage the uptake of incentives for favourable land management on existing and potential sites within the Morecambe Bay area, Dartmoor, Exmoor and Herefordshire, especially through existing ESA and Countryside Stewardship schemes. (ACTION: CC, CCW, EN, MAFF)

5.1.2 Ensure the habitat requirements of this species are considered when drawing up or reviewing management prescriptions and grants in ESAs and other agri-environmental schemes, with particular attention to the need for bracken control. (ACTION: MAFF, WOAD)

5.1.3 Encourage the uptake of the Woodland Grant Scheme for coppice restoration and management in the Morecambe Bay area. (ACTION: FA)

5.2 Site safeguard and management

5.2.1 Ensure that at least 20 colonies lie within SSSIs across the current geographical range of the species. (ACTION: CCW, EN)

5.2.2 Encourage favourable management for the species on existing sites and seek to restore favourable management to former sites where opportunities for colonisation or re-introduction exist. (ACTION: CCW, EN)

5.3 Species management and protection

5.3.1 Following restoration of the habitat, encourage the spread of the butterfly to 10 additional sites by 2005, using re-introduction techniques if necessary. (ACTION: CCW, EN)

5.4 Advisory

5.4.1 Produce a guide for landowners and managers in target areas advising on how to manage land for the butterfly. (ACTION: CCW, EN)

5.5 Future research and monitoring

5.5.1 Promote research into the butterfly's ecological requirements to identify the management and conservation needs of the butterfly, including research on habitat management techniques and their impact on this species (especially in bracken habitats). (ACTION: CCW, EN, JNCC)

5.5.2 Investigate the effects of habitat loss and isolation of colonies on genetic variation and population viability. (ACTION: ITE)

5.5.3 Survey all former and potential sites to identify precise breeding areas and suitable sites for re-introduction. (ACTION: CCW, EN, JNCC)

5.5.4 Continue current butterfly monitoring transects on existing sites, collating and analysing data annually to compare trends at individual sites. (ACTION: CCW, EN, JNCC)

5.5.5 Pass information gathered during survey and monitoring of this species to JNCC or BRC so that it can be incorporated in national databases. (ACTION: CCW, EN)

5.5.6 Provide information annually to the World Conservation Monitoring Centre on the UK status of the species to contribute to maintenance of an up-to-date global red lists. (ACTION: JNCC)

5.6 Communications and publicity

5.6.1 Promote opportunities for the appreciation and conservation of the high brown fritillary and its habitat. (ACTION: CCW, EN)

APHODIUS NIGER (A DUNG BEETLE)

1. CURRENT STATUS

1.1 This beetle depends on cattle dung trodden into the water's edge. In the UK, it has only ever been found in the New Forest, Hampshire, with all the records from the edge of a single spring-time pond on Balmer Lawn. However there is a suggestion of another population from a single specimen found in flood litter of a river in a different catchment.

1.2 This dung beetle is listed as endangered in the GB Red List.

2. CURRENT FACTORS CAUSING LOSS OR DECLINE

2.1 Changes in grazing and the introduction of helminthicides to cattle.

3. CURRENT ACTION

3.1 The New Forest is an SSSI and a candidate SAC under the EC Habitats Directive.

3.2 English Nature is formulating a policy on the use of helminthicides on NNRs and SSSIs.

4. ACTION PLAN OBJECTIVES AND TARGETS

4.1 Maintain and, if feasible, enhance the known population at its current site.

4.2 Carry out research to determine why the species has such a restricted distribution and to clarify habitat needs.

4.3 Survey to confirm the presence and location of other populations by the year 2000.

5. PROPOSED ACTION WITH LEAD AGENCIES

5.1 Policy and legislation

5.1.1 Seek to develop policy on the use of helminthicides in the New Forest. (ACTION: MAFF)

5.2 Site safeguard and management

5.2.1 Seek to protect only known extant population, and any newly discovered sites, by ensuring that local catchment and water management plans take into account the needs of the species, once these are defined. (ACTION: NRA)

5.2.2 Encourage favourable management for this species at known sites, and implement policy on Helminthicides on relevant SSSI's, when formulated. (ACTION: EN)

5.3 Species management and protection

5.3.1 No action proposed.

5.4 Advisory

5.4.1 Provide advice to the New Forest Verderers and graziers concerning the probable toxic effects of helminthicides on the beetle. (ACTION: EN)

5.5 Future research and monitoring

5.5.1 Promote surveys to determine the presence and location of a population at a second site by the year 2000. (ACTION: EN)

5.5.2 Promote research into the beetle's ecology to investigate the reasons for its restricted distribution, its habitat management needs, and to determine its vulnerability to helminthicides. (ACTION: EN)

5.5.3 Pass information gathered during survey and monitoring of this species to JNCC or BRC so that it can be incorporated in national databases. (ACTION: EN)

5.5.4 Provide information annually to the World Conservation Monitoring Centre on the UK status of the species to contribute to maintenance of an up-to-date global red lists. (ACTION: JNCC)

5.6 Communications and publicity

5.6.1 No action proposed.

HORNET ROBBERFLY (ASILUS CRABRONIFORMIS)

I. CURRENT STATUS

1.1 This large and spectacular fly is found in unimproved grassland and heath in southern England and Wales. However, these habitats have shown significant decline in range and quality in recent years, with fragmentation enhancing the difficulties facing this insect. Since 1970 the hornet robberfly has been recorded from only about 40 ten km squares: in Hampshire, for example, it has been lost from six of its seven chalk grassland sites over the last few years.

1.2 The fly's larvae are believed to prey on the larvae of large dung beetles and the adult flies feed on a variety of insects, including grasshoppers, dung beetles and flies. As such, it requires suitable grassland sward to support its prey community.

2. CURRENT FACTORS CAUSING LOSS OR DECLINE

2.1 Loss of unimproved grassland and heath leading to habitat fragmentation.

2.2 Use of persistent parasite treatments for stock (e.g. ivermectins) which kill dung beetle hosts.

2.3 Changes in stock management.

3. CURRENT ACTION

3.1 A population on a National Trust property in Wiltshire has been monitored for several years by the warden.

3.2 Two SSSIs in Wales are under management agreements to ensure that agricultural usage is consistent with the needs of the robberfly.

4. ACTION PLAN OBJECTIVES AND TARGETS

4.1 Ensure the continued survival of the species in England and Wales in at least 40 regular sites.

5. PROPOSED ACTION WITH LEAD AGENCIES

5.1 Policy and legislation

5.1.1 Produce a policy statement on the use of ivermectins in SSSIs and nature reserves. (ACTION: CCW, EN)

5.1.2 Ensure that the effects of new veterinary chemicals on non-target species and their environment are taken into account when considering approval for release of these product for general use. (ACTION: MAFF, WOAD)

5.2 Site safeguard and management

5.2.1 Consider trial land management schemes in about five areas where the robberfly occurs, to test the effects of alternative methods of grassland and stock management on this species. (ACTION: CCW, MAFF, WOAD)

5.2.2 Promote favourable management in all SSSIs and nature reserves where the species occurs or formerly occurred. (ACTION: CCW, EN)

5.3 Species management and protection

5.3.1 No specific action proposed.

5.4 Advisory

5.4.1 Produce a leaflet on appropriate management for circulation to land owners and managers of sites where the robberfly occurs, or was once present. (ACTION: CCW, EN)

5.5 Future research and monitoring

5.5.1 Survey sites or districts where the species has been reported since 1960, to determine the current distribution. (ACTION: CCW, EN)

5.5.2 Promote research into the fly's ecology, especially its habitat requirements, population dynamics, dispersal abilities, larval hosts and adult prey and the importance of metapopulation structure to their survival. (ACTION: CCW, EN)

5.5.3 Promote investigate into the effects of ivermectins on the robberfly, and the use of alternative methods of stock parasite treatment that are less harmful. (ACTION: MAFF, WOAD)

5.5.4 Encourage monitoring of known sites for this species, seeking to include, where possible, information provided by local naturalists and site managers on the history of site management and the effects of ivermectin treatments on local robberfly populations. (ACTION: CCW, EN)

5.5.5 Pass information gathered during survey and monitoring of this species to JNCC or BRC so that it can be incorporated in national databases. (ACTION: CCW, EN)

5.5.6 Provide information annually to the World Conservation Monitoring Centre on the UK status of the species to contribute to maintenance of an up-to-date global red lists. (ACTION: JNCC)

5.6 Communications and publicity

5.6.1 Use this large and attractive fly to highlight the conservation issues facing insects associated with dung. (ACTION: CCW, EN)

BEMBIDION ARGENTEOLUM (A GROUND BEETLE)

1. CURRENT STATUS

1.1 This ground beetle is localised, but very widely distributed over parts of northern and central Europe. It is rare and declining in Scandinavia, but still abundant on the Karellion Peninsula of Russia across to Siberia. Within the UK there are recent records from Rye Harbour in Sussex, which possible relate to immigrants from the Continent, and pre-1923 records from several sites on Lough Neagh in Northern Ireland. On Lough Neagh recent searches have failed to re-find the species and it is presumed threatened or extinct.

1.2 As with the reed marsh beetle (*Stenus palposus*), the species probably occurs only within damp, fine sand on the margins of large freshwater bodies, but it may also occur on silty sands around lagoons or sand pits.

1.3 The species is considered to be nationally threatened, and of equivalent status to endangered within the GB Red List.

2. CURRENT FACTORS CAUSING LOSS OR DECLINE

2.1 Trampling by cattle.

2.2 Sand extraction from or near suitable beaches.

2.3 Rotting algal accumulations on suitable beaches.

3. CURRENT ACTION

3.1 Possible sites around Lough Neagh are all within an ASSI.

4. ACTION PLAN OBJECTIVES AND TARGETS

4.1 Survey to determine whether the species survives on Lough Neagh.

4.2 If it is re-found at Lough Neagh, protect and manage all sites to ensure its continued survival.

4.3 Determine the status of the species at Rye Harbour.

5. PROPOSED ACTION WITH LEAD AGENCIES

5.1 Policy and legislation

5.1.1 No action proposed.

5.2 Site safeguard and management

5.2.1 If the beetle is re-found at Lough Neagh, take appropriate action to guard against the damaging effects of cattle trampling, sand extraction and accumulations of rotting algae. (ACTION: DoE(NI))

5.2.2 If a breeding population has established at Rye Harbour, take measures to protect and manage the site. (ACTION: EN)

5.3 Species management and protection

5.3.1 If the species is re-found at Lough Neagh, consider scheduling it within the Wildlife (Northern Ireland) Order 1985. (ACTION: DoE(NI))

5.4 Advisory

5.4.1 No action proposed.

5.5 Future research and monitoring

5.5.1 Carry out further surveys to confirm the presence or absence of the species on Lough Neagh. (ACTION: DoE(NI))

5.5.2 If re-found at Lough Neagh, investigate the habitat requirements of the beetle. (ACTION: DoE(NI))

5.5.3 Survey to determine whether the species persists at Rye Harbour as a breeding population or whether the records there are of vagrant individuals only. (ACTION: EN)

5.5.4 Pass information gathered during survey and monitoring of this species to JNCC or BRC so that it can be incorporated in national databases. (ACTION: EN, DoE(NI))

5.5.5 Provide information annually to the World Conservation Monitoring Centre on the UK status of the species to contribute to maintenance of an up-to-date global red lists. (ACTION: JNCC)

5.6 Communications and publicity

5.6.1 No action proposed.

PEARL-BORDERED FRITILLARY (*BOLORIA EUPHROSYNE*)

1. CURRENT STATUS

1.1 The pearl-bordered fritillary was formerly widespread and locally abundant through much of Britain, but has declined very rapidly over the last 50 years in the south of England, and is now extinct over large parts of its former range. Its main centres of distribution are in parts of Wales and southern England, although it is still widespread and abundant at localities in north-west England and in the Highlands of Scotland. It is absent from Northern Ireland. In southern England few large colonies are known, many are small and highly vulnerable to extinction, and the rate of loss of sites is estimated at 39% per decade in central southern England.

1.2 The butterfly breeds either in woodland clearings or unimproved grassland habitats with scattered scrub or abundant bracken.

1.3 The pearl-bordered fritillary is listed on Schedule 5 of the WCA 1981 (in respect of sale only).

2. CURRENT FACTORS CAUSING LOSS OR DECLINE

2.1 Loss of open clearings and canopy gaps within modern high forest systems.

2.2 Cessation of grazing on unimproved grassland and abandonment of traditional bracken and gorse management.

3. CURRENT ACTION

3.1 A full action plan is being prepared by Butterfly Conservation.

3.2 The species has been re-introduced to at least two reserves in England, and conservation management has been implemented on several others.

3.3 New conservation initiatives are being planned by Butterfly Conservation with Forest Enterprise and the Forest Authority, to include targeting of the Woodland Improvement Grant towards coppice restoration.

3.4 The species is included in the Scottish Diurnal Lepidoptera Project which is mapping all known records in Scotland and developing habitat management guidelines for the sites in Scotland where it occurs.

4. ACTION PLAN OBJECTIVES AND TARGETS

4.1 Obtain accurate data on distribution and abundance by 1998.

4.2 Halt the current decline by the year 2005, through maintaining viable networks of populations in core areas of distribution.

4.3 Encourage restoration of suitable habitats throughout the butterfly's former range, with the long-term aim of re-introducing the species to at least 3 sites per previously occupied county.

5. PROPOSED ACTION WITH LEAD AGENCIES

5.1 Policy and legislation

5.1.1 Encourage extensive grazing regimes in acid grassland/bracken mosaics where the butterfly survives, promoting the uptake of ESA and Countryside Stewardship and other agreements as appropriate. (ACTION: CC, CCW, EN, MAFF, SNH, SOAEFD, WOAD)

5.1.2 Encourage appropriate woodland management in occupied sites through the Woodland Grant Scheme. (ACTION: FA)

5.1.3 Ensure the habitat requirements of this species are considered when drawing up or reviewing management prescriptions and grants in ESAs and other agri-environmental schemes, with particular attention to the need for bracken control. (ACTION: MAFF, SOAEFD, WOAD)

5.2 Site safeguard and management

5.2.1 Seek to ensure that three large or medium-sized colonies are notified in each Biogeographic Zone or equivalent where the species occurs. (ACTION: CCW, SNH)

5.2.2 Encourage sympathetic habitat management at all sites containing large or medium-sized colonies. (ACTION: CCW, EN, SNH)

5.2.3 Where feasible, encourage restoration of suitable habitats throughout the butterfly's former range to aid restoration programmes. (ACTION: CCW, EN, SNH)

5.3 Species management and protection

5.3.1 Following feasibility assessments and habitat restoration, where necessary, seek to restore populations to at least three sites per previously occupied county. (ACTION: EN)

5.4 Advisory

5.4.1 Ensure site managers are aware of the presence, legal protection and importance of conserving this species, and appropriate methods of management and restoration for its conservation. (ACTION: CCW, EN, SNH)

5.5 Future research and monitoring

5.5.1 Collate all recent records and update national distribution map by 1998. (ACTION: BRC, JNCC)

5.5.2 Promote surveys to identify the locations of large and medium-sized colonies and to identify potential sites for re-introduction. (ACTION: CCW, EN, SNH)

5.5.3 Encourage further research on habitat requirements and habitat management techniques, especially in unimproved grassland/bracken habitats. (ACTION: CCW, EN, SNH)

5.5.4 Encourage regular monitoring of extant sites, collating transect data annually and using this information to compare trends on individual sites. (ACTION: EN, JNCC, SNH)

5.5.5 Pass information gathered during survey and monitoring of this species to JNCC or BRC so that it can be incorporated in national databases. (ACTION: EN, SNH)

5.5.6 Provide information annually to the World Conservation Monitoring Centre on the UK status of the species to contribute to maintenance of an up-to-date global red lists. (ACTION: JNCC)

5.6 Communications and publicity

5.6.1 No action proposed.

SHRILL CARDER BEE (BOMBUS SYLVARUM)

1. CURRENT STATUS

1.1 This bee was widespread and common in the 19th and early 20th centuries, especially in southern England. However, post-1960 records suggest a decline to only one third of the previous distribution by the 1970s, with just seven sites reliably identified in the south and east of the British Isles in the 1980s. This decline has been attributed to changes in agricultural practices resulting in the loss of foraging and nesting sites in herb-rich rough grasslands such as headlands.

1.2 This species is widespread in continental Europe but is likely to be in decline in areas of extensive farming and limited habitat.

2. CURRENT FACTORS CAUSING LOSS OR DECLINE

2.1 Loss of herb-rich grasslands through agricultural intensification.

3. CURRENT ACTION

3.1 The JNCC has produced an outline action plan for threatened bees in the genus *Bombus*.

4. ACTION PLAN OBJECTIVES AND TARGETS

4.1 Survey to determine the current status of the bee by 2000.

4.2 Identify its precise habitat requirements by 2000.

4.3 Identify and maintain all strong populations.

4.4 Ensure the long-term survival of the bee in the UK using habitat restoration and re-introductions as necessary.

5. PROPOSED ACTION WITH LEAD AGENCIES

5.1 Policy and legislation

5.1.1 No action proposed.

5.2 Site safeguard and management

5.2.1 Consider notifying sites supporting viable populations of the shrill carder bee as SSSIs, where this is necessary to secure appropriate management. (ACTION: CCW)

5.2.2 Consider whether appropriate land management schemes can assist in encouraging the maintenance and, if necessary, restoration of herb-rich grasslands at known sites for this bee. (ACTION: EN, MAFF)

5.2.3 If less than 20 populations exist, use habitat restoration and re-introductions as necessary to secure the survival of the bee in the UK. (ACTION: CCW, EN)

5.3 Species management and protection

5.3.1 Consider establishing a captive breeding population with a view to undertaking re-introductions. (ACTION: EN)

5.4 Advisory

5.4.1 Provide advice on suitable management for relevant land managers. (ACTION: CCW, EN)

5.5 Future research and monitoring

5.5.1 Promote ecological research, to establish the habitat requirements of this species, the factors limiting breeding success at existing sites, dispersal ability and appropriate re-introduction methods. (ACTION: CCW, EN)

5.5.2 Promote surveys to determine the current status of the bee by the year 2000. (ACTION: CCW, EN)

5.5.3 Undertake surveys monitor the status of known sites and to establish whether suitable receptor sites exist for re-establishing populations. (ACTION: EN)

5.5.4 Encourage further research to identify the level of threat posed to this species by the introduction of non-native species and strains of *Bombus* used in pollinating greenhouses. (ACTION: ITE)

5.5.5 Pass information gathered during survey and monitoring of this species to JNCC or BRC so that it can be incorporated in national databases. (ACTION: CCW, EN)

5.5.6 Provide information annually to the World Conservation Monitoring Centre on the UK status of the species to contribute to maintenance of an up-to-date global red lists. (ACTION: JNCC)

5.6 Communications and publicity

5.6.1 Use this species to promote appreciation and conservation of threatened species of bumblebee and their habitats. (ACTION: CCW, EN)

CALLICERA SPINOLAE (A HOVERFLY)

1. CURRENT STATUS

1.1 This large, metallic-bronze hoverfly is apparently rare in western Europe and is believed to be on the verge of extinction in the UK. Historically it has been found at seven sites, all in East Anglia, but is now thought to survive at only one of these, a parkland in Cambridgeshire, where it is reduced to breeding in rot holes in two beech trees. The species is recognised as a quality indicator species for dead wood (saproxylic) habitats in Europe.

1.2 The hoverfly is listed as endangered on the GB Red List.

2. CURRENT FACTORS CAUSING LOSS OR DECLINE

2.1 Loss of old parkland trees through old age, windblow or felling.

3. CURRENT ACTION

3.1 The species is being monitored at its remaining known site. One of the two trees it uses fell in a gale in early 1995 but the main trunk has now been pushed upright.

3.2 A project to provide artificial breeding sites has begun.

4. ACTION PLAN OBJECTIVES AND TARGETS

4.1 Ensure the continued survival of the known population, including by notification as SSSI.

4.2 Attempt to locate further populations by the year 2000 and conserve any that are found.

5. PROPOSED ACTION WITH LEAD AGENCIES

5.1 Policy and legislation

5.1.1 No action proposed.

5.2 Site safeguard and management

5.2.1 Seek to ensure the long-term continuity of suitable habitat, including appropriate management at the current site, in particular maintenance of the two known breeding trees and the ivy on which the adults feed. (ACTION: EN)

5.2.2 Prepare and implement long term management plans for all current and identified sites. (ACTION: EN)

5.2.3 Review the need to notify the site as an SSSI pending the completion of surveys designed to discover whether this species still occurs at other sites. (ACTION: EN)

5.3 Species management and protection

5.3.1 Provide artificial breeding habitat at current and recent sites, if sufficient natural habitat is lacking. (ACTION: EN)

5.4 Advisory

5.4.1 Ensure land managers and owners at sites are aware of the presence and importance of conserving this species, and appropriate methods of management for its conservation. (ACTION: EN)

5.5 Future research and monitoring

5.5.1 Survey historic and other potential East Anglian sites, particularly parklands, to ascertain the true distribution of the species. (ACTION: EN)

5.5.2 Monitor the remaining populations and promote research into the feasibility and use of artificial breeding sites. (ACTION: EN)

5.5.3 Encourage research on the ecology and distribution of this species in Europe, particularly the reasons for its decline, and use the information and expertise gained towards its conservation in the UK. (ACTION: EN, JNCC)

5.5.4 Pass information gathered during survey and monitoring of this species to JNCC or BRC so that it can be incorporated in national databases. (ACTION: EN)

5.5.5 Provide information annually to the World Conservation Monitoring Centre on the UK status of the species to contribute to maintenance of an up-to-date global red lists. (ACTION: JNCC)

5.6 Communication and publicity

5.6.1 Use this hoverfly to promote interest in the conservation of insects relying on dead wood. (ACTION: EN)

BLUE GROUND BEETLE (*CARABUS INTRICATUS*)

1. CURRENT STATUS

1.1 This large colourful beetle is known to be in decline in Europe and is considered threatened in the Netherlands, Belgium, Luxembourg and Denmark. Its status elsewhere is uncertain. It has always been rare in the UK, with records from only 12 sites in Devon and Cornwall. In 1994, a survey found the beetle at just two of these sites, both small woodlands on the edge of Dartmoor within a few kilometres of each other. It may, however, still occur at five other sites where the habitat remains suitable.

1.2 The blue ground beetle is found only in mature beech and oak woodland with little ground vegetation and high humidity. It is considered to be an indicator species for deadwood in Europe. It cannot fly, so its dispersal abilities are limited.

1.3 This beetle is listed as vulnerable by the IUCN Red Data list and endangered in the GB Red List.

2. CURRENT FACTORS CAUSING LOSS OR DECLINE

2.1 Development of dense ground vegetation due to lack of grazing or canopy break up.

2.2 Loss of suitable deciduous woodland, including coniferisation and removal of deadwood.

3. CURRENT ACTION

2.1 A survey of known sites was carried out in 1994 under EN's Species Recovery Programme, and management recommendations made. Further surveying and captive breeding is being carried out by a volunteer.

2.2 Part of one site where the beetle still occurs is a NNR which is being managed by EN for the beetle. Two former sites are SSSIs, and another is a Cornwall Wildlife Trust reserve.

4. ACTION PLAN OBJECTIVES AND TARGETS

4.1 Survey former sites to establish range and population by 1998.

4.2 Identify precise habitat requirements by the year 2000.

4.3 R-establish self-sustaining populations at a minimum of 5 sites by 2005.

5. PROPOSED ACTION WITH LEAD AGENCIES

5.1 Policy and legislation

5.1.1 No action proposed.

5.2 Site safeguard and management

5.2.1 Following further survey and research to identify the precise requirements for this species, encourage favourable management within occupied woodlands. (ACTION: EN, FA)

5.3 Species management and protection

5.3.1 Ensure that self-sustaining populations are established at a minimum of 5 sites by 2005, through habitat management, and re-introduction if necessary. (ACTION: EN)

5.4 Advisory

5.4.1 Ensure landowners and managers of former and current sites are aware of the presence of the species, or potential of their land to support it, and appropriate methods of management for its conservation. (ACTION: EN)

5.4.2 Ensure that the relevant groups and societies are aware of the ecological implications of collecting this species. (ACTION: EN)

5.5 Future research and monitoring

5.5.1 Complete surveys of all previous sites by 1998 to establish the range and population size. (ACTION: EN)

5.5.2 Promote ecological research on the species and identify habitat its requirements by 2000. (ACTION: EN)

5.5.3 Identify suitable re-introduction sites and promote research to determine appropriate re-introduction techniques. Consider captive breeding if necessary. (ACTION: EN)

5.5.4 Encourage research on the ecology and distribution of this species on a European level and use the information and expertise gained towards its conservation in the UK. (ACTION: JNCC)

5.5.5 Pass information gathered during survey and monitoring of this species to JNCC or BRC so that it can be incorporated in national databases. (ACTION: EN)

5.5.6 Provide information annually to the World Conservation Monitoring Centre on the UK status of the species to contribute to maintenance of an up-to-date global red lists. (ACTION: JNCC)

5.6 Communications and publicity

5.6.2 Use the blue ground beetle to raise awareness of the implications of the importance of woodland management. (ACTION: EN)

CATHORMIOCERUS BRITANNICUS (A BROAD-NOSED WEEVIL)

1. CURRENT STATUS

1.1 This species of broad-nosed weevil may be endemic to the UK. It was first discovered at Tintagel, Cornwall in 1908. Since then it has only been found at a few coastal cliff sites on the Lizard Peninsula, and on one roadside bank in Dorset. It is usually found in short, herb-rich grassland at the edge of cliffs, though it has also been found in taller swards. The preferred adult food plants are plantains, especially ribwort (*Plantago lanceolata*), and the larvae probably feed on plant roots. Little else is known about its ecology.

1.2 The species is listed as endangered in the GB Red List.

2. CURRENT FACTORS CAUSING LOSS OR DECLINE

2.1 Lack of grazing of coastal cliff slopes.

3. CURRENT ACTION

3.1 English Nature commissioned a report in 1993 on the conservation of the five British species of *Cathormiocerus*, including *C. britannicus*.

3.2 Most of the known Cornish sites are National Trust properties, and are SSSIs.

3.3 The roadside verge site in Dorset has been brought to the attention of the County Council with a view to getting it recognised as a priority for protection and appropriate management.

4. ACTION PLAN OBJECTIVES AND TARGETS

4.1 Survey all current, former and likely sites to confirm status and distribution by 2005.

4.2 Conduct research to determine habitat preferences and the reasons for the weevil's limited distribution.

4.3 Protect all known sites and ensure that they are appropriately managed.

5. PROPOSED ACTION WITH LEAD AGENCIES

5.1 Policy and legislation

5.1.1 Encourage grazing of known and likely coastal cliff grassland sites for the weevil; consider promoting the up-take of Countryside Stewardship, as appropriate. (ACTION: EN, MAFF)

5.2 Site safeguard and management

5.2.1 Seek to ensure that the roadside verge site in Dorset is protected and appropriately managed. (ACTION: Dorset County Council)

5.2.2 Following further research to identify more precise habitat requirements, encourage appropriate grazing and cutting of sites in Cornwall. (ACTION: EN)

5.3 Species management and protection

5.3.1 No action proposed.

5.4 Advisory

5.4.1 Ensure that the owners and managers of all sites are aware of the presence and importance of conserving the beetle, and its conservation requirements. (ACTION: EN)

5.5 Future research and monitoring

5.5.1 Attempt to establish the conservation status of this weevil by the year 2000 through surveys of current, former and likely sites, focusing on western Cornwall, but including suitable terrain as far east as Dorset. (ACTION: EN)

5.5.2 Promote ecological research to determine more clearly the habitat requirements of this species to inform management advice, and through a trial period of site management and recording and assessment, assess which would be the most effective conservation action. (ACTION: EN)

5.5.3 Pass information gathered during survey and monitoring to JNCC or BRC so that it can be incorporated in a national database and contribute to the maintenance of an up-to-date Red List. (ACTION: EN)

5.6 Communications and publicity

5.6.1 Use the problems faced by this rare, endemic weevil to draw attention to the need for coastal cliff grassland management, especially grazing. (ACTION: EN)

CHRYSOTOXUM OCTOMACULATUM (A HOVERFLY)

1. CURRENT STATUS

1.1 This hoverfly is an attractive black and yellow wasp mimic. In the UK it is confined to southern England, with historic records from 11 ten km squares covering the dry heaths of east Dorset, the New Forest and the western Weald. It is currently believed to be undergoing a dramatic population decline within all its known sites, with only six records since 1980 from just four 10 km squares, mostly in Surrey. It is suspected that the larvae are predators on aphids living in ant nests.

1.2 The distribution of this species throughout Europe is not known, but this hoverfly is listed as vulnerable on the GB Red List.

2. CURRENT FACTORS CAUSING LOSS OR DECLINE

2.1 The reasons for the current population decline are not well understood, but may include habitat destruction due to afforestation, tourism or increased recreation, lack of heathland management leading to loss of bare ground or disturbed soil, and unplanned summer fires.

3. CURRENT ACTION

3.1 EN funded a survey of Dorset sites in 1995.

4. ACTION PLAN OBJECTIVES AND TARGETS

4.1 Maintain all existing populations.

4.2 Survey all present and past sites to establish current status by the year 2000.

4.3 Conduct research on the hoverfly's specific ecological requirements, to inform habitat management.

5 PROPOSED ACTIONS WITH LEAD AGENCIES

5.1 Policy and legislation

5.1.1 Encourage the uptake of appropriate land management schemes (e.g. Countryside Stewardship) on sites where the species is known, or is likely to occur. (ACTION: EN, MAFF)

5.1.2 Seek to avoid inappropriate afforestation of occupied sites. (ACTION: FA)

5.1.3 Seek to discourage inappropriate recreational and tourist use of present and potential sites. (ACTION: CC, LAs, Sports Council)

5.2 Site safeguard and management

5.2.1 Promote the sympathetic management of current and former sites to aid conservation of this species. (ACTION: EN)

5.2.2 Prepare and implement long-term management plans for all sites. (ACTION: EN)

5.3 Species management and protection

5.3.1 Consider the use of captive breeding to increase population size and to research the life history. (ACTION: EN)

5.4 Advisory

5.4.1 Ensure that landowners and managers are aware of the presence and importance of conserving this species, and appropriate methods of management for its conservation. (ACTION: EN)

5.5 Future research and monitoring

5.5.1 Encourage research to identify the ecological requirements of this species in order to help underpin habitat management advice. (ACTION: EN)

5.5.2 Survey all known, former and potential heathland sites to establish the current status by the year 2000. (ACTION: EN)

5.5.3 Encourage regular monitoring of remaining sites, ensuring the inclusion of immature stages as well as adults. (ACTION: EN)

5.5.4 Encourage research on the ecology and status of this species in Europe and use the information gained towards its conservation in the UK. (ACTION: JNCC)

5.5.5 Pass information gathered during survey and monitoring of this species to JNCC or BRC so that it can be incorporated in national databases. (ACTION: EN)

5.5.6 Provide information annually to the World Conservation Monitoring Centre on the UK status of the species to contribute to maintenance of an up-to-date global red lists. (ACTION: JNCC)

5.6 Communication and publicity

5.6.1 Use this species to highlight the effects heathland management may have on resident fauna and flora. (ACTION: EN)

SOUTHERN DAMSELFLY (COENAGRION MERCURIALE)

1. CURRENT STATUS

1.1 This globally threatened damselfly breeds in heathland streams and runnels and, more rarely, rhos pasture, chalk streams and calcareous mires. It has a restricted distribution in continental Europe, where its centre of population is the south west, and it can also be found in North Africa. It is threatened throughout most of its range.

1.2 This damselfly has suffered a 30% decline in its UK distribution since 1960. Since 1980 it has been recorded from 24 ten km squares in Devon, Dorset, Hampshire, Mid Glamorgan, the Gower Peninsula, Pembrokeshire and Anglesey, with the largest populations being in the New Forest and Pembrokeshire.

1.3 This species is listed on Annex II of the EC Habitats Directive, and Appendix II of the Bern Convention. It is listed as rare in the GB Red List.

2. CURRENT FACTORS CAUSING LOSS OR DECLINE

2.1 Loss of suitable habitat due to lack of appropriate heathland management, including reduced grazing and over-deepening of shallow breeding streams.

2.2 Drainage and dredging of breeding sites.

3. CURRENT ACTION

3.1 Some management work has been carried out by RSPB and EN on sites in Devon and Dorset. Monitoring is being undertaken at some English sites.

3.2 Studies on the biology of this species are being carried out by members of the British Dragonfly Society.

3.3 Surveys of current and former sites in Devon and Dorset were funded by EN in 1994.

3.4 Six sites have been proposed as SACs under the EC Habitats Directive.

3.5 The species is currently being considered for full protection under Schedule 5 of the WCA 1981.

4. ACTION PLAN OBJECTIVES AND TARGETS

4.1 Maintain the current status of the species in the UK, preventing further loss of breeding populations in England and Wales.

4.2 If feasible, re-introduce species to 5 former sites by 2005.

5. PROPOSED ACTIONS WITH LEAD AGENCIES

5.1 Policy and legislation

5.1.1 Encourage the uptake of beneficial land management schemes on land adjacent to occupied sites, including design (or cessation) of drainage schemes, and other agri-environmental measures. (ACTION: CCW, EN, MAFF, WOAD)

5.2 Site safeguard and management

5.2.1 Consider notifying additional sites with large breeding centres as SSSIs. (ACTION: CCW)

5.2.2 Encourage the sympathetic management of all occupied and nearby sites, especially appropriate grazing management. (ACTION: CCW, EN, LAs)

5.2.3 Ensure that, where possible, the hydrology of occupied sites remains favourable. (ACTION: NRA)

5.3 Species management and protection

5.3.1 Following further survey and identification of suitable sites, seek to re-establish populations at five former sites. (ACTION: CCW, EN)

5.4 Advisory

5.4.1 Ensure relevant land owners, managers and all others involved in the management of sites which support this species are aware of its presence and rarity, and appropriate methods of habitat management for its conservation. (ACTION: CCW, EN, NRA)

5.5 Future research and monitoring

5.5.1 Encourage further research into the damselfly's ecological requirements throughout its range in England and Wales, especially to identify precise habitat requirements and appropriate re-introduction techniques. (ACTION: CCW, EN)

5.5.2 Promote regular monitoring of extant sites, seeking to identify any further threats to the species. (ACTION: EN)

5.5.3 Encourage research on the ecology and status of this species with European partners, and use the information and expertise gained towards its conservation in the UK. (ACTION: JNCC)

5.5.4 Pass information gathered during survey and monitoring of this species to JNCC or BRC so that it can be incorporated in national databases. (ACTION: CCW, EN)

5.5.5 Provide information annually to the World Conservation Monitoring Centre on the UK status of the species to contribute to maintenance of an up-to-date global red lists. (ACTION: JNCC)

5.6 Communications and publicity

5.6.1 Use this species to promote awareness of the importance of heathland, chalk streams and mire habitats to species conservation. (ACTION: CCW, EN)

SPECKLED FOOTMAN MOTH (*COSCINIA CRIBRARIA*)

I. CURRENT STATUS

1.1 Although collectors report seeing large numbers of the speckled footman moth in the UK in the late nineteenth century, the resident sub-species (*C.c. bivittata*) has suffered a major decline in range and population size. By the early 1990s records were restricted to only a thin scattering of the moth, all from heathlands in the Wareham area of south-east Dorset. The species has not been reported from its other former sites in Hampshire since 1960 and no strong colony is currently known.

1.2 The speckled footman moth is scattered throughout Europe south to the Mediterranean and North Africa, and east to Siberia. It is protected in Hungary and the former west Germany. It is listed as vulnerable on the GB Red List.

2. CURRENT FACTORS CAUSING LOSS OR DECLINE

2.1 The loss of suitable habitat due to development, plantation forestry and subsequent encroachment of conifer seedlings, drainage work, extensive heathland fires, scrub encroachment and changes in the heathland resulting from inappropriate management.

3. CURRENT ACTION

3.1 Initial searches were conducted by Butterfly Conservation volunteers and others in 1995, but could not locate the species.

4. ACTION PLAN OBJECTIVES AND TARGETS

4.1 Carry out research to identify habitat requirements and appropriate habitat management by 2000.

4.2 Locate and maintain viable populations at all known sites.

4.3 Restore the species to its former range in the UK by the year 2010.

5. PROPOSED ACTION WITH LEAD AGENCIES

5.1 Policy and legislation

5.1.1 No action proposed.

5.2 Site safeguard and management

5.2.1 Following research to identify habitat requirements of this species, promote the appropriate management of sites by liaison with landowners and managers. (ACTION: EN)

5.3 Species management and protection

5.3.1 Following feasibility assessments, seek to restore the species to its former range in the UK as a series of 15 self-sustaining populations, by the year 2010. (ACTION: EN)

5.4 Advisory

5.4.1 Ensure landowners and managers are aware of the presence and importance of conserving this species, and appropriate methods of management for its conservation. (ACTION: EN)

5.5 Future research and monitoring

5.5.1 Promote research into the habitat requirements of this species to inform habitat management advice. (ACTION: EN)

5.5.2 Carry out systematic surveys of all known former and likely sites, to confirm the range and status of the moth in the UK. (ACTION: EN)

5.5.3 Encourage research on the ecology and status of this species at an international level and seek to establish whether the subspecies *C.c. bivittata* is endemic to Britain. (ACTION: EN, JNCC)

5.5.4 Encourage regular monitoring of known sites and use the information gained to identify any further threats to the species. (ACTION: EN)

5.5.5 Pass information gathered during survey and monitoring of this species to JNCC or BRC so that it can be incorporated in national databases. (ACTION: EN)

5.5.6 Provide information annually to the World Conservation Monitoring Centre on the UK status of the species to contribute to maintenance of an up-to-date global red lists. (ACTION: JNCC)

5.6 Communications and publicity

5.6.1 Seek to improve co-ordination and dialogue between collectors, landowners, site managers and conservation agencies to raise awareness of the moth. (ACTION: EN)

CRYPTOCEPHALUS CORYLI (A LEAF BEETLE)

1. CURRENT STATUS

1.1 This beetle was widespread in the southern half of England in the middle of this century, but is now known only from single sites in Surrey and Berkshire and, infrequently, from a number of sites on the Lincolnshire Coversand Heaths. In the south, it occurs on hazel in woodland edges or rides, or hedgerows, while in the north it lives on young birch in heathland.

1.2 The species is listed as endangered in the GB Red List.

2. CURRENT CAUSES OF LOSS AND DECLINE

2.1 The reasons for the decline are not well understood, but may be related to the reduction in coppicing.

2.2 The beetle is at risk from clearance of birch from heathland

3. CURRENT ACTION

3.1 None known.

4. ACTION PLAN OBJECTIVES AND TARGETS

4.1 Determine the reasons for the decline by the year 2000.

4.2 Survey to establish whether the beetle exists at other sites.

4.3 Maintain the beetle at all known sites and, where possible, enhance populations.

4.4 If feasible, re-introduce the beetle to three sites by the year 2005.

5. PROPOSED ACTION WITH LEAD AGENCIES

5.1 Policy and legislation

5.1.1 No action proposed.

5.2 Site safeguard and management

5.2.1 Ensure that the Wildlife Enhancement Scheme on the Coversand Heaths takes into account the needs of the beetle. (ACTION: EN)

5.2.2 Following further investigation of the ecological requirements of this species, encourage coppice management of part of the sites in Surrey and Berkshire on a trial basis. (ACTION: EN, FA)

5.3 Species management and protection

5.3.1 Following further survey and research, seek to re-introduce the species to three sites within its former range by the year 2000. (ACTION: EN)

5.4 Advisory

5.4.1 Ensure that relevant land owners and conservation advisers are aware of the importance of birch scrub for this species. (ACTION: EN)

5.5 Future research and monitoring

5.5.1 Surveys all former and potential sites to determine the current distribution of the species in the UK. (ACTION: EN)

5.5.2 Encourage research on the ecological requirements of this species to underpin appropriate management advice, and seek to establish the reasons for its decline by the year 2000. (ACTION: EN)

5.5.3 Pass information gathered during survey and monitoring of this species to JNCC or BRC so that it can be incorporated in national databases. (ACTION: EN)

5.5.4 Provide information annually to the World Conservation Monitoring Centre on the UK status of the species to contribute to maintenance of an up-to-date global red lists. (ACTION: JNCC)

5.6 Communications and publicity

5.6.1 Use this species to highlight the conservation value of scrub. (ACTION: EN)

CRYPTOCEPHALUS EXIGUUS (A LEAF BEETLE)

1. CURRENT STATUS

1.1 Little is known of this beetle, other than it is associated with wetlands. During the last century it was recorded from various sites in the Norfolk Broads and Lincolnshire fens but, since 1910, it has been known from only a single site, Pashford Poors Fen in Suffolk. It has not been seen since 1986.

1.2 The beetle is listed as endangered in the GB Red List.

2. CURRENT FACTORS CAUSING LOSS OR DECLINE

2.1 The only known site in Suffolk is threatened by lowering of the water table due to drainage of adjacent land.

3. CURRENT ACTION

3.1 The site is an SSSI and a Suffolk Wildlife Trust reserve.

3.2 Two surveys for the species have recently been carried out, but without success. Given that the species' microhabitat is unknown, survey is being continued in the hope that it may be found.

4. ACTION PLAN OBJECTIVES AND TARGETS

4.1 Survey to determine by the year 2000 whether the species is extinct or not.

4.2 If re-found, maintain and enhance the surviving population.

4.3 If re-found and the water table cannot be restored and, if feasible, translocate the species to at least five former sites by the year 2005.

4.4 Promote research to identify the ecological requirements of this species.

5. PROPOSED ACTION WITH LEAD AGENCIES

5.1 Policy and legislation

5.1.1 Following further research to identify the ecological requirements of the species, seek to ensure that these are taken into account in water management plans of the remaining or newly discovered sites. (ACTION: EN, IDB, NRA)

5.2 Site safeguard and management

5.2.1 If the species is re-found, seek to restore the water table to its former level by 2005. (ACTION: EN, NRA)

5.2.2 Assuming the species survives and water levels permit, seek to ensure that the site is managed appropriately once the beetle's habitat requirements are known. (ACTION: EN)

5.3 Species management and protection

5.3.1 If the water table cannot be restored, and following feasibility assessments, seek to translocate the species to at least five former sites by the year 2005. (ACTION: EN)

5.4 Advisory

5.4.1 No action proposed.

5.5 Future research & monitoring

5.5.1 Survey to determine, by 2000, whether the species still occurs at Pashford Poors Fen. (ACTION: EN)

5.5.2 If the species is re-found, carry out research to determine its ecological and management needs. (ACTION: EN)

5.5.3 Pass information gathered during survey and monitoring to JNCC or BRC so that it can be incorporated in a national database and contribute to the maintenance of an up-to-date Red List. (ACTION: EN)

5.6 Communications and publicity

5.6.1 Use this species to demonstrate the impact of the loss of wetland habitats on UK flora and fauna. (ACTION: EN)

MARSH FRITILLARY (EURODRYAS AURINIA)

1. CURRENT STATUS

1.1 The marsh fritillary butterfly is declining in almost every European country and is now extinct in northern Belgium. The UK is now believed to be one of the major European stronghold for the species, but even here it has declined substantially over the last 150 years. In Britain, its range has reduced by over 62%, and it has recently disappeared from most of eastern England and eastern Scotland. It is still quite widespread in parts of south-west England and Wales, but colonies are estimated to be disappearing at a rate of well over 10% per decade. In Ireland, the butterfly's range is thought to have contracted by 50%.

1.2 Surveys in 1990 indicated that there were 228 definite colonies in England, 111 in Wales, 35 in Scotland and 58 in Northern Ireland, in about 20 key areas. 44% of colonies known in Britain are within SSSIs, and 11 within NNRs.

1.3 The marsh fritillary breeds in two main habitats, damp neutral or acid grasslands (Rhos pastures) and dry chalk and limestone grasslands. Colonies are often small and prone to extinction, so extensive networks of habitat patches which permit re-colonisation are essential to their long term survival.

1.4 The butterfly is listed on Annex II of the EC Habitats Directive and Appendix II of the Bern Convention It is also protected under Schedule 5 of the WCA 1981 (in respect of sale only), and fully protected under Schedule 5 and 7 of the Wildlife Order (Northern Ireland) 1985.

2. CURRENT FACTORS CAUSING LOSS OR DECLINE

2.1 Agricultural improvement of marshy and chalk/limestone grasslands.

2.2 Afforestation and development of habitats.

2.3 Changes in grazing stock and practice.

2.4 Increasing fragmentation and isolation of habitats.

3. CURRENT ACTION

3.1 A full species action plan has been prepared by Butterfly Conservation.

3.2 Conservation management for the butterfly is being carried out on many nature reserves and SSSIs/ASSIs.

3.3 Survey and monitoring work is being undertaken by a variety of bodies, including a survey commissioned by SNH of two areas of western Scotland in 1994. CCW have almost completed a full survey of Wales.

3.4 SNH has funded a post-graduate student to collaborate with the Scottish Diurnal Lepidoptera Project to establish 5 monitoring sites and collate vegetational data at a further two.

3.5 Two sites have been proposed for designation as SACs under the EC Habitats Directive.

3.6 The species is being considered for full protection under the WCA 1981.

4. ACTION PLAN OBJECTIVES AND TARGETS

4.1 Halt current decline and maintain the present range of the species.

4.2 Maintain at least five large populations within 20 pre-determined key areas.

4.3 Ensure that a minimum number of colonies are protected within SSSIs.

5. PROPOSED ACTION WITH LEAD AGENCIES

5.1 Policy and legislation

5.1.1 Promote favourable land management on occupied grasslands, and those within dispersal range of existing populations, through management agreements and appropriate schemes, for example: ESA, Countryside Stewardship, and Tir Cymen. (ACTION: CC, CCW, EN, DANI, DoE(NI), LAs, MAFF, SNH, SOAEFD, WOAD)

5.1.2 Discourage the afforestation of occupied sites or sites within dispersal distance. (ACTION: FA)

5.1.3 Set the criteria for, then identify key areas within which large populations will be maintained. (ACTION: CCW, DoE(NI), EN, SNH)

5.2 Site safeguard and management

5.2.1 Seek to ensure that at least five large (1,000+ adults) or medium-sized (100 - 1,000 adults) colonies are notified as SSSI/ASSI per key area. (ACTION: CCW, DoE(NI), EN, SNH)

5.2.2 Ensure that at least 20 colonies lie within SSSIs across the current geographical range of the species. (ACTION: CCW, DoE(NI), EN, SNH)

5.2.3 Encourage favourable management of all known sites with large and medium populations, and of associated occupied or potential sites, to encourage the formation of site networks. (ACTION: CCW, DoE(NI), EN, SNH)

5.3 Species management and protection

5.3.1 No action proposed.

5.4 Advisory

5.4.1 Ensure information on the distribution of the marsh fritillary and the management of its habitat is available to all those who play a role in its conservation and recovery. (ACTION: CCW, DoE(NI), EN, SNH)

5.5 Future research and monitoring

5.5.1 Complete surveys to identify key areas and site networks. (ACTION: CCW, DoE(NI), EN, SNH)

5.5.2 Encourage further research on habitat management and assess the impact of such management on other important species associated with the same habitats. (ACTION: CCW, DoE(NI), EN, FC, SNH)

5.5.3 Encourage regular monitoring of a network of sites which are actively managed within the key areas and use the information gained to compare trends on individual sites and identify further threats to the species. (ACTION: CCW, DoE(NI), EN, SNH)

5.5.4 Pass information gathered during survey and monitoring of this species to JNCC or BRC so that it can be incorporated in national databases. (ACTION: CCW DoE(NI), EN, SNH)

5.5.5 Provide information annually to the World Conservation Monitoring Centre on the UK status of the species to contribute to maintenance of an up-to-date global red lists. (ACTION: JNCC)

5.6 Communications and publicity

5.6.1 Promote opportunities for the appreciation and conservation of the marsh fritillary and its habitat, and use the butterfly to illustrate the problems of habitat fragmentation. (ACTION: CCW, DoE(NI), EN, SNH)

NETTED CARPET MOTH (*EUSTROMA RETICULATUM*)

1. CURRENT STATUS

1.1 This moth has a localised distribution throughout Europe. In the UK it is restricted to 11 sites in Cumbria, where it has declined substantially since 1980, and to two small colonies in north-west Wales. The sole larval food plant, touch-me-not or yellow balsam (*Impatiens noli-tangere*), is also found naturally only in these areas. The plant occurs in wet woodland, by streams, seepages and lakesides. Both food plant and moth undergo great population fluctuations.

1.2 The moth is listed as vulnerable in the GB Red List.

2. CURRENT FACTORS CAUSING LOSS OR DECLINE

2.1 Increased shade in woodland through canopy closure, resulting in the loss of food plants.

2.2 Road-widening and maintenance, and alteration to local hydrology.

3. CURRENT ACTION

3.1 In England, this moth is the subject of a three year Species Recovery Programme project (1994-96) run by EN, The National Trust, Butterfly Conservation and Lancaster University, to determine optimum habitat management.

3.2 All populations of the food plant in north west Wales were surveyed in 1994 and larval monitoring was initiated.

4. ACTION PLAN OBJECTIVES AND TARGETS

4.1 Identify the precise habitat requirements of the species by 1997.

4.2 Ensure that all existing habitat is appropriately managed by the year 2000.

4.3 Increase the moth's population and range to its recorded optimum by 2005.

5. PROPOSED ACTION WITH LEAD AGENCIES

5.1 Policy and legislation

5.1.1 Encourage sympathetic woodland management where the moth is present. (ACTION: CCW, EN, FA)

5.1.2 Seek to ensure that road works do not affect colonies of the food plant. (ACTION: LAs)

5.2 Site safeguard and management

5.2.1 Consider notifying SSSIs to include all known colonies. (ACTION: EN, CCW)

5.2.2 Continue to develop and promote appropriate management of sites by liaison with land owners and managers. (ACTION: CCW, EN)

5.2.3 Consider habitat restoration within the dispersal range of existing colonies to increasing the current range of the moth in the UK to its recorded optimum, by 2005. (ACTION: CCW, EN, FA)

5.3 Species management and protection

5.3.1 Continue to encourage growth of the food plant colonies. (ACTION: CCW, EN)

5.4 Advisory

5.4.1 Ensure land owners and managers are aware of the presence and importance of conserving the species, and appropriate methods of management for its conservation. (ACTION: CCW, EN)

5.5 Future research and monitoring

5.5.1 Undertake research into the long-term population dynamics of the species, effects of habitat management and dispersal abilities of the moth. (ACTION: CCW, EN)

5.5.2 Undertake a systematic survey of potential habitats to locate any previously unknown or new colonies of the food plant. (ACTION: CCW, EN)

5.5.3 Encourage regular monitoring of extant sites. (ACTION: CCW, EN)

5.5.4 Pass information gathered during survey and monitoring of this species to JNCC or BRC so that it can be incorporated in national databases. (ACTION: CCW, EN)

5.5.5 Provide information annually to the World Conservation Monitoring Centre on the UK status of the species to contribute to maintenance of an up-to-date global red lists. (ACTION: JNCC)

5.6 Communications and publicity

5.6.1 Produce an illustrated leaflet on the current status and requirements of the moth. (ACTION: CCW, EN)

BLACK BOG ANT (FORMICA CANDIDA, FORMERLY KNOWN AS F. TRANSKAUCASICA)

1. CURRENT STATUS

1.1 In the UK the black bog ant is known from only a small number of bogs, wet heaths and mossy stream sides in Dorset and Hampshire, and from an isolated site near Carmarthen in Dyfed. The species seems to have disappeared from a number of its former strongholds in the New Forest, and has been recorded in only 9 one km squares there since 1975.

1.2 This species is listed as endangered in the GB Red List.

2. CURRENT FACTORS CAUSING LOSS OR DECLINE

2.1 Loss of permanent bog habitat through land drainage and the consequent lowering of the water table, agriculture and afforestation.

2.2 Natural succession, leading to the overgrowth of carr and scrub.

2.3 Excessive grazing pressure and trampling of nests.

2.3 Drought.

2.4 Pollution and eutrophication of watercourses.

2.5 Potential genetic isolation, inbreeding and loss of genetic fitness.

3. CURRENT ACTION

3.1 The Dyfed population is monitored annually, and drainage ditches are being dammed to maintain the water table.

4. ACTION PLAN OBJECTIVES AND TARGETS

4.1 Survey former sites and nearby suitable habitat to establish the true status of the species by 2000.

4.2 Maintain all known populations and encourage their growth.

4.3 Identify the precise habitat requirements of the species by 2000.

4.4 Restore at least 20 self-sustaining populations to the former range in the UK by the year 2005.

5. PROPOSED ACTIONS WITH LEAD AGENCIES

5.1 Policy and legislation

5.1.1 Seek to ensure that river management activities in occupied areas take into account the requirements of this ant. (ACTION: NRA)

5.1.2 Consider how policies and existing incentive schemes might be used to encourage landowners and managers to maintain water levels and water quality at occupied sites. (ACTION: MAFF, NRA, WOAD)

5.2 Site safeguard and management

5.2.1 Following further research to identify precise habitat requirements, review management in the New Forest (particularly stocking and grazing levels and forest management practice) and consider modifications in areas where this species would benefit. (ACTION: FA, FE)

5.2.2 Seek to secure sympathetic management of all known sites. (ACTION: CCW, EN)

5.2.3 Seek to ensure that water level management plans take into account the ecological requirements of this species where appropriate. (ACTION: EN, IDBs, NRA)

5.3 Species management and protection

5.3.1 Following feasibility assessments and identification of suitable sites, seek to restore at least 20 self-sustaining populations to former sites by the year 2005, using habitat restoration where necessary. (ACTION: CCW, EN)

5.3.2 Seek to ensure the survival of threatened nest sites through implementation of short-term remedial management action. (ACTION: CCW, EN)

5.4 Advisory

5.4.1 Ensure the provision of guidance on species and habitat management to site owners and managers. (ACTION: CCW, EN)

5.5 Future research and monitoring

5.5.1 Promote research into the ecology of the ant, including investigation of the genetic variation between colonies to ensure the maintenance of viable, but distinct, populations and to help identify suitable management methods. (ACTION: CCW, EN)

5.5.2 Survey all current and former sites to ascertain the current status of the species in the UK and to identify sites for translocation by the year 2000. (ACTION: CCW, EN)

5.5.3 Encourage regular monitoring of all extant populations and seek to identify any further threats to the species, in particular the effects of summer drought on populations size. (ACTION: CCW, EN)

5.5.4 Encourage research on the ecology and distribution of the species at an international level and use the information and expertise gained towards its conservation in the UK. (ACTION: CCW, EN, JNCC)

5.5.5 Pass information gathered during survey and monitoring of this species to JNCC or BRC so that it can be incorporated in national databases. (ACTION: CCW, EN)

5.5.6 Provide information annually to the World Conservation Monitoring Centre on the UK status of the species to contribute to maintenance of an up-to-date global red lists. (ACTION: JNCC)

5.6 Communications and publicity

5.6.1 Promote opportunities for the appreciation and conservation of the black bog ant and its habitat. (ACTION: CCW, EN)

NARROW-HEADED ANT (FORMICA EXSECTA)

I. CURRENT STATUS

I.1 This ant is localised, but widely distributed in Europe. It has been recorded in only two main habitat types in the UK: on lowland heathland in southern England and in native pine forests in the Scottish Highlands. Historical records suggest two population centres in England: one covering the Dorset heathlands, the New Forest and the Isle of Wight, and the other centred on the Bovey valley in Devon, with an outlying record from the north Cornish coast. Recent surveys failed to record the species from the former area, but colonies were found at four sites in Devon in the early 1990s, including Chudleigh Knighton Heath (80 nests) and Bovey Heathfield (5 nests). The remnant population in the Bovey Valley appears to be just viable.

I.2 Most historical records in Scotland originate from mid-Strathspey, with outlying locations in Easter Ross and Rannoch Moor. Scottish populations have recently been recorded in Glen More and the Abernethy Forest, and at Carrbridge.

I.3 Both main Devon sites are designated as SSSIs and one is a Devon Wildlife Trust reserve. Similarly, the Glen More site is within a reserve managed by the Scottish Wildlife Trust and Forest Enterprise. The Abernethy Forest is notified as a SSSI, with part of it an NNR, and is an RSPB reserve.

I.4 The narrow-headed ant is listed as endangered on the GB red List.

2. CURRENT FACTORS CAUSING LOSS OR DECLINE

2.1 The loss of suitable heathland due to destruction and inappropriate management, for example through agriculture and urban development, inappropriate afforestation, untimely and extensive fires, and encroachment by scrub, trees and bracken leading to shading out of nests and subsequent encouragement of competitive species of ant at sites in England.

2.2 Loss of natural and semi-natural habitats in Scotland, e.g. Caledonian Pine Forest, and the intensive management of moorland for game birds and red deer.

2.3 Motorcycle scrambling at Bovey Heathfield in England

2.4 Excessive grazing and inadequate browsing by inappropriate species of ponies in the New Forest, and the production of dense, single age heather (Calluna vulgaris) monoculture with reduced marginal scrub between heath and woodland.

2.5 Nutrient enrichment of soils and development of grass swath.

2.6 Habitat fragmentation leading to potential inbreeding and loss of genetic fitness in isolated populations.

3. CURRENT ACTION

3.1 A report on the distribution, ecology and conservation of the ant in Devon was prepared by Exeter University for WWF in 1993.

3.2 Management plans have been prepared for both Bovey Heathfield and Chudleigh Knighton Heath. The Chudleigh Knighton Heath plan is being implemented and is proving beneficial to the ant.

3.3 Further survey work is currently being undertaken on the Devon sites with funding from EN's Species Recovery Programme.

3.4 Surveys have been undertaken for this species in Glen More and Abernethy which located more than 80 nests.

4. ACTION PLAN OBJECTIVES AND TARGETS

4.1 Survey to confirm the distribution of the species in the UK by the year 2000.

4.2 Maintain and, if possible, enhance the two main Devon populations and those in Glen More through appropriate management.

4.3 Develop and implement artificial rearing and translocation techniques by 2000.

4.4 Re-establish 10 self-sustaining populations in appropriate locations in Dorset or the New Forest by 2005.

5. PROPOSED ACTIONS WITH LEAD AGENCIES

5.1 Policy and legislation

5.1.1 No action proposed.

5.2 Site safeguard and management

5.2.1 Seek to secure favourable management for this species at all existing sites, helping to prepare, and encouraging the implementation of, management plans including protecting existing sites from damaging activities. (ACTION: EN, SNH)

5.3 Species management and protection

5.3.1 Following further survey and research, and the identification of suitable sites, seek to restore 10 populations to former sites in Dorset or the New Forest by 2005, using artificial rearing techniques as necessary. (ACTION: EN)

5.4 Advisory

5.4.1 Ensure the provision of detailed guidance to site owners and managers regarding the management requirements of the species and its habitat. (ACTION: EN, FA, SNH)

5.5 Future research and monitoring

5.5.1 Promote research to identify the habitat requirements of this species, especially into colony structure and formation, genetic variation and integrity of colonies, competition with other ants, asexual reproduction, artificial rearing and translocation techniques. (ACTION: EN, SNH)

5.5.2 In co-ordination with other organisations, survey all former and existing sites in Scotland to ascertain the current status of the species in the country. (ACTION: SNH)

5.5.3 Encourage monitoring of existing populations and identify any further threats to the species. (ACTION: EN, SNH)

5.5.4 Encourage research on the ecology and distribution of this ant at an international level and use the information and expertise gained towards its conservation both in the UK and internationally. (ACTION: JNCC)

5.5.5 Pass information gathered during survey and monitoring of this species to JNCC or BRC so that it can be incorporated in national databases. (ACTION: EN, SNH)

5.5.6 Provide information annually to the World Conservation Monitoring Centre on the UK status of the species to contribute to maintenance of an up-to-date global red lists. (ACTION: JNCC)

5.6 Communications and publicity

5.6.1 Promote opportunities for the appreciation and conservation of the narrow headed ant and its habitat. (ACTION: EN, SNH)

BLACK-BACKED MEADOW ANT (*FORMICA PRATENSIS*)

1. CURRENT STATUS

1.1 This ant has been rare since it was first recorded in the UK. It was confined to a few sites around the Bournemouth and Wareham areas of Dorset but, despite a number of informal searches, there have been no sightings of this species since the 1980s, when two last known colonies in the Morden area disappeared. A population still exists on cliff top sites on the Channel Islands. This species has recently been considered to be the same species as *F. nigricans*, which has not been recorded reliably from the UK.

1.2 The black-backed meadow ant is widespread in Europe but is declining. It is listed as vulnerable by the IUCN/WCMC and as endangered in the GB Red List. It is possibly now extinct in the UK.

2. CURRENT FACTORS CAUSING LOSS OR DECLINE

2.1 Urban development on the heaths and cliff tops around Bournemouth.

2.2 Inappropriate management and excessive encroachment of scrub on open heath and rough grass. This may lead to the subsequent invasion of competitive southern wood ants (*F. rufa*).

3. CURRENT ACTION

3.1 Proposals are currently being considered for a captive breeding programme with a view to re-introduction to protected sites.

4. ACTION PLAN OBJECTIVES AND TARGETS

4.1 Survey to determine distribution and status of the ant by 2000.

4.2 If found to be present in the UK, clarify taxonomic status by 2005.

4.3 If still present, protect and manage all remaining populations.

4.4 If feasible, restore 10 populations to suitable former sites by the year 2005.

5. PROPOSED ACTION WITH LEAD AGENCIES

5.1 Policy and legislation

5.1.1 If colonies are re-discovered, encourage the uptake of management agreements and incentive schemes for the restoration or enhancement of suitable heathland in areas adjacent to known, or restored, colonies, and encourage the protection and regeneration of heathland within its former range to encourage expansion of existing colonies. (ACTION: EN, MAFF)

5.2 Site safeguard and management

5.2.1 Ensure the survival of any re-discovered or re-introduced populations through favourable management of sites. (ACTION: EN)

5.2.2 Seek to restore suitable habitat to former sites, with a view to re-introducing populations within the former range of the species. (ACTION: EN)

5.3 Species management and protection

5.3.1 Following further survey and assessment, and the identification of suitable former sites, seek to restore 10 self-sustaining populations within the former range of this ant on the British mainland, by the year 2005, using captive-bred individuals as necessary.

5.4 Advisory

5.4.1 If the species is re-discovered, ensure the land owners or managers are aware of the presence and importance of conserving the species, and appropriate methods of management to maintain and enhance populations. (ACTION: EN)

5.5 Future research and monitoring

5.5.1 Undertake a thorough systematic survey for the species to confirm its distribution and conservation status by the year 2000. (ACTION: EN)

5.5.2 Encourage investigation and confirm the taxonomic status of the species by the year 2005. (ACTION: ITE)

5.5.3 If re-introduction proves necessary, promote research to determine the most appropriate means. (ACTION: EN)

5.5.4 Encourage research on the habitat requirements of this species, including colony foundation, genetic variation and integrity, methods of artificially rearing this species and the myrecophile fauna associated with colonies. (ACTION: EN)

5.5.5 Encourage research on the ecology and conservation of this species at an international level and use the information and experience gained towards its conservation both in the UK and internationally. (ACTION: EN, JNCC)

5.5.6 If re-discovered in the UK, encourage monitoring of extant populations and seek to identify any other threats to the species. (ACTION: EN)

5.5.7 Pass information gathered during survey and monitoring of this species to JNCC or BRC so that it can be incorporated in national databases. (ACTION: EN)

5.5.8 Provide information annually to the World Conservation Monitoring Centre on the UK status of the species to contribute to maintenance of an up-to-date global red lists. (ACTION: JNCC)

5.6 Communications and publicity

5.6.1 No action proposed.

MOLE CRICKET (*GRYLLOTALPA GRYLLOTALPA*)

1. CURRENT STATUS

1.1 The mole cricket occurs throughout much of Europe, north Africa and western Asia, but is thought to be declining throughout its range. In the UK, the species used to occur in 33 vice-counties, mainly in southern England but also in southern Wales, western Scotland and Northern Ireland. By the mid 20th century its range had contracted substantially, to Dorset, Hampshire and Surrey. It may now be extinct, with the last confirmed record of a solitary specimen at Wareham, Dorset in 1988, but there have been several unconfirmed records since.

1.2 This large insect inhabits damp, but well-drained margins of wet areas. It prefers sandy soils, but has been found in grass tussocks in peaty areas and river silts. The cricket spends the majority of its life underground in a series of tunnels which it excavates. Both sexes can fly, assisting natural dispersal and colonisation.

1.3 The species is listed as endangered in the GB Red List, and is protected under Schedule 5 of the WCA 1981.

2. CURRENT FACTORS CAUSING LOSS OR DECLINE

2.1 Intensive mechanical cultivation or drainage of soils in arable and horticultural systems.

2.2 Lack of suitable grazing or cutting management in damp meadows, allowing the development of tall vegetation which makes the underlying soil too cold for breeding.

2.3 Heavy insecticide use.

3. CURRENT ACTION

3.1 A full species action plan was prepared by EN in 1995.

3.2 In 1994 a survey of known sites in Surrey, Hampshire and Dorset, and ecological work in Guernsey and the Netherlands, was grant-aided by EN under the Species Recovery Programme.

3.3 Appeals for information have been made in various journals in the last twenty years.

4. ACTION PLAN OBJECTIVES AND TARGETS

4.1 Locate and safeguard any surviving colonies by the year 2000.

4.2 Establish breeding colonies of the cricket in captivity by the year 2000.

4.3 If feasible, identify or establish 20 self-sustaining colonies throughout the cricket's former range by the year 2005.

5. PROPOSED ACTION WITH LEAD AGENCIES

5.1 Policy and legislation

5.1.1 Seek to ensure that the requirements of the mole cricket are taken into account in catchment management plans for occupied areas. (ACTION: NRA)

5.2 Site safeguard and management

5.2.1 Encourage sympathetic management of known or potential sites. (ACTION: EN)

5.2.2 Consider targeting an appropriate land management scheme such as Countryside Stewardship, the Habitat Scheme, or ESAs, to any area found to support the species, to encourage natural colonisation or to facilitate translocation. (ACTION: MAFF)

5.3 Species management and protection

5.3.1 Establish captive breeding populations, preferably using native stock, to facilitate re-introductions or translocations by the year 2000. (ACTION: EN)

5.3.2 Following further survey and assessment, and identification of suitable receptor sites within the former range, identify or establish a series of at least 20 self-sustaining colonies by the year 2005. (ACTION: EN)

5.4 Advisory

5.4.1 Provide advice on suitable management for the mole cricket to land owners, managers and advisory bodies. (ACTION: EN)

5.5 Future research and monitoring

5.5.1 Survey all suspected and recent sites to determine the status of the species by the year 2000 and encourage entomologists and others to look out for the mole cricket and report any finds. (ACTION: EN)

5.5.2 Promote research into selected aspects of mole cricket ecology to help define the habitat and site management requirements, and captive breeding techniques. (ACTION: EN, NRA)

5.5.3 Survey to identify potential sites for translocations. (ACTION: EN)

5.5.4 Encourage research on the ecology and conservation of this species at an international level and use the information and experience gained towards its conservation in the UK. (ACTION: EN, JNCC)

5.5.5 Pass information gathered during survey and monitoring of this species to JNCC or BRC so that it can be incorporated in national databases. (ACTION: EN)

5.5.6 Provide information annually to the World Conservation Monitoring Centre on the UK status of the species to contribute to maintenance of an up-to-date global red lists. (ACTION: JNCC)

5.6 Communications and publicity

5.6.1 Use this species to highlight the problems associated with loss of wetland edge. (ACTION: EN)

SILVER SPOTTED SKIPPER BUTTERFLY (*HESPERIA COMMA*)

I. CURRENT STATUS

I.I The silver-spotted skipper is widespread in central and southern Europe. In the UK it formerly occurred as far north as Yorkshire, and west to Devon, but underwent a rapid decline in the 1950s and, by 1982, was reduced to 49 localities in 10 areas. In 1980 is was confined to southern chalk downland grassland in southern England representing a decline in range of at least 89%. However, it has recently expanded its range a little, with a 30% increase in the North and South Downs since 1980.

I.2 Small local populations require high immigration from other nearby colonies to be self-sustaining, so networks of sites are essential to the long-term survival of small colonies.

I.3 The silver-spotted skipper is listed as rare in the GB Red List, and is protected under Schedule 5 of the WCA 1981 (in respect of sale only).

2. CURRENT FACTORS CAUSING LOSS OR DECLINE

2.1 Insufficient grazing by stock and rabbits.

2.2 Loss of unimproved calcareous grasslands and fragmentation of remaining habitats.

3. CURRENT ACTION

3.1 A full action plan is being prepared by Butterfly Conservation.

3.2 Conservation management is being implemented on several nature reserves and SSSIs.

3.3 Research on the genetics and metapopulation structure of the species is being conducted by Birmingham University under a NERC grant. Other local studies are being conducted by members of Butterfly Conservation.

4. ACTION PLAN OBJECTIVES AND TARGETS

4.1 Maintain populations throughout the current range, through conservation of large colonies and/or networks of smaller populations.

4.2 Conduct strategic re-introductions to large sites or a network of small sites.

4.3 Ensure that a minimum number of colonies are protected within SSSIs.

5. PROPOSED ACTION WITH LEAD AGENCIES

5.1 Policy and legislation

5.1.1 Promote favourable land management on occupied grasslands and those within dispersal range of existing colonies through appropriate schemes (e.g. ESAs, Countryside Stewardship, etc.). (ACTION: CC, EN, MAFF)

5.1.2 Encourage approval of licensing trials of rabbit VHD vaccine in the UK. (ACTION: MAFF)

5.2 Site safeguard and management

5.2.1 Ensure that at least 20 colonies lie within SSSIs across the current geographical range of the species. (ACTION: EN)

5.2.2 Encourage appropriate management of all known sites with large populations, and associated occupied or potential sites, to encourage the formation of networks. (ACTION: EN)

5.3 Species management and protection

5.3.1 Conduct strategic re-introductions into suitably restored habitat, if beyond the limits of natural spread. (ACTION: EN)

5.4 Advisory

5.4.1 Advise site managers on appropriate habitat management, possibly through the production of an advisory guide. (ACTION: EN)

5.5 Future research and monitoring

5.5.1 Define the terms 'large' and 'medium-sized colonies' to assist in prioritising conservation action. (ACTION: EN)

5.5.2 Survey to identify suitable sites for re-introduction. (ACTION: EN)

5.5.3 Investigate rabbit VHD and likely impacts on silver-spotted skipper habitat. (ACTION: EN)

5.5.4 Investigate the suitability of creating new habitats for the species through restoration of inappropriately managed areas. (ACTION: EN)

5.5.5 Encourage regular monitoring of extant sites, continuing existing transects on known sites, and using the information to identify further threats to the species. (ACTION: EN)

5.5.6 Conduct further research on ideal management regimes (e.g., non-rotational regimes) (ACTION: EN)

5.5.7 Encourage research on the ecology and conservation of this species on an international level and use the information and experience gained towards its conservation in the UK. (ACTION: EN, JNCC)

5.5.8 Pass information gathered during survey and monitoring of this species to JNCC or BRC so that it can be incorporated in national databases. (ACTION: EN)

5.5.9 Provide information annually to the World Conservation Monitoring Centre on the UK status of the species to contribute to maintenance of an up-to-date global red lists. (ACTION: JNCC)

5.6 Communications and publicity

5.6.1 Promote opportunities for the appreciation and conservation of this butterfly and its habitat, and use the species to illustrate the problems of habitat fragmentation. (ACTION: EN)

BRIGHT WAVE MOTH (*IDAEA OCHRATA*)

I. CURRENT STATUS

1.1 This moth is a coastal species which occurs along sandy shingle beaches and on sand hills. It has been recorded regularly since 1980 from just three areas of coast, in Suffolk, Essex and Kent, and may be declining at two of these. Sporadic records from other places suggest that the moth may sometimes be a windblown vagrant. The bright wave moth has also been recorded from Spain, North Africa, central and southern Europe and northern Iran. Little is known about its ecology.

1.2 The species is listed as rare in the GB Red List, but may be re-graded as vulnerable.

2. CURRENT FACTORS CAUSING LOSS OR DECLINE

2.1 Tidal erosion at the Essex sites.

2.2 Recreational pressures on upper beaches.

3. CURRENT ACTION

3.1 None known.

4. ACTION PLAN OBJECTIVES AND TARGETS

4.1 Identify the precise habitat requirements of this species.

4.2 Maintain viable populations within currently occupied areas and, if feasible, restore to 1980 distribution.

5. PROPOSED ACTION WITH LEAD AGENCIES

5.1 Policy and legislation

5.1.1 No action proposed.

5.2 Site safeguard and management

5.2.1 Encourage measures to reduce tidal erosion at Essex sites. (ACTION: LAs)

5.2.2 Prevent damage to occupied beaches caused by recreational use. (ACTION: LAs)

5.2.3 Encourage appropriate management of all occupied sites, and of suitable sites within the moth's dispersal range. (ACTION: EN)

5.2.4 Attempt to link up isolated colonies by suitable habitat management between them. (ACTION: EN)

5.3 Species management and protection

5.3.1 Following feasibility assessment and identification of suitable sites, seek to restore population to 1980 levels, using re-introductions if necessary. (ACTION: EN)

5.4 Advisory

5.4.1 Produce a leaflet on the current status and breeding requirements of the moth for site owners and managers. (ACTION: EN)

5.5 Future research and monitoring

5.5.1 Conduct research into the habitat requirements, population dynamics and dispersal abilities of the moth to aid conservation management. (ACTION: EN)

5.5.2 Encourage research on the status and distribution of this species on an international level and use the information gained towards its conservation in the UK (ACTION: EN, JNCC)

5.5.3 Pass information gathered during survey and monitoring of this species to JNCC or BRC so that it can be incorporated in national databases. (ACTION: EN)

5.5.4 Provide information annually to the World Conservation Monitoring Centre on the UK status of the species to contribute to maintenance of an up-to-date global red lists. (ACTION: JNCC)

5.6 Communications and publicity

5.6.1 Promote opportunities for the appreciation and the conservation of the bright wave moth and its habitat. (ACTION: EN)

VIOLET CLICK BEETLE (*LIMONISCUS VIOLACEUS*)

1. CURRENT STATUS

1.1 The violet click beetle, which appears to be very rare throughout its European range, is known in the UK from only two localities: Windsor Forest, Berkshire and Bredon Hill, Worcestershire. There is also one historic record from Tewkesbury which may have referred to a site in east Gloucestershire, but probably refers to Bredon Hill, where it was re-discovered in 1989. It breeds in hollows in the trunks of ancient trees, beech in Windsor Forest and ash at Bredon Hill. It is probable that a site would require a large population of trees to support the species.

1.2 The beetle is listed in Annex II of the EC Habitats Directive and Schedule 5 of the WCA 1981. It is also listed as endangered in the GB Red List.

2. CURRENT FACTORS CAUSING LOSS OR DECLINE.

2.1 Lack of suitable ancient trees at the current sites leading to habitat fragmentation due to the age-structure of the tree population.

3. CURRENT ACTION

3.1 Both known sites are SSSIs and part of the Bredon locality is an NNR. Both sites are candidate SACs under the EC Habitats Directive.

3.2 An experiment providing breeding sites has been successful, and fallen trees have been re-assembled.

3.3 A conservation strategy is being prepared under EN's Species Recovery Programme.

4. ACTION PLAN OBJECTIVES AND TARGETS

4.1 Protect all trees known or suspected to be used for breeding by the beetle, and the sites they stand in.

4.2 Ensure appropriate habitat management, especially the long-term continuity of habitat.

4.3 Survey other likely sites to determine the distribution of the species by the year 2000.

5. PROPOSED ACTION WITH LEAD AGENCIES

5.1 Policy and legislation

5.1.1 No action proposed.

5.2 Site safeguard and management

5.2.1 Encourage favourable management at both sites where the species is currently known to occur, and of any new sites, to ensure the long-term continuity of habitat. (ACTION: EN)

5.3 Species management and protection

5.3.1 Continue to experiment with artificial sites for breeding as necessary, and consider the need for translocations within sites. (ACTION: EN)

5.4 Advisory

5.4.1 Continue to offer advice to the Crown Estate at Windsor and to the landowners at Bredon on the importance of the species and its needs. (ACTION: EN)

5.4.2 Ensure the provision of advice to woodland owner/ managers on the rapid propagation of large trees in suitable locations as potential habitats for the future. (ACTION: FA)

5.5 Future research and monitoring

5.5.1 Encourage survey to identify any further sites that may exist, especially in the Cotswolds in the vicinity of the single, historic Tewkesbury record. (ACTION: EN)

5.5.2 Promote further research into the species' microhabitat needs, dispersal abilities and into non-destructive monitoring techniques. (ACTION: EN)

5.5.3 Encourage further research on the distribution and ecology of this species with European partners. (ACTION: JNCC)

5.5.4 Pass information gathered during survey and monitoring of this species to JNCC or BRC so that it can be incorporated in national databases. (ACTION: EN)

5.5.5 Provide information annually to the World Conservation Monitoring Centre on the UK status of the species to contribute to maintenance of an up-to-date global red lists. (ACTION: JNCC)

5.6 Communications and publicity

5.6.1 Use the violet click beetle as a flagship species to publicise the value of ancient trees to threatened invertebrates and other wildlife. (ACTION: EN)

STAG BEETLE (*LUCANUS CERVUS*)

I. CURRENT STATUS

I.I This large and conspicuous beetle is rare and protected in some European countries, but is still widespread in southern England, especially the Thames valley, north Essex, south Hampshire and West Sussex. It also occurs fairly frequently in the Severn valley and coastal areas of the south-west. Outside these areas the records are sparse and often old, indicating some contraction of the beetle's range.

I.2 The stag beetle can be found in broadleaved woodland, parks, other pasture woodland and gardens. The larvae live in the decaying wood of deciduous trees, often in roots and stumps, and take at least three and a half years to become fully grown.

I.3 The stag beetle is listed on Annex II of the EC Habitats Directive.

2. CURRENT FACTORS CAUSING LOSS OR DECLINE

2.1 Loss of habitat through the removal of stumps and other dead wood.

2.2 Collection for sale may be a contributory factor.

3. CURRENT ACTION

3.1 The JNCC has been encouraging people to record sightings through articles in Wildlife Trust newsletters and similar publications.

3.2 3 sites have been proposed as SACs for this species under the EC Habitats Directive.

4. ACTION PLAN OBJECTIVES AND TARGETS

4.1 Raise awareness of the threats to, and the European importance of, the species among local conservation groups and communities.

4.2 Identify a series of key sites and monitor these to establish long-term trends.

4.3 Maintain strong populations at key sites throughout the current range.

4.4 Carry out further research to establish habitat requirements.

5. PROPOSED ACTION WITH LEAD AGENCIES

5.I Policy and legislation

5.I.I Encourage the retention of dead wood within broadleaved woods and parks throughout the current range of the beetle. (ACTION: FA, LAs)

5.2 Site safeguard and management

5.2.1 Encourage appropriate habitat management, including the retention of dead wood, for all sites where the beetle is known to occur. (ACTION: EN, FA, LAs)

5.2.2 Seek to protect and ensure favourable management of a network of key sites throughout the range of the beetle. (ACTION: EN, FA, LAs)

5.2.3 Ensure that Site Management Statements take account of the requirements of this species on occupied SSSIs. (ACTION: EN)

5.3 Species management and protection

5.3.1 Consider adding this species to Schedule 5 of the WCA 1981. (ACTION: EN, JNCC)

5.4 Advisory

5.4.1 Ensure landowners and managers are aware of the presence and importance of conserving this species, and appropriate methods of management for its conservation. (ACTION: EN)

5.4.2 Ensure the relevant societies and organisations are aware of the ecological implications of collecting this species. (ACTION: EN)

5.5 Future research and monitoring

5.5.1 Undertake surveys to establish more precisely the current distribution and identify key sites for conservation action. (ACTION: EN)

5.5.2 Promote research to clarify the precise habitat requirements of the species and the effects of collection on populations. (ACTION: EN)

5.5.3 Pass information gathered during survey and monitoring of this species to JNCC or BRC so that it can be incorporated in national databases. (ACTION: EN)

5.5.4 Provide information annually to the World Conservation Monitoring Centre on the UK status of the species to contribute to maintenance of an up-to-date global red lists. (ACTION: JNCC)

5.6 Communications and publicity

5.6.1 Develop and implement a high profile strategy for raising public awareness (especially at the local community level) of the conservation needs of the stag beetle, in particular its reliance upon dead wood. (ACTION: EN)

LARGE COPPER BUTTERFLY (*LYCAENA DISPAR*)

1. CURRENT STATUS

1.1 The large copper butterfly became extinct in the UK in 1851. It was last recorded at Bottisham Fen in Cambridgeshire and, although the species was never widespread, there is good evidence that its former range also included Lincolnshire, Huntingdonshire, Norfolk and Somerset. A rare Dutch subspecies, *L. dispar batavus*, was introduced to Woodwalton Fen in Cambridgeshire in 1927. The population has subsequently had to be re-introduced or supplemented on several occasions, from captive stock.

1.2 The butterfly is listed as a globally threatened species by IUCN/WCMC. It is listed in Appendix II of the Bern Convention and Annexes II and IV of the EC Habitats Directive. It is protected under Schedule 5 of the WCA 1981 (in respect of sale only).

2. CURRENT CAUSES OF LOSS AND DECLINE

2.1 Loss of open fenland habitat due to drying out and encroachment of carr woodland.

2.2 Successful re-establishment of the large copper is severely limited by the small size and isolation of remaining fenland fragments.

3. CURRENT ACTION

3.1 A full species action plan is being prepared by Butterfly Conservation.

3.2 The species has been re-introduced with partial success to Woodwalton Fen, a NNR.

3.3 A project is being undertaken at Keele University to determine the feasibility of a large copper re-establishment programme in the UK.

4. ACTION PLAN OBJECTIVES AND TARGETS

4.1 Identify areas of suitable habitat in which to re-establish this species, encouraging restoration and maintenance of habitat as required.

4.2 If suitable habitat is located, consider further strategic re-introductions.

5. PROPOSED ACTION WITH LEAD AGENCIES

5.1 Policy and legislation

5.1.1 No action proposed.

5.2 Site safeguard and management

5.2.1 Continue appropriate management of the Woodwalton Fen site and of any other potential re-introduction sites. (ACTION: EN)

5.3 Species management and protection

5.3.1 No action proposed.

5.4 Advisory

5.4.1 No action proposed.

5.5 Future research and monitoring

5.5.1 Promote research to identify the precise requirements of the univoltine race of the large copper and appropriate management techniques. (ACTION: EN)

5.5.2 Survey potential sites for re-introduction and compile a list of candidate sites by 1998. (ACTION: EN)

5.5.3 Pass information gathered during survey and monitoring of this species to JNCC or BRC so that it can be incorporated in national databases. (ACTION: EN)

5.5.4 Provide information annually to the World Conservation Monitoring Centre on the UK status of the species to contribute to maintenance of an up-to-date global red lists. (ACTION: JNCC)

5.6 Communications and publicity

5.6.1 Use this species to highlight the importance of conserving fenland, and other wetland, habitats. (ACTION: EN)

LARGE BLUE BUTTERFLY (*MACULINEA ARION*)

I. CURRENT STATUS

I.I The range of the large blue butterfly is declining rapidly in Europe, with less than 10 colonies surviving in most northern countries. The butterfly once occurred in about 90 colonies in Britain, but declined rapidly in the 1950s and became extinct in 1979. It has since been re-established successfully at five sites in south west England using Swedish stock.

1.2 It is listed as a globally threatened species by IUCN/WCMC, and is listed on Appendix II of the Bern Convention and Annex IV of the EC Habitats Directive. It is protected under Schedule 2 of the Conservation (Natural Habitats, etc.) Regulations 1994 and Schedule 5 of the WCA 1981.

2. CURRENT FACTORS CAUSING LOSS OR DECLINE

2.1 Loss of habitat, combined with lack of grazing or other appropriate management.

3. CURRENT ACTION

3.1 The Joint Committee for the Conservation of the Large Blue Butterfly was formed in 1962.

3.2 The butterfly has been re-established at five sites in England under EN's Species Recovery Programme, after considerable research by ITE.

3.3 A full action plan for this species has been published by Butterfly Conservation.

4. ACTION PLAN OBJECTIVES AND TARGETS

4.1 Consolidate the five re-established populations in England, aiming to achieve colonies containing 400 to 5,000 adults in each.

4.2 Re-establish populations at a further 5 former sites in southern England by 2005.

5. PROPOSED ACTIONS WITH LEAD AGENCIES

5.1 Policy and legislation

5.1.1 Ensure the requirements of this species are taken into account when preparing management prescriptions in ESAs and other agri-environment schemes. (ACTION: MAFF, EN)

5.2 Site safeguard and management

5.2.1 Encourage the favourable management of relevant SSSIs. (ACTION: EN)

5.2.2 Seek to secure positive management of appropriate areas adjacent to existing colonies to ensure a suitable sward and scrub-free habitat, planting wild thyme from a local source if necessary. (ACTION: EN)

5.3 Species management and protection

5.3.1 Re-establish a further five populations as suitable sites by 2005. (ACTION: EN)

5.3.2 Arrange low-key wardening to prevent illegal collecting or accidental disturbance, and to help with monitoring. (ACTION: EN)

5.4 Advisory

5.4.1 Produce an advisory leaflet on how to manage land for this species, and circulate it to landowners and managers in suitable areas adjacent to target sites. (ACTION: EN)

5.4.2 Ensure the relevant societies and organisations are aware of the legal and ecological implications of collecting this species. (ACTION: EN)

5.5 Future research and monitoring

5.5.1 Compile a priority list of potentially suitable sites for re-establishment. (ACTION: EN)

5.5.2 Encourage regular monitoring of extant sites and seek to identify further threats to the species. (ACTION: EN)

5.5.3 Pass information gathered during survey and monitoring of this species to JNCC or BRC so that it can be incorporated in national databases. (ACTION: EN)

5.5.4 Provide information annually to the World Conservation Monitoring Centre on the UK status of the species to contribute to maintenance of an up-to-date global red lists. (ACTION: JNCC)

5.6 Communications and Publicity

5.6.1 Maintain confidentiality about site locations. (ACTION: EN)

HEATH FRITILLARY (*MELLICTA ATHALIA*)

1. Current status

1.1 This butterfly is widespread and often abundant in continental Europe, but has declined in many countries. In the UK, it is confined to southern England, where it was formerly locally abundant in parts of the south west and south east. It has declined severely during this century, with just 43 colonies known in 1989, including 2 sites in Essex where it has been successfully re-introduced since 1984. The butterfly's main centres of distribution are Exmoor, east Cornwall and the Blean Woods of Kent, where it breeds on heathland, species-rich grassland and coppiced woodland respectively.

1.2 The heath fritillary is listed as vulnerable on the GB Red List, and is protected under Schedule 5 of the WCA 1981.

2. CURRENT FACTORS CAUSING LOSS OR DECLINE

2.1 Reduction of coppice area and increased isolation of new clearings in Kent.

2.2 Abandonment or inappropriate management of species-rich grasslands in the south-west.

3. CURRENT ACTION

3.1 A full species action plan is being prepared by Butterfly Conservation.

3.2 Conservation management is being undertaken by EN on two nearby sites in Cornwall, and on several nature reserves in Kent.

3.3 EN has a management agreement with the private owner of a large block of woodland in Kent containing several colonies.

3.4 Trial habitat management is being conducted by the National Trust on heathland habitat on Exmoor.

3.5 Butterfly Conservation are attempting to re-introduce the species to a site in Devon.

4. ACTION PLAN OBJECTIVES AND TARGETS

4.1 Restore to 1980 status in Kent (i.e. approximately 25 inter-connected colonies of variable sizes) by 2005, carrying out re-introductions if necessary.

4.2 Maintain the range and population sizes in east Cornwall, Devon and Exmoor, carrying out re-introductions as necessary.

4.3 Maintain the re-introduced populations in Essex.

5. Proposed action with lead agencies

5.1 Policy and legislation

5.1.1 Consider improving financial incentives for coppice management in Blean Woods, Kent. (ACTION: EN)

5.1.2 Promote the uptake of favourable land management agreements on existing and potential sites within Cornwall, Devon and Exmoor, especially through ESAs and Countryside Stewardship Schemes. (ACTION: CC, EN, MAFF)

5.2 Site safeguard and management

5.2.1 Promote positive management for the species on all sites within the main centres of distribution to maintain and enhance populations. (ACTION: EN, FA)

5.2.2 Seek to restore favourable management on sites where re-introduction is necessary. (ACTION: EN)

5.2.3 Consider the need to notify sites as SSSI. (ACTION: EN)

5.3 Species management and protection

5.3.1 Promote strategic re-introduction into suitably restored habitats, particularly in Kent. (ACTION: EN)

5.4 Advisory

5.4.1 Ensure land owners and managers are aware of the presence and legal status of the species, and appropriate methods of habitat management for its conservation. (ACTION: EN)

5.5 Future research and monitoring

5.5.1 Promote further research into species' requirements to aid conservation management. (ACTION: EN)

5.5.2 Survey to identify potential re-introduction sites. (ACTION: EN)

5.5.3 Investigate genetic variation and population variability to underpin translocation programmes. (ACTION: EN)

5.5.4 Continue existing monitoring transects in known sites and encourage regular monitoring of all large/medium colonies to identify any threats to the species. (ACTION: EN)

5.5.5 Pass information gathered during survey and monitoring of this species to JNCC or BRC so that it can be incorporated in national databases. (ACTION: EN)

5.5.6 Provide information annually to the World Conservation Monitoring Centre on the UK status of the species to contribute to maintenance of an up-to-date global red lists. (ACTION: JNCC)

5.6 Communications and publicity

5.6.1 Promote opportunities for the appreciation and conservation of the heath fritillary and its habitat. (ACTION: EN)

OBEREA OCULATA (A LONGHORN BEETLE)

I. CURRENT STATUS

I.I This large, colourful and attractive beetle was formerly recorded in Cumbria, Kent and Oxfordshire, and was common throughout the East Anglian fens in the 19th century. However, since 1890 it has been found only in a small area of fenland in the immediate vicinity of Wicken Fen in Cambridgeshire.

I.2 The species is listed as endangered on the GB Red List.

2. CURRENT FACTORS CAUSING LOSS OR DECLINE

2.1 The reasons for the past decline are not known.

3. CURRENT ACTION

3.1 Wicken Fen, the core of the species' present distribution, is a NNR managed by the National Trust.

4. ACTION PLAN OBJECTIVES AND TARGETS

4.1 Maintain and, if possible, enhance the surviving population.

4.2 Promote research to determine the ecological requirements of this species and underpin management advice.

4.3 If possible, re-introduce to at least two sites by 2005.

5. PROPOSED ACTION WITH LEAD AGENCIES

5.1 Policy and legislation

5.1.1 Seek to ensure that relevant catchment management plans and water abstraction policies take into account the needs of this species. (ACTION: NRA)

5.2 Site safeguard and management

5.2.1 Seek to secure favourable management of the NNR and its surroundings, encouraging the up-take of Countryside Stewardship or other agreements as appropriate. (ACTION: EN, MAFF)

5.3 Species management and protection

5.3.1 Following feasibility assessment and the identification of suitable sites, seek to re-introduce to at least two sites within the former range of the species by 2005. (ACTION: EN)

5.4 Advisory

5.4.1 Ensure that the managers of Wicken Fen and adjoining land are aware of the habitat requirements of the beetle, as far as they are known. (ACTION: EN)

5.5 Future research and monitoring

5.5.1 Promote research into the species' ecology, to determine its habitat management needs and the feasibility of re-introductions. (ACTION: EN)

5.5.2 Pass information gathered during survey and monitoring of this species to JNCC or BRC so that it can be incorporated in national databases. (ACTION: EN)

5.5.3 Provide information annually to the World Conservation Monitoring Centre on the UK status of the species to contribute to maintenance of an up-to-date global red lists. (ACTION: JNCC)

5.6 Communications and publicity

5.6.1 Use this beetle as a flagship species to publicise fen and carr conservation and also to popularise beetle conservation in general. (ACTION: EN)

PANAGAEUS CRUX-MAJOR (A GROUND BEETLE)

I. CURRENT STATUS

1.1 Although formerly very widespread in wetlands in south Wales and England, as far north as Yorkshire, this colourful ground beetle is currently known from only three sites in the UK. One is on flood meadows in the Lower Derwent Valley in Yorkshire, and the other two are in dune systems: Tywyn Burrows in Dyfed and Saltfleetby-Theddlethorpe in Lincolnshire.

1.2 The species is listed as vulnerable in the GB Red List.

2. CURRENT FACTORS CAUSING LOSS OR DECLINE

2.1 Lack of grazing on wet pasture or dune slacks leading to growth of scrub or coarse grassland.

3. CURRENT ACTION

3.1 Two of the species' sites are NNRs and the third, which is a Ministry of Defence training area, is designated an SSSI.

4. ACTION PLAN OBJECTIVES AND TARGETS

4.1 Maintain and enhance all current populations.

4.2 Survey to locate further populations by 2000.

4.3 If less than five sites are found by 2000 and, if feasible, re-establish in at least two former sites by 2005.

5. PROPOSED ACTION WITH LEAD AGENCIES

5.1 Policy and legislation

5.1.1 Seek to ensure that relevant catchment management plans and water abstraction policies take into account the needs of this species. (ACTION: NRA)

5.2 Site safeguard and management

5.2.1 Encourage sympathetic management of all sites where the species occurs, as far as knowledge of its habitat requirements allow. (ACTION: CCW, EN)

5.3 Species management and protection.

5.3.1 If the species is found at less than five sites, following feasibility assessment and the identification of suitable sites, seek to re-establish populations in at least two former sites by 2005. (ACTION: CCW, EN)

5.4 Advisory

5.4.1 No action proposed.

5.5 Future research and monitoring

5.5.1 Promote survey work to establish whether the beetle occurs at any further sites by 2000. (ACTION: CCW, EN)

5.5.2 Encourage research into the species' ecology to determine its habitat management needs. (ACTION: CCW, EN)

5.5.3 Pass information gathered during survey and monitoring of this species to JNCC or BRC so that it can be incorporated in national databases. (ACTION CCW, EN)

5.5.4 Provide information annually to the World Conservation Monitoring Centre on the UK status of the species to contribute to maintenance of an up-to-date global red lists. (ACTION: JNCC)

5.6 Communications and publicity

5.6.1 Use this colourful and bizarre species as a flagship to publicise dune and flood meadow wetland conservation, and to popularise ground beetle conservation. (ACTION: CCW, EN)

A ROVE BEETLE (STENUS PALPOSUS)

1. CURRENT STATUS

1.1 This rove beetle occurs only within fine, damp sand on the margins of large freshwater bodies from the water's edge to about 2 metres up the beach. It is a boreal relict, with a widespread but very localised distribution across northern Europe, stretching eastwards to the Caspian Sea and north to Finland. The European range is highly fragmented and the species is threatened over much of this. Within the UK, the beetle has been reliably recorded from only one small area on the north west corner of Lough Neagh in Northern Ireland. Former sites may have been affected by a lowering of the water table of the Lough in the 1950s.

1.2 The species is considered to be nationally and globally threatened, and of equivalent status to endangered within the GB Red List.

2. CURRENT FACTORS CAUSING LOSS OR DECLINE

2.1 Trampling by cattle and humans.

2.2 Sand extraction from the rear of the beach, from the beach itself and from the adjacent bed of Lough Neagh.

3. CURRENT ACTION

3.1 The site is within Lough Neagh ASSI.

4. ACTION PLAN OBJECTIVES AND TARGETS

4.1 Ensure that the known population is maintained through appropriate site protection and management.

4.2 Locate and conserve any other extant populations around Lough Neagh by 1998.

5. PROPOSED ACTION WITH LEAD AGENCIES

5.1 Policy and legislation

5.1.1 No action proposed.

5.2 Site safeguard and management

5.2.1 Ensure that the management statement for the Lough Neagh ASSI takes the needs of the beetle into account. (ACTION: DoE(NI))

5.2.2 Control the numbers of grazing animals on the beach. (ACTION: DoE(NI))

5.2.3 Ensure that sand extraction at Lough Neagh does not threaten the habitat of the beetle. (ACTION: DoE(NI))

5.3 Species management and protection

5.3.1 Consider scheduling the species within the Wildlife (Northern Ireland) Order 1985. (ACTION: DoE(NI))

5.4 Advisory

5.4.1 Provide advice on land management to all those who own or manage land adjoining the site. (ACTION: DoE(NI))

5.5 Future research and monitoring

5.5.1 Carry out further surveys to determine whether the beetle occurs elsewhere on Lough Neagh by 1998. (ACTION: DoE(NI))

5.5.2 Investigate the environmental factors which are beneficial to the beetle. (ACTION: DoE(NI))

5.5.3 Pass information gathered during survey and monitoring of this species to JNCC or BRC so that it can be incorporated in national databases. (ACTION: DoE(NI))

5.5.4 Provide information annually to the World Conservation Monitoring Centre on the UK status of the species to contribute to maintenance of an up-to-date global red lists. (ACTION: JNCC)

5.6 Communications and publicity

5.6.1 No action proposed.

TACHYS EDMONDSI (A GROUND BEETLE)

1. CURRENT STATUS

1.1 This ground beetle is endemic to the UK. It has only ever been found in bogs in the New Forest, living among live *Sphagnum* moss. However, it has not been seen in the last 20 years and may now be extinct.

1.2 The species is currently listed as rare on the GB Red List, but this is under review.

2. CURRENT FACTORS CAUSING LOSS OR DECLINE

2.1 The reasons for the decline of this species are uncertain, but may have been the result of land drainage, prolonged drought, or fires.

3. CURRENT ACTION

3.1 The New Forest sites are within an SSSI and a candidate SAC under the EC Habitats Directive.

4. ACTION PLAN OBJECTIVES AND TARGETS

4.1 Determine by the year 2000 whether the species is extinct.

4.2 If re-found, maintain and enhance surviving populations.

5. PROPOSED ACTION WITH LEAD AGENCIES

5.1 Policy and legislation

5.1.1 If re-found, seek to ensure the needs of this species are taken into account in relevant catchment management plans and local water abstraction policies, once these are identified. (ACTION: NRA)

5.2 Site safeguard and management

5.2.1 If the species is found to survive, following research to identify its habitat requirements, seek to ensure appropriate management of sites. (ACTION: EN)

5.3 Species management and protection

5.3.1 No action proposed.

5.4 Advisory

5.4.1 No action proposed.

5.5 Future research and monitoring

5.5.1 Survey for the species at its former sites, and in other apparently suitable habitat in the New Forest, to determine whether it is still present, by the year 2000. (ACTION: EN)

5.5.2 If found, undertake research to determine species' habitat requirements, vulnerability and conservation management needs. (ACTION: EN)

5.5.3 Pass information gathered during survey and monitoring of this species to JNCC or BRC so that it can be incorporated in national databases. (ACTION: EN)

5.5.4 Provide information annually to the World Conservation Monitoring Centre on the UK status of the species to contribute to maintenance of an up-to-date global red lists. (ACTION: JNCC)

5.6 Communications and publicity

5.6.1 If the species is not found after further survey, use it to highlight the problems of extinction facing species endemic to the UK. (ACTION: EN)

OTHER INVERTEBRATES

ANISUS VORTICULUS (A SNAIL)

1. CURRENT STATUS

1.1 This snail is local throughout its central and southern European range. It occurs in unpolluted, calcareous waters in well-vegetated marsh drains and is usually found with a number of other molluscs which are rare and vulnerable, including *Segmentina nitida*.

1.2 In Britain, since 1965 it has been recorded at about fifteen sites, in Norfolk, Suffolk, Middlesex and Sussex, but living colonies have not been confirmed outside East Anglia for over ten years. In 1994, systematic sampling on the Pevensey Levels in Sussex, formerly a well known site, failed to produce any live records. The reasons for this decline are not clear. The species seems to have re-colonised at least one ditch system in Suffolk, possibly as a result of improved water quality.

1.3 This snail is listed as vulnerable in the GB Red List.

2. CURRENT FACTORS CAUSING LOSS OR DECLINE

2.1 The main threats possibly include over-frequent ditch clearance, nutrient enrichment due to fertiliser applications, and conversion of grazing levels to arable farming with associated water table lowering.

3. CURRENT ACTION

3.1 EN funded a survey of the molluscs of Pevensey Levels in 1994.

3.2 The Conchological Society of Great Britain and Ireland has surveyed most of the recent sites for this species.

4. ACTION PLAN OBJECTIVES AND TARGETS

4.1 To maintain populations at least 15 sites.

4.2 Produce management advice by the year 2000.

4.3 Establish baseline monitoring data for all known populations by the year 2000.

5. PROPOSED ACTION WITH LEAD AGENCIES

5.1 Policy and legislation

5.1.1 Identify water quality requirements and take account of these standards when setting standards in watercourses occupied by this species, seeking to restore clear, unpolluted water to ditches to provide opportunities for expansion or re-colonisation. (ACTION: EN, IDBs, NRA)

5.1.2 Ensure the needs of this species are taken into account if considering extending ESAs over grazing marshes occupied by the snail. (ACTION: MAFF)

5.2 Site safeguard and management

5.2.1 Seek to ensure that management plans prepared for existing and newly discovered sites take into account of the presence and requirements of the species on a case-by-case basis. (ACTION: EN)

5.2.2 Establish and implement a ditch management cycle that allows the re-colonisation of cleaned stretches from adjacent sections, taking into account the length of rotation necessary to avoid the ditch becoming choked with emergent vegetation. (ACTION: EN, IDBs, NRA,)

5.2.3 Seek to ensure that Water Level Management Plans take into account the ecological requirements of this species, where appropriate. (ACTION: IDBs, NRA)

5.3 Species management and protection

5.3.1 Following further research and monitoring, prepare advice on habitat management to favour this species, by the year 2000. (ACTION: EN)

5.4 Advisory

5.4.1 Ensure that land managers are aware of the presence and vulnerability of this species, and appropriate methods of land and water management for its protection. (ACTION: EN)

5.5 Future research and monitoring

5.5.1 Within a single season, undertake a survey of all post-1965 live recorded sites to establish an accurate distributional baseline for the species. Then monitor using fixed point monitoring stations at each of the existing sites. (ACTION: EN)

5.5.2 Promote further study on the ecological requirements of this species, including the effects of changes in water quality on survival and current management of habitats containing healthy populations. (ACTION: EN)

5.5.3 Survey poorly recorded areas to discover if further colonies exist. (ACTION: EN)

5.5.4 Encourage research on the ecology and distribution of this species on an international level and use the information and expertise gained towards its conservation in the UK. (ACTION: EN, JNCC)

5.5.5 Pass information gathered during survey and monitoring of this species to JNCC or BRC so that it can be incorporated in national databases. (ACTION: EN)

5.5.6 Provide information annually to the World Conservation Monitoring Centre on the UK status of the species to contribute to maintenance of an up-to-date global red lists. (ACTION: JNCC)

5.6 Communications and publicity

5.6.1 No action proposed

WHITE-CLAWED CRAYFISH (*AUSTROPOTAMOBIUS PALLIPES*)

1. CURRENT STATUS

1.1 In Europe this crayfish was formerly widespread in France, Spain and Italy, but populations are now confined to a diminishing number of areas. It is the only species of freshwater crayfish which is native to the UK. It is widespread in clean, calcareous streams, rivers and lakes in England and Wales and occurs in a few areas in Northern Ireland, but many populations have been lost since the 1970s.

1.2 This species is listed in Appendix III of the Bern Convention and Annexes II and V of the EC Habitats Directive. It is classed as globally threatened by IUCN/WCMC. It is protected under Schedule 5 of the WCA in respect of taking from the wild and sale, and is proposed for addition to Schedule 5 of the Wildlife (Northern Ireland) Order 1985.

2. CURRENT FACTORS CAUSING LOSS OR DECLINE

2.1 Crayfish plague, a disease caused by the fungus *Aphanomyces astaci* which is carried by some North American crayfish including the signal crayfish *Pacifastacus leniusculus*. Spores from the fungus can also be transmitted by a variety of other means, including water, fish and damp equipment.

2.2 Direct competition for food and habitat from non-native crayfish: three non-native crayfish species are now breeding in the wild.

2.3 Habitat modification and management of waterbodies.

2.4 Pollution, particularly pesticides and sewage.

3. CURRENT ACTION

3.1 JNCC published an action plan in 1994 for the conservation of the white-clawed crayfish in the UK.

3.2 MAFF and SOAEFD are to use fisheries legislation to regulate the keeping of non-native crayfish species to protect native crayfish and habitats in England, Wales and Scotland.

3.3 NRA has commissioned research regarding future management for the species, and published a leaflet on crayfish plague, with a guide to identifying both native and introduced species.

3.4 Nottingham University and the Biological Records Centre (ITE) hold and update a database on crayfish in the UK. Various surveys are being undertaken.

3.5 The three species of non-native crayfish established in the wild are listed on Schedule 9 of the WCA which makes it an offence to release or allow them to escape into the wild.

3.6 Four sites have been proposed as candidate SACs for this species, under the EC Habitats Directive.

4. ACTION PLAN OBJECTIVES AND TARGETS

4.1 Attempt to maintain the present distribution of this species by limiting the spread of crayfish plague, limiting the spread of non-native species, and by maintaining appropriate habitat conditions.

5. PROPOSED ACTION WITH LEAD AGENCIES

5.1 Policy and legislation

5.1.1 Designate "no-go" areas for the keeping of non-native crayfish under the Import of Live Fish (England and Wales) Act 1980 and the Import of Live Fish (Scotland) Act 1978. (ACTION: MAFF, SOAEFD, WOAD)

5.1.2 Section 14 of the WCA and Article 15 of the Wildlife (Northern Ireland) Order should be used to prevent the further spread of non-native crayfish into areas which contain natural populations. (ACTION: DANI, MAFF, SOAEFD, WOAD)

5.1.3 The use of byelaws to control baiting with crayfish by anglers should be reviewed. (ACTION: NRA)

5.1.4 Seek to control the keeping of non-native crayfish which are not yet established in the wild, and the trade of non-native crayfish as pets for other ornamental purposes throughout the UK. (ACTION: DANI, MAFF)

5.2 Site safeguard and management

5.2.1 Consider designating further sites vital for the white-clawed crayfish as SSSI/ASSIs. (ACTION: CCW, DoE(NI))

5.2.2 Ensure appropriate habitat management is undertaken. (ACTION: CCW, EN, NRA)

5.3 Species management and protection

5.3.1 Establish the feasibility of eradicating non-native crayfish populations from the wild where they threaten sensitive sites or important populations of native crayfish. (ACTION: CCW, EN, NRA)

5.3.2 If feasible, instigate and support re-introduction programmes to selected sites. (ACTION: CCW, EN, NRA)

5.3.3 Licences should not be issued for the release of non-native crayfish to sites where there are inadequate precautions to prevent escape within "no-go" areas. (ACTION: DANI, MAFF, SOAEFD, WOAD)

5.4 Advisory

5.4.1 Provide advice for those involved in the conservation of this species and the management of non-native crayfish populations. (ACTION: CCW, DANI, DoE(NI), EN, MAFF, NRA, SNH, SOAEFD, WOAD)

5.4.2 Provide advice on disinfection procedures to prevent the transmission of crayfish plague. (ACTION: CCW, EN, NRA)

5.5 Future research and monitoring

5.5.1 Make inventories of SSSIs/ASSIs which contain native crayfish populations. Monitor populations in protected areas. Maintain the detailed databases on the distribution of the native and non-native crayfish held at Nottingham University and the Biological Records Centre. (ACTION: CCW, JNCC, NRA)

5.5.2 Investigate the potential for recovery of native crayfish in areas affected by crayfish plague, and the feasibility of re-introducing the species to these areas. (ACTION: CCW, DoE(NI), NRA,)

5.5.3 Assess the morphological and genetic variability

across the range before decisions are made on stocks for re-introduction programmes. (ACTION: CCW, EN,)

5.5.4 Pass information gathered during survey and monitoring of this species to JNCC or BRC so that it can be incorporated in national databases. (ACTION: CCW, EN)

5.5.5 Provide information annually to the World Conservation Monitoring Centre on the UK status of the species to contribute to maintenance of an up-to-date global red lists. (ACTION: JNCC)

5.6 Communications and publicity

5.6.1 Increase public awareness of the presence of this species in local rivers and the threats to its existence. Publicise the need for conservation and how the public can help by contributing records to the databases on distribution. (ACTION: CCW, DoE(NI), EN, NRA)

5.6.2 Ensure that anglers (and others using the aquatic environment), and visitors to nature reserves and SSSI/ASSIs containing the crayfish, are made aware of the risks of spreading crayfish plague on equipment and of the legislative controls on release of non-native species. (ACTION: CCW, DoE(NI), EN, NRA)

SANDBOWL SNAIL (*CATINELLA ARENARIA*)

I. CURRENT STATUS

1.1 The sandbowl snail is very localised throughout its European range. In the UK it is known from only three sites in England, including Sunbiggin Tarn in Cumbria and Braunton Burrows in Devon. It was also previously known from Glamorgan, Wales.

1.2 The species is listed as vulnerable on the IUCN/WCMC red list and as endangered in the GB Red List and is protected under Schedule 5 of the WCA 1981.

2. CURRENT FACTORS CAUSING LOSS OR DECLINE

2.1 The species is under threat at Braunton Burrows, a sand dune system, from lack of grazing and a falling water table resulting from drainage of adjacent land. It is threatened at the Cumbrian sites by drainage and tramping.

3. CURRENT ACTION

3.1 Both Braunton Burrows and Sunbiggin Tarn are SSSIs. Braunton Burrows is also a NNR and Biosphere Reserve.

3.2 A water level management plan for Braunton Burrows and Marsh is to be prepared by the NRA, IDB and EN in 1995/96.

4. ACTION PLAN OBJECTIVES AND TARGETS

4.1 Ensure that viable populations are maintained at all known sites.

4.2 Restore grazing and a high water table to Braunton Burrows by the year 2000.

4.3 Carry out surveys to locate any other sites for the species.

5. PROPOSED ACTION WITH LEAD AGENCIES

5.1 Policy and legislation

5.1.1 Seek to ensure that local water abstraction policies take into consideration the need to conserve this species. (ACTION: NRA)

5.2 Site safeguard and management

5.2.1 Encourage resumption of an appropriate level of grazing on Braunton Burrows by the year 2000. (ACTION: EN, MoD)

5.2.2 Seek to restore water levels in ditches on the marshes adjacent to Braunton Burrows to their 1970s levels by the year 2000, through the production and implementation of a water level management plan. (ACTION: EN, IDB, NRA).

5.2.3 Develop and implement a management plan for Sunbiggin Tarn. (ACTION: EN)

5.2.4 Seek to protect any new sites that may be found and ensure appropriate management. (ACTION: EN, NRA)

5.3 Species management and protection

5.3.1 No action proposed.

5.4 Advisory

5.4.1 Ensure that land managers at new sites are aware of the presence and importance of conserving this species and appropriate methods of management for its conservation. (ACTION: EN)

5.5 Future research and monitoring

5.5.1 Survey to identify sites for this species in other dune slacks and calcareous upland fens and flushes in Cumbria. (ACTION: EN)

5.5.2 Encourage regular monitoring of extant sites and seek to identify any further threats to the species. (ACTION: EN)

5.5.3 Encourage research on the ecology and distribution of this species with European partners and use the information and expertise gained towards its conservation in the UK. (ACTION: JNCC)

5.5.4 Pass information gathered during survey and monitoring of this species to JNCC or BRC so that it can be incorporated in national databases. (ACTION: EN)

5.5.5 Provide information annually to the World Conservation Monitoring Centre on the UK status of the species to contribute to maintenance of an up-to-date global red lists. (ACTION: JNCC)

5.6 Communications and publicity

5.6.1 No action proposed.

IVELL'S SEA ANEMONE (*EDWARDSIA IVELLI*)

1. CURRENT STATUS

1.1 Ivell's sea anemone is known from only one location in the world - Widewater Lagoon in West Sussex. It was last seen in 1983 and is now possibly extinct.

1.2 It is as a globally threatened species listed by IUCN/WCMC and is protected under Schedule 5 of the WCA 1981.

2. CURRENT FACTORS CAUSING LOSS OR DECLINE

2.1 Reduced seawater penetration and water infusion from adjacent marshes.

2.2 Pollution, especially agrochemical run-off from gardens.

3. CURRENT ACTION

3.1 A management plan has been drafted for Widewater Lagoon and will be implemented as the site is a proposed priority SAC under the EC Habitats Directive.

4. ACTION PLAN OBJECTIVES AND TARGETS

4.1 Establish whether the species survives at its sole recorded site.

4.2 Restore the habitat through improvement of water quality and quantity.

4.3 If the species is re-discovered, consider translocating individuals to other sites.

5. PROPOSED ACTION WITH LEAD AGENCIES

5.1 Policy and legislation

5.1.1 No action proposed.

5.2 Site safeguard and management

5.2.1 Implement the management plan for the site. (ACTION: EN, LA)

5.3 Species management and protection

5.3.1 Survey Widewater Lagoon by 1998 to find out whether the species still survives. If it does, restore the habitat and consider translocating the species to other sites. (ACTION: EN)

5.4 Advisory

5.4.1 No action proposed.

5.5 Future research and monitoring

5.5.1 Continue to search for this species through surveys of brackish lagoon habitat. (ACTION: EN, JNCC)

5.5.2 Pass information gathered during survey and monitoring of this species to JNCC or BRC so that it can be incorporated in national databases. (ACTION: EN)

5.5.3 Provide information annually to the World Conservation Monitoring Centre on the UK status of the species to contribute to maintenance of an up-to-date global red lists. (ACTION: JNCC)

5.6 Communications and Publicity

5.6.1 No action proposed.

MEDICINAL LEECH (*HIRUDO MEDICINALIS*)

I. CURRENT STATUS

I.I The medicinal leech has been recorded in 24 European countries in recent years, but is very scarce in France and Belgium. There are probably no more than 20 isolated populations of the medicinal leech remaining in the UK. Existing sites are widely scattered and may be found in Kent, Dorset, Cumbria, Anglesey, east Norfolk, Argyll and Islay. The wide distribution may be due to 19th and early 20th century trade in this species, and the release of imported leeches may have supplemented British populations. The largest remaining population, at Lydd, is thought to number several thousand.

I.2 The medicinal leech is listed on Appendix III of the Bern Convention, Appendix II of CITES and Annex V of the Habitats Directive. It is listed as vulnerable by the IUCN and as rare in the GB Red List. It is protected under Schedule 5 of the WCA 1981.

2. CURRENT FACTORS CAUSING LOSS OR DECLINE

2.1 Loss of ponds through water abstraction, natural vegetational succession and infilling.

2.2 Loss of stock-grazed ponds.

3. CURRENT ACTION

3.1 To increase the availability of breeding habitat, a new pond was dug by the FA and CCW in 1995 adjacent to an existing population in Newborough Forest, Anglesey.

3.2 12 sites have been designated as SSSIs.

3.3 The leech is included in SNH's species action programme; all of its known sites are being visited, populations assessed and site-specific management guidelines are being developed.

4. ACTION PLAN OBJECTIVES AND TARGETS

4.1 Survey to determine full extent of distribution by the year 2000.

4.2 Safeguard all known sites.

4.3 Where appropriate, enhance existing populations through pond creation, supplementing with translocation if necessary

4.4 Ensure that wild stock is not used for medicinal purposes.

5. PROPOSED ACTION WITH LEAD AGENCIES

5.1 Policy and legislation

5.1.1 Consider encouragement for sympathetic land-use around all occupied ponds including the use of financial incentives. (ACTION: LAs, MAFF, NRA, SOAEFD, WOAD)

5.2 Site safeguard and management

5.2.1 Consider designating additional SSSIs for the species where this is necessary to secure appropriate management. (ACTION: CCW)

5.2.2 Seek to secure favourable management for the species at all occupied sites, including ensuring that suitable hosts are available. (ACTION: CCW, EN, SNH)

5.2.3 Where appropriate, consider the creation of new pond habitat within 200 metres of existing sites. (ACTION: CCW, EN, SNH)

5.2.4 If appropriate, developing and implement a policy on translocation of leeches to new sites. (ACTION: CCW, EN, SNH)

5.3 Species management and protection

5.3.1 Retain on Schedule 5 of the WCA 1981 and issue licences for non-damaging activities only. (ACTION: CCW, EN, SNH)

5.4 Advisory

5.4.1 Provide management advice to owners or managers of leech ponds. (ACTION: CCW, EN, NRA, RPBs, SNH)

5.4.2 Ensure the relevant societies and organisations are aware of the ecological and legal implications of collecting this species. (ACTION: CCW, EN, SNH)

5.5 Future research and monitoring

5.5.1 Survey to identify the population status at all known and likely leech sites by the year 2000. (ACTION: CCW, EN, SNH)

5.5.2 Encourage regular monitoring of extant sites and identify any further threats to the species. (ACTION: CCW, EN, SNH)

5.5.3 Promote further research on the ecological requirements of this species to identify habitat requirements and the most appropriate methods for re-introduction or translocation. (ACTION: CCW, EN, SNH)

5.5.4 Pass information gathered during survey and monitoring of this species to JNCC or BRC so that it can be incorporated in national databases. (ACTION: CCW, EN, SNH)

5.5.5 Provide information annually to the World Conservation Monitoring Centre on the UK status of the species to contribute to maintenance of an up-to-date global red lists. (ACTION: JNCC)

5.6 Communications and publicity

5.6.1 Advise relevant medical research institutions on the status of the leech and encourage use of alternative species for research. (ACTION: CCW, EN, SNH)

FRESHWATER PEARL MUSSEL (*MARGARITIFERA MARGARITIFERA*)

I. CURRENT STATUS

1.1 Since 1950 the freshwater pearl mussel has been recorded from 151 ten km squares in Britain and 14 ten km squares in Northern Ireland. The British range is to the north and west of a line running from Scarborough in Yorkshire to Beer Head in Devon. Many populations may not have produced young for over 30 years as site records are often based on observers only finding dead shells. In Ireland the mussel occurs throughout the country, being widespread in the south and west. It has, however, declined in the east, and recruitment rates are not known for most populations.

1.2 The species is dependent on the presence of salmonid fish as hosts for its larvae.

1.3 This mussel is classed as vulnerable on the IUCN/WCMC RDL. It is listed on Annexes II and IV of the EC Habitats Directive and Appendix II of the Bern Convention and is protected under Schedule 5 of the WCA 1981 (for killing and injuring only) and the Wildlife Order (Northern Ireland) 1985. It is currently being considered for increased protection under the WCA 1981.

2. CURRENT FACTORS CAUSING LOSS OR DECLINE

2.1 Poor water quality, including nutrient enrichment (which also affects the numbers of host fish).

2.2 Habitat removal and alteration through development, drainage schemes, flow regulation and fisheries management.

2.3 A decline in populations of host fish.

2.4 Conifer planting, exacerbating the effects of river acidification.

2.5 Amateur pearl fishing, aided by improved accessibility.

2.6 Poor land management in the catchment (e.g. overgrazing leading to to sedimentation from soil erosion).

3. CURRENT ACTION

3.1 SNH have commissioned and received advice on the feasibility of conducting a national survey and developed a methodology for monitoring key sites around Scotland. Some surveying was undertaken at key sites in 1994 and 1995. A project investigating threats to pearl mussels began in 1995, supported by SNH and the University of Aberdeen.

3.2 EN and the NRA have completed a survey of sites in England in 1995.

3.3 EN has prepared a species action plan.

3.4 CCW surveyed the River Wye in 1992/93.

4. ACTION PLAN OBJECTIVES AND TARGETS

4.1 Establish the current status of the mussel throughout the UK, and its ecological requirements at all stages of the life cycle.

4.2 Maintain, and where possible increase the size of existing populations.

4.3 Encourage re-colonisation of this species into at least 10 suitable former areas by 2005.

4.4 Establish educational and monitoring programmes.

4.5 Determine the effects of controlled exploitation in fished rivers, and enforce legislation on pearl fishery practices.

5. PROPOSED ACTION WITH LEAD AGENCIES

5.1 Policy and legislation

5.1.1 Identify water quality requirements for the species and seek to ensure that these form the basis for setting Statutory Water Quality Objectives, including Special Ecosystem Standards for sites occupied by the pearl mussel. (ACTION: DoE, DoE(NI), NRA, RPBs, SOAEFD, WO)

5.1.2 Seek to ensure that catchment management plans, flood defence activities, water level management plans and freshwater fisheries management take account of the requirements of this mussel. (ACTION: DoE(NI), IDBs, NRA, MAFF, RPBs, SOAEFD, WOAD)

5.1.3 Encourage favourable land management within catchments where the river supports major populations of the mussel, through appropriate land management and grant schemes. (ACTION: DANI, FA, MAFF, SOAEFD, WOAD)

5.2 Site safeguard and management

5.2.1 Consider designating centres of large, self-sustaining populations as SSSI/ASSI, and designate SACs for the most important ones. (ACTION: CCW, DoE, DoE(NI), SOAEFD, WO)

5.3 Species management and protection

5.3.1 Review the protection given to the species under the WCA 1981. (ACTION: DoE, JNCC)

5.3.2 Consider re-introduction into formerly occupied areas if conditions become ecologically suitable, using appropriate stock to maintain regional genetic variation. (ACTION: CCW, EN, SNH)

5.4 Advisory

5.4.1 Provide advice to river and land managers, water bailiffs and local police in relevant areas on the presence and legal status of this species, and appropriate methods of management for its conservation. (ACTION: CCW, DoE(NI), EN, NRA, RPBs, SNH)

5.5 Future research and monitoring

5.5.1 Identify catchments where there is the best chance of re-establishing this species. (ACTION: CCW, DoE(NI), EN, NRA, RPBs, SNH)

5.5.2 Carry out research to investigate key threats; fish hosts; life cycle and life history in different places; tolerance to variation in acidity; genetic variation; viability of re-seeding populations, and the effects of commercial exploitation. (ACTION: CCW, EN, DoE(NI), NRA, RPBs, SNH)

5.5.3 Establish the current status of populations throughout the UK. (ACTION: CCW, DoE(NI), EN, SNH)

5.5.4 Encourage regular monitoring of known populations and seek to identify further threats to the species. (ACTION: CCW, DoE(NI), EN, SNH)

5.5.5 Pass information gathered during survey and monitoring of this species to JNCC or BRC so that it can be incorporated in national databases. (ACTION: CCW, DoE(NI), EN, SNH)

5.5.6 Provide information annually to the World Conservation Monitoring Centre on the UK status of the species to contribute to maintenance of an up-to-date global red lists. (ACTION: JNCC)

5.6 Communications and publicity

5.6.1 Promote awareness of the threats to the species and publicise the legal protection afforded to it. (ACTION: CCW, EN, DoE(NI), NRA, RPBs, SNH)

5.6.2 Consider convening a conference on the conservation of freshwater mussels in the UK, to promote co-ordination of effort. (ACTION: JNCC)

GLUTINOUS SNAIL (MYXAS GLUTINOSA)

1. CURRENT STATUS

1.1 This north European aquatic snail is currently known from only one site in the UK, near Oxford, although fresh shells have been discovered at a second site. The species has not been found recently at a number of formerly well-known sites.

1.2 The glutinous snail is regarded as vulnerable throughout Europe and is recorded as endangered in the GB RED List and globally threatened by the IUCN/WCMC. It is protected under Schedule 5 of the WCA 1981.

2. CURRENT FACTORS CAUSING LOSS OR DECLINE

2.1 This snail occurs in clear, hard water which is free from fine sediment and nitrate/phosphate pollution. It shows a preference for firm substrates. Consequently, it is susceptible to a wide range of physical disturbance and pollutants.

3. CURRENT ACTION

3.1 The species is monitored at its remaining site, and a management plan has been written. The site is a proposed LNR. A recent survey of suitable nearby sites was carried out, but found no more colonies.

4. ACTION PLAN, OBJECTIVES AND TARGETS

4.1 Ensure the known remaining population is maintained and protected.

4.2 Locate any other populations by 2000 and seek to maintain them.

4.3 Secure improvements in water quality and habitat suitability at the remaining site.

4.4 Gain detailed knowledge of the ecology of the species.

5. PROPOSED ACTIONS WITH LEAD AGENCIES

5.1 Policy and legislation

5.1.1 No action proposed.

5.2 Site safeguard and management

5.2.1 Encourage good water quality in the catchment area of the remaining site. (ACTION: NRA)

5.2.2 Implement the management plan for the remaining site. (ACTION: EN)

5.2.3 Consider the need to notify the site as an SSSI. (ACTION: EN)

5.3 Species management and protection

5.3.1 No action proposed.

5.4 Advisory

5.4.1 Following suitable research on the ecology of this species, ensure the provision of advice on population and habitat management. (ACTION: EN)

5.5 Future research and monitoring

5.5.1 Undertake ecological studies, including a description of current and desired water quality and flow and the physical habitat. (ACTION: EN, NRA)

5.5.2 Survey all sites where the snail has been recorded this century by the year 2000. (ACTION: CCW, EN)

5.5.3 Encourage research on the ecology and distribution of this species with European partners and use the information and experience gained towards its conservation. (ACTION: EN, JNCC)

5.5.4 Continue monitoring existing population and seek to identify any further threats to the species. (ACTION: EN)

5.5.5 Pass information gathered during survey and monitoring of this species to JNCC or BRC so that it can be incorporated in national databases. (ACTION: EN)

5.5.6 Provide information annually to the World Conservation Monitoring Centre on the UK status of the species to contribute to maintenance of an up-to-date global red lists. (ACTION: JNCC)

5.6 Communications and publicity

5.6.1 No action proposed.

STARLET SEA ANEMONE (*NEMATOSTELLA VECTENSIS*)

1. CURRENT STATUS

1.1 The starlet sea anemone occurs in only a few coastal lagoons in the Isle of Wight, Sussex, Hampshire, and in Dorset and along the East Anglian coast. It may also occur in some brackish ponds and ditches.

1.2 The species is listed as vulnerable by IUCN/WCMC and rare on the GB Red List and is protected under Schedule 5 of the WCA 1981.

2. CURRENT FACTORS CAUSING LOSS OR DECLINE

2.1 Loss and damage to lagoon and other sheltered brackish water habitats caused by pollution, drainage and other activities.

2.2 Isolation of pools leading to fragmentation of populations.

2.3 Coastal defence works and associated infilling.

3. CURRENT ACTION

3.1 Saline lagoons are a priority habitat under the EC Habitats Directive.

4. ACTION PLAN OBJECTIVES AND TARGETS

4.1 Maintain and protect viable populations at all known localities.

4.2 Assess status in brackish ponds and ditches.

4.3 If feasible, re-introduce to 5 sites by the year 2005.

5. PROPOSED ACTION WITH LEAD AGENCIES

5.1 Policy and legislation

5.1.1 Seek to ensure that sea defence strategies and structures take account of the requirements of the anemone, including opportunities to create brackish lagoons and ditches. (ACTION: EN, LAs, NRA, MAFF)

5.2 Site safeguard and management

5.2.1 Maintain and, where possible, increase the amount of brackish lagoon habitat and ditches in occupied areas and in areas within the dispersal range of this species, to encourage expansion of existing colonies. (ACTION: EN, LAs, MAFF, NRA)

5.2.2 Promote the implementation of practices to encourage the formation and development of brackish lagoons and sheltered brackish water habitats at suitable sites. (ACTION: EN, LAs, NRA)

5.2.3 Continue programme to conserve lagoon habitats under the EC Habitats Directive, to benefit this species. (ACTION: DoE, EN, JNCC)

5.2.4 Consider the need to notify sites for this species as SSSI. (ACTION: EN)

5.3 Species management and protection

5.3.1 Following feasibility assessment and the identification of suitable sites, seek to re-introduce to at least 5 populations to formerly occupied localities, once conditions are suitable. (ACTION: EN)

5.4 Advisory

5.4.1 No action proposed.

5.5 Future research and monitoring

5.5.1 Promote surveys to determine the full extent of the species' distribution, especially in brackish ponds and ditches. (ACTION: EN)

5.5.2 Seek to identify former sites suitable for re-introduction. (ACTION: EN)

5.5.3 Encourage regular monitoring of existing populations and identify any further threats to the species. (ACTION: EN)

5.5.4 Pass information gathered during survey and monitoring of this species to JNCC or BRC so that it can be incorporated in national databases. (ACTION: EN)

5.5.5 Provide information annually to the World Conservation Monitoring Centre on the UK status of the species to contribute to maintenance of an up-to-date global red lists. (ACTION: JNCC)

5.6 Communications and publicity

5.6.1 Use this species to highlight the conservation value of lagoons. (ACTION: EN)

5.5.3 Pass information gathered during survey and monitoring of this species to JNCC or BRC so that it can be incorporated in national databases. (ACTION CCW, EN)

5.5.4 Provide information annually to the World Conservation Monitoring Centre on the UK status of the species to contribute to maintenance of an up-to-date global red lists. (ACTION: JNCC)

5.6 Communications and publicity

5.6.1 Use this colourful and bizarre species as a flagship to publicise dune and flood meadow wetland conservation, and to popularise ground beetle conservation. (ACTION: CCW, EN)

FRESHWATER PEA MUSSEL (*PISIDIUM TENUILINEATUM*)

1. CURRENT STATUS

1.1 The freshwater pea mussel has a localised distribution in Britain, occurring in central southern England and at a few isolated sites on the Welsh borders. Since 1950 it has been recorded in 16 ten km squares, but the precise distribution is uncertain as the genus *Pisidium* consists of a number of very small mussels which are often ignored due to difficulties in identification for the non-specialist. However, the species appears to have declined within many canal and river sites to the north of London.

1.2 The freshwater pea mussel is rare throughout its European range, from the Mediterranean to the south of Sweden. It is listed as rare in the GB Red List.

2. CURRENT FACTORS CAUSING LOSS OR DECLINE

2.1 The reasons for both the rarity and the recent decline are unknown, but are likely to include a decline in water quality and possibly inappropriate water channel management.

3. CURRENT ACTION

3.1 The Conchological Society of Great Britain and Ireland has surveyed most of the recent sites for this species.

4. ACTION PLAN OBJECTIVES AND TARGETS

4.1 Research the ecology of the species.

4.2 Carry out surveys to establish the full extent of the current distribution by 2000.

4.3 Maintain the present distribution.

5. PROPOSED ACTION WITH LEAD AGENCIES

5.1 Policy and legislation

5.1.1 No action proposed.

5.2 Site safeguard and management

5.2.1 Seek to ensure sympathetic water channel management within occupied sites. (ACTION: British Waterways Board, EN, NRA)

5.2.2 Promote water course protection in areas adjacent to former sites to assist re-establishment. (ACTION: EN, NRA)

5.3 Species management and protection

5.3.1 No action proposed.

5.4 Advisory

5.4.1 Promote land and water management practices for site managers and land owners. (ACTION: EN, NRA)

5.5 Future research and monitoring

5.5.1 Undertake a survey of all post-1950 sites by 2000, to establish the current distribution of the species. (ACTION: CCW, EN, NRA)

5.5.2 Research ecological requirements of the species, including habitat requirements. (ACTION: CCW, EN, JNCC)

5.5.3 Survey poorly recorded areas to discover if further colonies exist. (ACTION: CCW, EN)

5.5.4 Encourage regular monitoring of extant populations, initiating the use of several fixed point monitoring stations. (ACTION: EN)

5.5.5 Encourage research on the ecology and conservation of this species on an international level and use the information gained towards its conservation in the UK. (ACTION: CCW, EN, JNCC)

5.5.6 Pass information gathered during survey and monitoring of this species to JNCC or BRC so that it can be incorporated in national databases. (ACTION: CCW, EN)

5.5.7 Provide information annually to the World Conservation Monitoring Centre on the UK status of the species to contribute to maintenance of an up-to-date global red lists. (ACTION: JNCC)

5.6 Communications and publicity

5.6.1 No action proposed.

DEPRESSED RIVER MUSSEL (*PSEUDANODONTA COMPLANATA*)

1. CURRENT STATUS

1.1 This mussel is seriously threatened throughout its European range. In the UK since 1950 it has been recorded from 63 ten km squares in England and Wales- from Somerset, through the Welsh borders to south Yorkshire. However, the species is easily overlooked, and may be more common than thought. The UK probably has the healthiest populations in Europe, with the possible exception of Finland.

2. CURRENT FACTORS CAUSING LOSS OR DECLINE

2.1 The threats to this species are not fully known, but are likely to include water pollution, physical disturbance of river banks and channels, drought, and the collection of individuals for garden ponds and aquaria.

3. CURRENT ACTION

3.1 Cambridge University are surveying some sites.

4. ACTION PLAN OBJECTIVES AND TARGETS

4.1 Identify and maintain key populations by the year 2000.

4.2 Research the ecology and habitat preferences of this species.

5. PROPOSED ACTION WITH LEAD AGENCIES

5.1 Policy and legislation

5.1.1 Identify water quality requirements for the mussel and seek to ensure maintain favourable water quality at key sites. (ACTION: DoE, NRA, WO)

5.1.2 Seek to ensure that local flood defence activities and water level management plans take account of the requirements of the species. (ACTION: NRA)

5.2 Site safeguard and management

5.2.1 Seek to identify key sites throughout the range of this species, and ensure that suitable habitat is maintained within them. (ACTION: CCW, EN, NRA)

5.3 Species management and protection

5.3.1 Following further assessment of the effects of collecting on this species, consider adding this mussel to Schedule 5 of the WCA 1981. (ACTION: EN)

5.4 Advisory

5.4.1 Following further research to determine the habitat requirements of this species, provide advice to all river managers in areas where this mussel occurs. (ACTION: CCW, EN, NRA)

5.5 Future research and monitoring

5.5.1 Undertake studies to identify water quality, flow and habitat requirements for this species. (ACTION: CCW, EN, NRA)

5.5.2 Carry out surveys to establish the distribution of the species, and the location of key populations by 2000. (ACTION: CCW, EN, NRA)

5.5.3 Undertake further research to assess the impact of collecting on the population of this species. (ACTION: CCW, EN, JNCC)

5.5.4 Encourage research on the ecology and distribution of this species to determine its status in Europe. (ACTION: CCW, EN, JNCC)

5.5.5 Encourage regular monitoring of known populations and seek to identify any further threats to the species. (ACTION: CCW, EN, JNCC)

5.5.6 Pass information gathered during survey and monitoring of this species to JNCC or BRC so that it can be incorporated in national databases. (ACTION: CCW, EN)

5.5.7 Provide information annually to the World Conservation Monitoring Centre on the UK status of the species to contribute to maintenance of an up-to-date global red lists. (ACTION: JNCC)

5.6 Communications and publicity

5.6.1 No action proposed.

SHINING RAM'S-HORN SNAIL (*SEGMENTINA NITIDA*)

1. CURRENT STATUS

1.1 This snail lives in unpolluted, usually calcareous water in the ponds and drains of grazing marshes. It is often associated with a rich variety of freshwater molluscs, including other rare species. It can be found locally throughout Europe, northwards to southern Scandinavia.

1.2 In Britain, the shining ram's-horn has shown a dramatic decline this century. Since 1950 it has been recorded in about 12 ten km squares, but in the early years of the century it was known from about 90 sites over a much wider area. It is now confined to the Norfolk Broads and Pevensey levels, with small colonies possibly still present on the Lewes Levels and a site in east Kent.

1.3 The species is listed as endangered in the GB Red List.

2. CURRENT FACTORS CAUSING LOSS OR DECLINE

2.1 The reasons for the decline of this species are not clearly understood, but it is believed that the following are the main threats: over-frequent ditch clearance, eutrophication due to fertiliser run-off, and conversion of grazing levels to arable farming, with associated water table lowering.

3. CURRENT ACTION

3.1 EN funded a survey of the molluscs of the Pevensey Levels in 1994.

3.2 The Conchological Society of Great Britain and Ireland has surveyed most of the recent sites for this species.

4. ACTION PLAN OBJECTIVES AND TARGETS

4.1 Research the ecology of the species to understand why it is declining.

4.2 Identify and maintain all existing populations by the year 2000.

4.3 Enable existing populations to increase in size and spread in range.

4.4 Produce management advice by the year 2000.

5. PROPOSED ACTION WITH LEAD AGENCIES

5.1 Policy and legislation

5.1.1 Seek to maintain favourable water quality at currently occupied, and any newly discovered sites. (ACTION: NRA)

5.1.2 Ensure the needs of this species are taken into account when considering any possible expansion of ESAs to cover marshes containing occupied water courses. (ACTION: MAFF)

5.2 Site safeguard and management

5.2.1 Consider the development of safeguards in SSSI management plans, both where the snail is already present and where it has the potential to colonise. (ACTION: EN)

5.2.2 Develop a ditch management cycle that allows the re-colonisation of cleaned stretches from adjacent sections. (ACTION: EN, IDBs, NRA)

5.3 Species management and protection

5.3.1 No action proposed.

5.4 Advisory

5.4.1 Produce land and water management guidelines for site managers and land owners by the year 2000. (ACTION: EN, NRA)

5.5 Future research and monitoring

5.5.1 Undertake a survey of all post-1950 sites by the year 2000, to establish the current distribution of the species. (ACTION: EN)

5.5.2 Promote research on ecological requirements of the species, including habitat requirements. (ACTION: EN)

5.5.3 Encourage research on the ecology and distribution of this species to ascertain its status in Europe. (ACTION: EN, JNCC)

5.5.4 Encourage regular monitoring of known sites, including the use of fixed point monitoring stations. (ACTION: EN)

5.5.5 Pass information gathered during survey and monitoring of this species to JNCC or BRC so that it can be incorporated in national databases. (ACTION: EN)

5.5.6 Provide information annually to the World Conservation Monitoring Centre on the UK status of the species to contribute to maintenance of an up-to-date global red lists. (ACTION: JNCC)

5.6 Communications and publicity

5.6.1 No action proposed.

NARROW-MOUTH WHORL SNAIL (VERTIGO ANGUSTIOR)

1. CURRENT STATUS

1.1 This localised European species occurs in damp, short grass and moss on marshes, including salt marshes, or among flood debris. It is known in the UK from only eight sites in England and Wales, and one in Scotland. It is also known from a further 15 sites in the Republic of Ireland.

1.2 The snail is nationally and globally threatened and is included on Annex II of the EC Habitats Directive. It is listed as vulnerable on the IUCN/WCMC red list and endangered on the GB Red List.

2. CURRENT FACTORS CAUSING LOSS OR DECLINE

2.1 The habitat of this snail is very vulnerable to changes in hydrological conditions, reduced grazing pressure and physical disturbance.

3. CURRENT ACTION

3.1 Four sites are SSSIs, and three of them are also NNRs. Three sites have been proposed as SACs under the EC Habitats Directive.

3.2 Population monitoring is being carried out by CCW on two sites in Wales.

3.3 Trials are being undertaken by CCW to re-create upper saltmarsh for this species on one site in Wales.

4. ACTION PLAN OBJECTIVES AND TARGETS

4.1 Ensure that all remaining populations are maintained, protected and, if possible, enhanced.

4.2 Undertake further surveys of former sites and likely sites to determine the current distribution of this species by the year 2000.

5. PROPOSED ACTION WITH LEAD AGENCIES

5.1 Policy and legislation

5.1.1 Seek to ensure that appropriate catchment management plans, flood defence activities, water level management plans, sea defence strategies and structures take account of the requirements of this species. (ACTION: CCW, EN, IDBs, NRA, LAs, MAFF, SNH, SOAEFD, WOAD).

5.2 Site safeguard and management

5.2.1 Seek to secure appropriate management of all known sites for this species. (ACTION: CCW, EN, SNH)

5.2.2 Seek to ensure that all relevant SSSI and NNR management plans take into account the needs of the species. (ACTION: CCW, EN)

5.2.3 Consider the need for further sites to be notified as SSSI. (ACTION: CCW, EN, SNH)

5.3 Species management and protection

5.3.1 Ensure that all remaining populations are maintained and enhanced, if possible, particularly the Oxwich and East Anglian sites. (ACTION: CCW, EN, SNH)

5.4 Advisory

5.4.1 Ensure that land owners and managers are aware of the presence and importance of conserving this species and, following further research to identify the requirements of this species, provide advice on appropriate methods of management for its conservation. (ACTION: CCW, EN, NRA, SNH)

5.5 Future research and monitoring

5.5.1 Promote research into the ecology of this species to improve management advice, having regard to the very fragile nature of the colonies. (ACTION: CCW, EN, JNCC, SNH)

5.5.2 Survey all known historic locations by the year 2000 to discover whether species is still present at any of them. (ACTION: EN)

5.5.3 Ensure all known colonies are mapped in detail to assist with management, and encourage regular monitoring to help identify any further threats to the species. (ACTION: CCW, EN, SNH)

5.5.4 Survey other areas in Scotland to determine if the species occurs elsewhere. (ACTION: SNH)

5.5.5 Encourage research on the ecology and conservation of this species with European partners. (ACTION: CCW, EN, JNCC, SNH)

5.5.6 Pass information gathered during survey and monitoring of this species to JNCC or BRC so that it can be incorporated in national databases. (ACTION: CCW, EN, SNH)

5.5.7 Provide information annually to the World Conservation Monitoring Centre on the UK status of the species to contribute to maintenance of an up-to-date global red lists. (ACTION: JNCC)

5.6 Communications and publicity

5.6.1 No action proposed.

ROUND-MOUTHED WHORL SNAIL (*VERTIGO GENESII*)

I. CURRENT STATUS

I.I In the UK a small population of this snail exists at one site in England, Teesdale in Durham, although a second site has recently been identified in Scotland. Elsewhere in Europe, it occurs in the Alps and mountains of central Scandinavia, where it is also very local.

1.2 The snail is listed on Annex II of the EC Habitats Directive. It is listed as vulnerable on the IUCN/WCMC global list and as endangered in the GB Red List.

2. CURRENT FACTORS CAUSING LOSS OR DECLINE

2.1 No major threats to the species are currently known at its UK sites, although it would be very susceptible to changes in hydrology or an increase in trampling.

3. CURRENT ACTION

3.1 The Teesdale site is an SSSI and NNR and has been proposed as an SAC under the EC Habitats Directive.

4. ACTION PLAN OBJECTIVES AND TARGETS

4.1 Establish the status of the species and search for further populations.

4.2 Protect and maintain any newly discovered populations.

4.3 Ensure the known populations receive maximum protection.

5. PROPOSED ACTION WITH LEAD AGENCIES

5.1 Policy and legislation

5.1.1 None proposed.

5.2 Site safeguard and management

5.2.1 Ensure that the habitat remains stable in a favourable condition, in particular with regard to hydrology and recreational use. (ACTION: NRA, RPB)

5.3 Species management and protection

5.3.1 No action proposed.

5.4 Advisory

5.4.1 Ensure that all parties concerned with the management and future of the sites occupied by this species fully understand the vulnerability of this species and importance of conserving it. (ACTION: EN, SNH)

5.5 Future research and monitoring

5.5.1 Carry out surveys at potentially suitable sites to discover any other populations. (ACTION: CCW, EN, SNH)

5.5.2 Encourage regular monitoring of known, and any newly discovered, sites. (ACTION: EN, SNH)

5.5.3 Encourage research on the ecology and conservation of this species on an international level and use the information gained towards its conservation in the UK. (ACTION:EN, JNCC, SNH)

5.5.4 Pass information gathered during survey and monitoring of this species to JNCC or BRC so that it can be incorporated in national databases. (ACTION: EN, SNH)

5.5.5 Provide information annually to the World Conservation Monitoring Centre on the UK status of the species to contribute to maintenance of an up-to-date global red lists. (ACTION: JNCC)

5.6 Communications and publicity

5.6.1 No action proposed.

VERTIGO GEYERI (A WHORL SNAIL)

1. CURRENT STATUS

1.1 This is a rare alpine snail found in northern Europe. It occurs only on tufa-depositing springs and is known from only two sites in England and one in Wales. It has also recently been found at sites in Scotland.

1.2 It is listed on Annex II of the EC Habitats Directive. It is listed as vulnerable on the IUCN/WCMC red list and endangered on the GB Red List.

2. CURRENT FACTORS CAUSING LOSS OR DECLINE

2.1 None known for certain, although the habitat is vulnerable to destruction from changes in hydrology or grazing levels, or trampling by humans and animals.

3. CURRENT ACTION

3.1 All known sites in England and Wales are designated SSSIs, and part of the Welsh site is an NNR. Two sites have been proposed as SACs under the EC Habitats Directive.

3.2 A survey of sites for this species is being carried out in Scotland.

4. ACTION PLAN OBJECTIVES AND TARGETS

4.1 Maintain known populations.

4.2 Survey to establish the current distribution of the species by the year 2000.

5. PROPOSED ACTION WITH LEAD AGENCIES

5.1 Policy and legislation

5.1.1 Ensure that appropriate catchment management plans take into account the requirements of the species. (ACTION: NRA, RPBs)

5.1.2 Seek to ensure that water abstraction policies in the locality of known, or newly-discovered sites take full account of the need to protect the snail. (ACTION: NRA, RPBs)

5.2 Site safeguard and management

5.2.1 Seek to protect and ensure appropriate management of all sites, including the use of positive management agreements where possible. (ACTION: EN, NRA, RPBs, SNH)

5.3 Species management and protection

5.3.1 Ensure all known populations are maintained. (ACTION: CCW, EN, SNH)

5.4 Advisory

5.4.1 Ensure landowners and managers are aware of the presence, vulnerability and importance of conserving this species, and provide advice on appropriate methods of management for their conservation. (ACTION: CCW, EN, SNH)

5.5 Future research and monitoring

5.5.1 Surveys to determine whether this species occurs in other tufa-depositing springs and calcareous upland fens and flushes, having regard to the fragile nature of the habitat, by the year 2000. (ACTION: CCW, EN, SNH)

5.5.2 Encourage regular monitoring of extant, and any newly discovered, colonies and identify any further threats to the species. (ACTION: CCW, EN, SNH)

5.5.3 Encourage further research on the ecological requirements of this species to underpin management advice. (ACTION: CCW, EN, JNCC, SNH)

5.5.4 Encourage research on the ecology and conservation of this species at an international level and use the information and experience gained towards its conservation in the UK. (ACTION: CCW, EN, JNCC, SNH)

5.5.5 Encourage monitoring of extant, and newly discovered, colonies. (ACTION: CCW, EN, SNH)

5.5.6 Pass information gathered during survey and monitoring of this species to JNCC or BRC so that it can be incorporated in national databases. (ACTION: CCW, EN, SNH)

5.5.7 Provide information annually to the World Conservation Monitoring Centre on the UK status of the species to contribute to maintenance of an up-to-date global red lists. (ACTION: JNCC)

5.6 Communications and publicity

5.6.1 No action proposed.

DESMOULIN'S WHORL SNAIL (*VERTIGO MOULINSIANA*)

1. CURRENT STATUS

1.1 This species was formerly considered threatened on a global scale but new records suggest that this is not the case. In the UK, Desmoulin's whorl snail is known from a series of sites in England stretching in a broad band from Dorset to Norfolk. It is restricted to long-established calcareous wetlands, usually where there is a tall growth of sedges (*Carex* spp), saw-sedge (*Cladium mariscus*), reed-grass (*Glyceria maxima*) or reed (*Phragmites australis*) and a wide variety of other emergent waterside vegetation.

1.2 This snail is listed on Annex II of the EC Habitats Directive, and is listed as rare in the GB Red List.

2. CURRENT FACTORS CAUSING LOSS OR DECLINE

2.1 Destruction of wetlands.

2.2 Habitat degradation, particularly as a result of changes in hydrology.

3. CURRENT ACTION

3.1 JNCC and EN have funded a series of surveys at selected sites to determine the distribution and habitat requirements of the snail.

3.2 Four sites have been proposed as SACs under the EC Habitats Directive.

4. ACTION PLAN OBJECTIVES AND TARGETS

4.1 Maintain viable populations of the snail across its current range to ensure favourable conservation status.

4.2 Survey to determine the full extent of the snail's current distribution and precise habitat requirements.

5. PROPOSED ACTION WITH LEAD AGENCIES

5.1 Policy and legislation

5.1.1 Consider providing incentives for wetland management and restoration under appropriate agri-environment programmes in areas where the snail occurs, particularly where such incentives could contribute to the maintenance or restoration of water quality and quantity. (ACTION: MAFF)

5.1.2 Ensure the requirements of this species are taken into account when considering any possible extension of ESAs to cover marshes containing occupied water courses. (ACTION: MAFF)

5.1.3 Seek to ensure that local flood defence activities and water level management plans take account of the requirements of the species. (ACTION: NRA)

5.2 Site safeguard and management

5.2.1 Seek to ensure that local water abstraction policies take account of the need to protect the snail. (ACTION: NRA)

5.2.2 Encourage the sympathetic management of occupied wetland sites. (ACTION: EN, NRA)

5.3 Species management and protection

5.3.1 No action proposed.

5.4 Advisory

5.4.1 Ensure landowners and managers are aware of the presence and importance of conserving this snail, and appropriate methods of habitat management for its conservation. (ACTION: EN)

5.5 Future research and monitoring

5.5.1 Undertake further surveys in selected areas to clarify current distribution. (ACTION: EN)

5.5.2 Promote ecological research to determine habitat requirements more fully, to inform management advice. (ACTION: EN, NRA)

5.5.3 Pass information gathered during survey and monitoring of this species to JNCC or BRC so that it can be incorporated in national databases. (ACTION: EN)

5.5.4 Provide information annually to the World Conservation Monitoring Centre on the UK status of the species to contribute to maintenance of an up-to-date global red lists. (ACTION: JNCC)

5.6 Communications and publicity

5.6.1 No action proposed.

FLOWERING PLANTS

RIBBON-LEAVED WATER-PLANTAIN (*ALISMA GRAMINEUM*)

1. CURRENT STATUS

1.1 This short-lived perennial aquatic is now confined to two sites in the UK: a shallow lake in Worcestershire, where it has been known for many years, and a drainage channel in Lincolnshire, where it was rediscovered in 1991 after a 20 year absence from the site. It was formerly recorded from two other sites in Norfolk and Cambridgeshire in the 1970s, but has disappeared from both sites. This aquatic plantain is rare and sporadic in mainland Europe, where it is probably declining. Populations fluctuate markedly from year to year, but the reasons are largely unknown.

1.2 The plant is currently protected by Schedule 8 of the WCA.

2. CURRENT FACTORS CAUSING LOSS OR DECLINE

2.1 Eutrophication of water bodies and associated algal growth.

2.2 Competition from coarse marginal and aquatic species.

3. CURRENT ACTION

3.1 The Worcestershire site is an SSSI, with a management agreement currently in operation.

3.2 This species is the subject of an EN Species Recovery Programme project, which includes investigating the feasibility of re-introducing the plant to the former sites in Cambridgeshire and Norfolk.

4. ACTION PLAN OBJECTIVES AND TARGETS

4.1 Protect species at existing sites and ensure continued survival of viable populations.

4.2 Restore to five formerly occupied sites by the year 2005.

5. PROPOSED ACTIONS WITH LEAD AGENCIES

5.1 Policy and legislation

5.1.1 Identify water quality requirements which will maintain population levels at all known sites, and use these as a basis for setting standards. (ACTION: EN, JNCC, NRA)

5.2 Site safeguard and management

5.2.1 Ensure appropriate management of water bodies containing this species. (ACTION: EN)

5.2.2 Identify the habitat requirements of this species through research, and institute suitable management practices to ensure continued survival of the Lincolnshire population. (ACTION: EN)

5.3 Species management and protection

5.3.1 Collect and deposit seed in the National Seed Bank at Wakehurst Place and give encouragement to keeping plants in cultivation. (ACTION: EN, JNCC, RBG Kew)

5.3.2 Encourage regeneration from the natural seed bank at former sites, if conditions still remain suitable. (ACTION: EN)

5.3.3 Continue to investigate the feasibility of re-introducing plants to suitable sites if natural regeneration fails, once they can be propagated. (ACTION: EN, JNCC)

5.4 Advisory

5.4.1 Ensure that relevant landowners and local authorities are aware of the presence of this species, the legal protection afforded it, and appropriate methods of management. (ACTION: EN)

5.5 Future research and monitoring

5.5.1 Investigate the source of enrichment at the Worcestershire site and monitor water quality at all extant sites. (ACTION: EN, JNCC, NRA)

5.5.2 Survey former sites to see whether any suitable habitat remains and attempt natural regeneration or reintroduction where feasible. (ACTION: EN, JNCC)

5.5.3 Promote ecological research on this species to identify optimum conditions for growth and reproduction. (ACTION: EN, JNCC)

5.5.4 Encourage research on the ecology and conservation of this species on a international level, including the reasons for its decline and distribution, and use the information and expertise gained towards its conservation in the UK. (ACTION: EN, JNCC)

5.5.5 Pass information gathered during survey and monitoring of this species to JNCC or BRC so that it can be incorporated in national databases. (ACTION: EN)

5.5.6 Provide information annually to the World Conservation Monitoring Centre on the UK status of the species, to contribute to maintenance of an up-to-date global Red Data List. (ACTION: JNCC)

5.6 Communications and publicity

5.6.1 None proposed.

CREEPING MARSHWORT (*APIUM REPENS*)

1. CURRENT STATUS

1.1 This marshwort is a small, creeping umbellifer which grows in open, wet, usually base-rich permanent pasture subject to winter flooding. It occurs through central and southern Europe, and North Africa. This species has been recorded from sites in Oxfordshire and Buckinghamshire, Scotland, south east Yorkshire, Norfolk and Suffolk, with two putative sites in the Thames Valley persisting until 1960 and 1970. It is now restricted to one meadow in Oxfordshire, designated an SSSI, where the population is thought to be approximately 100 plants.

1.2 Recent taxonomic investigations appear to have indicated that this species co-exists, but does not hybridise, with *Apium nodiflorum*, although the two species may be almost indistinguishable in the field. However, doubt has been cast on the reliability of the conclusions drawn from genetic tests.

1.3 Creeping marshwort is listed in Annex II and IV of the EC Habitats Directive, Appendix I of the Bern Convention, and is protected under Schedule 4 of the Conservation (Natural Habitats, etc.) Regulations 1994 and Schedule 8 of the WCA 1981.

2. CURRENT FACTORS CAUSING LOSS OR DECLINE

2.1 Agricultural intensification, including the use of herbicides, control of winter flooding, overgrazing and ploughing.

3. CURRENT ACTION

3.1 This species is the subject of an EN Species Recovery Programme. In conjunction with this, the Oxford Rare Plants Group is monitoring the existing population of creeping marshwort and drawing up a detailed action plan for the species.

3.2 Plants from the extant population in Oxfordshire are being cultivated in Oxford Botanic Gardens and the Royal Botanic Gardens at Wakehurst.

3.3 Last surviving site in Oxfordshire has been proposed as an SAC under the EC Habitats Directive.

4. ACTION PLAN OBJECTIVES AND TARGETS

4.1 Maintain the population at the Oxfordshire site.

4.2 Restore to two Thames Valley sites by 2005.

4.3 Identify suitable sites for re-introduction and encourage suitable management of former sites, particularly those in the Thames Valley, to encourage germination of any seed remaining viable.

5. PROPOSED ACTION WITH LEAD AGENCIES

5.1 Policy and legislation

5.1.1 Encourage landowners of former sites where this species could be re-established in Oxfordshire to enter into the Upper Thames Tributaries ESA Scheme (particularly the owners of the two sites which survived until the 1970s), and encourage appropriate management of these sites. (ACTION: ADAS, EN)

5.2 Site safeguard and management

5.2.1 Ensure management plans for the current SSSI take account of the ecological requirements of this species. (ACTION: EN)

5.2.2 Encourage the consideration of this species in water level management plans if this proves to be an important factor in their habitat requirements. (ACTION: NRA)

5.3 Species management and protection

5.3.1 Encourage management at all former sites to enable any buried seed which is still viable to germinate. (ACTION: EN)

5.3.2 If natural regeneration is unsuccessful, re-introduce cultivated plants to suitable sites in the Thames Valley, ensuring correct conditions are provided. (ACTION: EN)

5.3.3 Keep plants in cultivation and collect seed, where possible, for the national seed bank at Wakehurst Place. Plants (of both genotypes) have already been collected in the absence of viable seed and are in cultivation at Kew and Oxford Botanic Gardens. (ACTION: EN, JNCC)

5.4 Advisory

5.4.1 Ensure that Oxford City Council are aware of the presence, legal status and appropriate management procedures needed to protect and maintain the current population. (ACTION: EN)

5.5 Future research and monitoring

5.5.1 Carry out a thorough survey and regular monitoring of former sites to establish whether any suitable habitat remains for re-introduction or translocation. (ACTION: EN, JNCC)

5.5.2 Promote research into the ecological and habitat requirements of this species, relative to *A. nodiflorum*, to enable correct management procedures and re-introduction. This should include its reproductive biology and possible pollinators, tolerance of grazing and the effects of periodic submergence. (ACTION: EN, JNCC)

5.5.3 Promote further genetic research to clarify the taxonomy of this species. (ACTION: EN, JNCC)

5.5.4 Encourage research on this species on the ecology and conservation an international level at use the information and expertise gained towards its conservation in the UK. (ACTION: EN, JNCC)

5.5.5 Pass information gathered during survey and monitoring of this species to JNCC or BRC so that it can be incorporated in national databases. (ACTION: EN)

5.5.6 Provide information annually to the World Conservation Monitoring Centre on the UK status of the species to contribute to maintenance of an up-to-date global Red Data List. (ACTION: JNCC)

5.6 Communications and publicity

5.6.1 None proposed.

NORWEGIAN MUGWORT (ARTEMISIA NORVEGICA)

1. CURRENT STATUS

1.1 The Norwegian mugwort is a globally rare arctic alpine plant. In the UK it is found on only three mountain summits in Ross and Cromarty District and Sutherland in Northern Scotland. These plants are morphologically distinct from other populations of the species and have been described as variety *scotica*. Elsewhere, it occurs only in Norway and the Ural mountains.

2. CURRENT FACTORS CAUSING LOSS OR DECLINE

2.1 None known.

3. CURRENT ACTION

3.1 Two sites are designated as SSSIs.

4. ACTION PLAN OBJECTIVES AND TARGETS

4.1 Maintain all known populations.

4.2 Promote research into the ecological requirements of this species underlying its restricted distribution.

4.3 Identify and maintain any as yet undiscovered populations.

5. PROPOSED ACTIONS WITH LEAD AGENCIES

5.1 Policy and legislation

5.1.1 None proposed.

5.2 Site safeguard and management

5.2.1 Ensure SSSI management takes account of the ecological requirements of this species. (ACTION:SNH)

5.3 Species management and protection

5.3.1 Ensure no damaging activities affect the sites of the known populations. (ACTION: SNH)

5.4 Advisory

5.4.1 Ensure that relevant landowners and LAs are aware of the presence and importance of conserving this species. (ACTION: SNH)

5.5 Future research and monitoring

5.5.1 Undertake ecological studies of this species. This should include research into dispersal mechanisms and seed viability to help explain the very narrow distribution of the mugwort. (ACTION: SNH)

5.5.2 Seek to develop close links between Scottish experts and Norwegian and Russian counterparts to ensure an exchange of information on the ecology and conservation of this species. (ACTION: SNH)

5.5.3 Subject to confidentiality and data ownership, pass information gathered during survey and monitoring of this species to JNCC or BRC so that it can be incorporated in national databases. (ACTION: SNH)

5.5.4 Provide information annually to the World Conservation Monitoring Centre on the UK status of the species to contribute to maintenance of an up-to-date global Red Data List. (ACTION: JNCC)

5.6 Communications and publicity

5.6.1 None proposed.

MOUNTAIN SCURVY-GRASS (*COCHLEARIA MICACEA*)

1. CURRENT STATUS

1.1 Mountain scurvy-grass is an alpine species known only from naturally metalliferous soils on mountains in Scotland. It is relatively abundant and widespread and shows no sign of declining. The species appears to be endemic to the UK, pending clarification of the taxonomy of Norwegian plants of the same genus.

2. CURRENT FACTORS CAUSING LOSS OR DECLINE

2.1 None known.

3. CURRENT ACTION

3.1 A survey of the status of this plant was undertaken for SNH during 1994. Several sites were found to occur within existing SSSIs and NNRs.

4. ACTION PLAN OBJECTIVES AND TARGETS

4.1 Maintain a viable population on protected sites.

4.2 Safeguard any populations discovered in the future.

4.3 Define the taxonomic limits of its relationships with other *Cochlearia* species.

5. PROPOSED ACTIONS WITH LEAD AGENCIES

5.1 Policy and legislation

5.1.1 None proposed.

5.2 Site safeguard and management

5.2.1 Ensure all main sites are managed sympathetically for the species. (ACTION: SNH)

5.2.2 Seek to prevent damage by development activities on key sites through protective policies in local and structure plans. (ACTION: SNH, SOAEFD, LAs)

5.3 Species management and protection

5.3.1 No action required.

5.4 Advisory

5.4.1 Ensure that the relevant landowners, managers and LAs are aware of the presence and importance of conserving this species. (ACTION: SNH)

5.5 Future research and monitoring

5.5.1 Confirm the endemic status of the species through taxonomic comparisons with similar species from Scandinavia. (ACTION: SNH)

5.5.2 Complete sample surveys of current distribution. (ACTION: SNH)

5.5.3 Subject to confidentiality and data ownership, pass information gathered during survey and monitoring of this species to JNCC or BRC so that it can be incorporated in national databases. (ACTION: SNH)

5.5.4 Provide information annually to the World Conservation Monitoring Centre on the UK status of the species to contribute to maintenance of an up-to-date global Red Data List. (ACTION: JNCC)

5.6 Communications and publicity

5.6.1 None proposed.

LUNDY CABBAGE (*COINCYA WRIGHTII*)

1. CURRENT STATUS

1.1 The Lundy cabbage is a short-lived perennial which is endemic to the UK. It is confined to the south eastern cliffs and slopes of Lundy Island in the Bristol Channel and is host to an endemic beetle. Numbers of the plant contained within each population are known to fluctuate markedly, but on average consist of between 3000 and 5000 flowering plants together with similar numbers of non-flowering individuals.

1.2 The Lundy cabbage is listed as vulnerable on the GB Red List and is protected under Schedule 8 of the WCA 1981.

2. CURRENT FACTORS CAUSING LOSS OR DECLINE

2.1 Overgrazing.

2.2 Shading out and suppression by bracken and rhododendron.

3. CURRENT ACTION

3.1 English Nature provide support to the Landmark Trust to employ a warden for the island.

3.2 Most of the plants on Lundy occur within a SSSI for which there is a detailed management plan.

3.3 Lundy Island is subject to a Countryside Stewardship agreement, which includes the control of bracken and rhododendron.

3.4 Grazing regimes on the island are currently subject to review by EN and the Landmark Trust.

3.5 The plant is being monitored by the University of Leeds and English Nature.

4. ACTION PLAN OBJECTIVES AND TARGETS

4.1 Ensure the continued survival of a viable population on Lundy.

4.2 Continue research into the population dynamics and ecological requirements of the species to determine optimal management.

5. PROPOSED ACTIONS WITH LEAD AGENCIES

5.1 Policy and legislation

5.1.1 None proposed.

5.2 Site safeguard, land acquisition and management

5.2.1 Control bracken and rhododendron where these pose a threat to populations of the species. (ACTION: EN)

5.2.2 Prevent adverse effects to the species from grazing. (ACTION: EN)

5.2.3 When population densities are low, consider deliberate scarification of soil near established plants to encourage regeneration. (ACTION: EN)

5.3 Species management, protection and licensing

5.3.1 No additional action proposed.

5.4 Advisory

5.4.1 None proposed.

5.5 Future research and monitoring

5.5.1 Encourage further research to determine the population dynamics and habitat requirements of the species, including the extent of the seed bank and the effect of landslips on regeneration. (ACTION: EN)

5.5.2 Assess the effects of grazing from deer, goats, sheep and rabbits through the use of exclosure experiments, and modify level of grazing accordingly. (ACTION: EN)

5.5.3 Pass information gathered during survey and monitoring of this species to JNCC or BRC so that it can be incorporated in national databases. (ACTION: EN)

5.5.4 Provide information annually to the World Conservation Monitoring Centre on the UK status of the species to contribute to maintenance of an up-to-date global Red Data List. (ACTION: JNCC)

5.6 Communications and publicity

5.6.1 Use the presence of this species on Lundy to increase awareness of plant conservation issues amongst visitors to the island. (ACTION: EN)

WILD COTONEASTER (COTONEASTER CAMBRICUS/C. INTEGERRIMUS)

1. CURRENT STATUS

1.1 Wild cotoneaster is restricted to one locality in Wales, where only a handful of plants remain. Although considered by some to be endemic, the taxonomic status of the species is disputed, with some evidence suggesting that it may not only be the widespread *C. integerrimus*, but may also have a relatively recent continental origin and, therefore, not be native.

1.2 Whatever the taxonomic status of the plant, it has always been rare at the single site, reaching as few as six individuals in 1978. This has been increased to approximately 33 plants by the introduction of plants grown in cultivation. Natural recruitment to the site is poor, but one seedling plant was found in 1993 in an area where seeds were sown 10 years previously.

1.3 This species is listed as endangered on the GB Red List and is protected under Schedule 8 of the WCA 1981.

2. MAIN FACTORS CAUSING LOSS OR DECLINE

2.1 Over-grazing by feral goats and sheep hindering re-establishment.

2.2 Damage by climbers.

2.2 The spread of invasive non-native cotoneasters.

3. CURRENT ACTION

3.1 Most plants are within a Country Park owned and managed by the Local Authority. The site is also protected as an LNR and an SSSI.

3.2 Plants have been raised *ex situ* and transplanted back on to the site with varying success. The programme is monitored annually, along with the number and health of the plants.

3.3 Rock climbing is currently controlled by voluntary agreement.

4. ACTION PLAN OBJECTIVES AND TARGETS

4.1 Safeguard the current population at the one extant site.

4.2 Clarify the taxonomic status to ascertain whether the species is endemic.

4.3 Undertake ecological research to develop a better understanding of the species.

5. PROPOSED ACTIONS WITH LEAD AGENCIES

5.1 Policy and legislation

5.1.1 None proposed.

5.2 Site safeguard and management

5.2.1 Continue to control public access including climbing in areas where this species occurs, preferably through continued voluntary agreement. (ACTION: CCW)

5.2.2 Promote appropriate habitat management, including the control of invasive vegetation, particularly non-native cotoneasters. (ACTION: LA)

5.3 Species management and protection

5.3.1 Continue propagation of plants and maintain stocks in cultivation, but cease translocation into the wild pending the outcome of taxonomic and genetic studies. (ACTION: CCW, JNCC, LA)

5.3.2 Deposit seed with national seed bank at Wakehurst Place, keep plants in cultivation and formalise existing work at Treborth and Ness. (ACTION: CCW, LA)

5.3.3 Discourage illegal collecting of this species and ensure that offenders are prosecuted. (ACTION: CCW, JNCC, LAs, WO)

5.4 Advisory

5.4.1 Ensure that local botanical groups and other relevant organisations are aware of the legal and ecological implications of collecting this species. (ACTION: CCW, LAs)

5.5 Future research and monitoring

5.5.1 Undertake genetic research to clarify the taxonomy of the species. (ACTION: CCW, JNCC)

5.5.2 Carry out ecological research to identify the optimum conditions for growth and management requirements of this species. (ACTION: CCW, JNCC)

5.5.3 Seek to establish a formal monitoring programme for this species. (ACTION: CCW, JNCC)

5.5.4 Continue monitoring the effects of grazing on this species and modify accordingly. (ACTION: CCW, LA)

5.5.5 If found to be an established introduction, monitor the effects of the existing 33 plants (and progeny) on the native flora. (ACTION: CCW, JNCC)

5.5.6 Pass information gathered during survey and monitoring of this species to JNCC or BRC so that it can be incorporated in national databases. (ACTION: CCW)

5.5.7 Provide information annually to the World Conservation Monitoring Centre on the UK status of the species to contribute to maintenance of an up-to-date global Red Data List. (ACTION: JNCC)

5.6 Communication and publicity

5.6.1 The precise location of this species should remain secret because of the risk from collectors.

LADY'S SLIPPER ORCHID (*CYPRIPEDIUM CALCEOLUS*)

1. CURRENT STATUS

1.1 A large, attractive orchid growing on moderately grazed species-rich limestone grassland. The distribution was formerly widespread, though local, in parts of the North Pennines in Derbyshire, Yorkshire, Durham and Cumbria. It has suffered a severe decline and has survived naturally at only one location, where a combination of careful habitat management and wardening, together with vegetative propagation and re-establishment of material from *ex-situ* propagation, has led to a steady increase in the size of the colony. In 1995 plants derived from micro-propagation using wild seed were planted out at two sites in addition to the original wild site. Further plants, derived from wild stock, exist in cultivation.

1.2 Lady slipper orchid also occurs in Scandinavia, and southwards to northern Greece. It is listed as critically endangered on the GB Red List; Appendix II of the Bern Convention and Annexes II and IV of the Habitats Directive. It is protected under Schedule 4 of the Conservation (Natural Habitats, etc.) Regulations 1994 and Schedule 8 of the WCA 1981.

2. CURRENT FACTORS CAUSING LOSS OR DECLINE

2.1 Uprooting by gardeners, picking and trampling by botanists and others.

2.2 Habitat destruction due to increased grazing pressure.

3. CURRENT ACTION

3.1 This orchid has been subject to an EN Species Recovery Programme since 1992. This has included conserving native plants *in-situ* and in cultivation, genetic investigation of potential wild plants in cultivation to inform decisions on cross-pollination and *ex-situ* propagation to provide seedlings for re-stocking the native site and up to five former or other suitable sites.

4. ACTION PLAN OBJECTIVES AND TARGETS

4.1 Consolidate and extend the population, re-introducing or translocating it to five sites by 2004.

4.2 Enhance and safeguard the genetic variation of wild plants.

4.3 Safeguard sites and plants from damage.

4.4 Complete objectives of the EN Species Recovery Programme by April 1996.

5. PROPOSED ACTIONS WITH LEAD AGENCIES.

5.1 Policy and legislation

5.1.1 No action proposed.

5.2 Site safeguard and management

5.2.1 Ensure that the required habitat for this plant is maintained through appropriate management at the wild site and each of the (re)introduction sites. (ACTION: EN)

5.3 Species management and protection

5.3.1 Maintain the *ex-situ* conservation programme based on micro-propagation techniques. (ACTION: EN, JNCC, RBG Kew)

5.3.2 Maintain the conservation of the plants at wild sites through wardening, enforcement of the schedules of the WCA 1981 and other plant protection techniques as appropriate. (ACTION: EN)

5.3.3 Increase the genetic diversity through cross-pollination of existing wild stock with other native stock informed by genetic investigations. (ACTION: EN, RBG Kew)

5.3.4 Maintain the stock of the three (possibly four) known genotypes of wild origin in several 'safe' holdings. (ACTION: EN, JNCC)

5.3.5 Continue programme of range consolidation with a further five populations restored to suitable sites by 2004. (ACTION: EN)

5.3.6 Maintain seed at the national seed bank at Wakehurst Place, when appropriate methods are established. (ACTION: RBG - Kew, EN)

5.4 Advisory

5.4.1 When recovery is underway, ensure that landowners and managers are aware of the presence, legal status and importance of conserving this species, and appropriate methods of habitat management. (ACTION: EN)

5.5 Future research and monitoring

5.5.1 Complete survey and assessment of all former and potential sites for the (re)introduction of the species. (ACTION: EN)

5.5.2 Research the most appropriate methods to store seed for its long-term viability. (ACTION: EN, JNCC, RBG Kew)

5.5.3 Pass information gathered during survey and monitoring of this species to JNCC or BRC so that it can be incorporated in national databases. (ACTION: EN)

5.5.4 Provide information annually to the World Conservation Monitoring Centre on the UK status of the species to contribute to maintenance of an up-to-date global Red Data List. (ACTION: JNCC)

5.6 Communications and publicity

5.6.1 Enhance public knowledge of this species and the conservation issues exemplified by its near extinction and recovery, providing this does not compromise the conservation of the species or detract from the security of the sites. (ACTION: EN)

5.6.2 Establish plants at some sites specifically for public viewing and conservation interpretation. (ACTION: EN)

STARFRUIT (*DAMASONIUM ALISMA*)

1. CURRENT STATUS

1.1 Starfruit occurs in muddy or gravel margins of shallow ponds with seasonally fluctuating water levels on commons or village greens. It was formerly recorded in several English counties northwards Shropshire and Yorkshire but, by 1990, the species was restricted to three native sites: one in Surrey and two in Buckinghamshire. Populations of starfruit are subject to wide fluctuations: one site in Buckinghamshire produced 300 plants in 1992, following pond clearance, but a total of only 15 plants occurred in 1994 at two native sites - probably as a result of high winter rainfall.

1.2 The UK represents the northern edge of the species range, with a scattered distribution across Europe, from Spain to Asia Minor and North Africa. It is listed as endangered on the GB Red List and is protected under Schedule 8 of the WCA 1981.

2. CURRENT FACTORS CAUSING LOSS OR DECLINE

2.1 Neglect and mismanagement of ponds on grazed commons or greens, including over-shading by trees and shrubs, with associated collection of leaf litter and the excessive growth of submerged and marginal plants.

2.2 Loss of habitat through development, drainage and in-filling of pools and wet hollows.

2.3 Introduction of water level controls reducing seasonal fluctuations.

2.4 Introduction of invasive, non-native species of water plants.

3. CURRENT ACTION

3.1 Plantlife and EN have been undertaking recovery work on this species since 1990 to relocate former sites and establish whether any remain suitable for regeneration of the seed bank.

3.2 Re-introduction has been attempted at several sites including a pond created specially for starfruit in 1994. Long-term monitoring by Plantlife at these sites will determine whether re-introduction has been successful.

3.3 Work at the Royal Botanic Gardens Kew has included both seed storage and germination techniques (work supported by EN SRP).

4. ACTION PLAN OBJECTIVES AND TARGETS

4.1 Safeguard populations at all known sites, including considering SSSI notification.

4.2 Establish suitable conditions and restore to a minimum of ten former sites by 2004.

4.3 Organise long-term management of the restored ponds to ensure the plant's future survival.

5. PROPOSED ACTIONS WITH LEAD AGENCIES

5.1 Policy and legislation

5.1.1 No action proposed.

5.2 Site safeguard and management

5.2.1 Promote measures to maintain water quality at all extant sites. (ACTION: LA, NRA)

5.2.2 Control marginal and submerged vegetation in the area around any starfruit populations and ensure that bare substrate is provided for germination. (ACTION: EN, LAs)

5.2.3 Prepare and promote an appropriate water level management plan for sites containing this species. (ACTION: EN, NRA, LAs)

5.2.4 Restore appropriate management at former sites with a view to regeneration from seed bank or re-introduction. (ACTION:EN)

5.2.5 Consider the need to notify sites as SSSI. (ACTION: EN)

5.3 Species management and protection

5.3.1 Collect and deposit seed from all sites in the National Seed Bank. (ACTION: EN)

5.3.2 Continue programme of restoration and, following analysis of previous attempts, aim to restore ten populations to suitable sites by 2004. Where re-introduction is attempted, ensure the use of seed of local provenance only. (ACTION: EN)

5.4 Advisory

5.4.1 Ensure landowners, managers and local authorities are aware of the presence, legal status and importance of conserving this species and appropriate methods of habitat management. (ACTION: EN)

5.5 Future research and monitoring

5.5.1 Survey former sites with a view to regeneration of the seed bank or identification of suitable sites for re-introduction. (ACTION: EN)

5.5.2 Monitor population size, water quality and water levels at all sites regularly. (ACTION: EN)

5.5.3 Work closely with other European countries to establish the status, ecology and conservation requirements of this species and use information and expertise towards its conservation in the UK. (ACTION: EN, JNCC)

5.5.4 Pass information gathered during survey and monitoring of this species to JNCC or BRC so that it can be incorporated in national databases. (ACTION: EN)

5.5.5 Provide information annually to the World Conservation Monitoring Centre on the UK status of the species to contribute to maintenance of an up-to-date global Red Data List. (ACTION: JNCC)

5.6 Communications and publicity

5.6.1 Ensure local communities are made aware of the presence and importance of this species and the reasons for carrying out management. (ACTION: EN)

YOUNG'S HELLEBORINE (*EPIPACTIS YOUNGIANA*)

1. CURRENT STATUS

1.1 This orchid is endemic to the UK, occurring only on derelict spoil heaps where deciduous trees have colonised. It is known from only six sites in the UK - five in Scotland and one in northern England - but may also occur on a site in South Wales. However, one site in England was destroyed in 1986, and one in Scotland will be destroyed when mineral extraction occurs under an extant planning permission. Young's helleborine probably recently evolved as a stable hybrid of the broad-leaved and narrow-lipped varieties, and was first described in 1978.

1.2 The species is listed as endangered on the GB Red List, and is protected under Schedule 8 of the WCA 1981.

2. CURRENT FACTORS CAUSING LOSS OR DECLINE

2.1 Lack of management leading to canopy closure.

2.2 Extraction of spoil for use as ballast.

2.3 Destruction of spoil heaps.

3. CURRENT ACTION

3.1 Plantlife carried out a survey of the central Scottish sites during 1993/94.

4. ACTION PLAN OBJECTIVES AND TARGETS

4.1 Determine whether intervening to conserve this species is appropriate.

4.2 If intervention is appropriate, then maintain the extant populations.

4.3 Determine whether any suitable sites remain for translocation of plants from the site threatened with destruction.

5. PROPOSED ACTION WITH LEAD AGENCIES

5.1 Policy and legislation

5.1.2 Seek to ensure that all planning proposals, including those for mineral extraction and the destruction of spoil heaps, take into account the needs of this species. (ACTION: EN, LAs, SNH)

5.2 Site safeguard and management

5.2.1 Consider the need for management works, including canopy thinning and scrub clearance at the three known sites. (ACTION: EN, SNH)

5.2.2 Pending confirmation of the Welsh site, consider notifying it as a SSSI if this is necessary to secure appropriate management. (ACTION: CCW)

5.3 Species management, protection and licensing

5.3.1 No action proposed.

5.4 Advisory

5.4.1 Provide advice on taxonomic problems and management to site managers. (ACTION: EN, SNH)

5.5 Future research and monitoring

5.5.1 Promote investigation of the status of the populations at the known sites, and the possible fourth site in south Wales. (ACTION: CCW, EN, JNCC, SNH)

5.5.2 Consider the feasibility of translocating plants from the threatened Scottish site to a suitable receptor site. (ACTION: SNH)

5.5.3 Establish long-term monitoring programmes for each population. (ACTION: EN, JNCC, SNH)

5.5.4 Promote investigation of the ecological requirements of this species and the relationship with canopy density. (ACTION: EN, JNCC, SNH)

5.5.5 Subject to confidentiality and data ownership, pass information gathered during survey and monitoring of this species to JNCC or BRC so that it can be incorporated in national databases. (ACTION: CCW, EN, SNH)

5.5.6 Provide information annually to the World Conservation Monitoring Centre on the UK status of the species to contribute to maintenance of an up-to-date global Red Data List. (ACTION: JNCC)

5.6 Communications and publicity

5.6.1 None proposed.

EYEBRIGHTS (*EUPHRASIA* SPECIES ENDEMIC TO THE UK) (Including *E. cambrica, campbelliae, heslop-harrisonii, rivularis, rotundifolia and vigursii*)

1. CURRENT STATUS

1.1 This action plan covers a number of closely-related, rare, endemic eyebrights, some of which may be under-recorded because of problems in identification. These species should be considered as a group until their individual distributions are better known and their taxonomic status verified. At present, the taxonomic status of *E. rotundifolia* is uncertain and some, or all, of the records may turn out to be a hybrid species. *E. cambrica* is easily confused with the more common *E. ostenfeldii* and records for this species need to be verified at a number of sites.

1.2 Habitats include damp, lowland heaths (*E. vigursii* and *E. campbelliae*), maritime heaths and grassland (*E. cambrica, E. rivularis* and *E. rotundifolia*), dune grass and salt marsh (*E. heslop-harrisonii*). Most British sites appear to have stable populations which are under no particular threat, although *E. vigursii* has been lost at a number of heathland sites inland in Cornwall as a result of habitat destruction and is now known to be seriously threatened. Populations for all species can vary greatly from year to year depending on conditions. These species are not found in Northern Ireland.

2. CURRENT FACTORS CAUSING LOSS OR DECLINE

2.1 Loss of habitat, particularly inland heaths in Cornwall.

2.2 Lack of grazing.

3. CURRENT ACTION

3.1 SNH is supporting re-evaluation of the distribution of the endemic species in Scotland.

4. ACTION PLAN OBJECTIVES AND TARGETS

4.1 Clarify taxonomic status and distribution of threatened eyebrights.

4.2 Protect known populations until taxonomic status is clear.

4.3 Following survey and taxonomic review, protect populations of any endangered species.

4.4 Consider preparation of individual action plans for any species found to be endangered after taxonomic review.

5. PROPOSED ACTIONS WITH LEAD AGENCIES

5.1 Policy and legislation

5.1.1 No action proposed.

5.2 Site safeguard and land acquisition

5.2.1 Encourage suitable habitat management at sites, including the maintenance or restoration of grazing for those species, where necessary. (ACTION: CCW, EN, SNH)

5.2.2 Consider notifying key sites for threatened species as SSSIs where this is necessary to secure appropriate management. (ACTION: CCW, SNH)

5.3 Species management and protection

5.3.1 No action proposed.

5.4 Advisory

5.4.1 Ensure land owners and local voluntary conservation groups are aware of the presence and importance of conserving these species, and that advice on appropriate methods of habitat management is available. (ACTION: CCW, EN, SNH)

5.5 Future research and monitoring

5.5.1 Promote morphological and genetic investigations to clarify the taxonomy of these species. (ACTION: CCW, EN, RBG Kew and Edinburgh SNH)

5.5.2 Undertake a survey of all known, and former, sites to ascertain the distribution of the species. (ACTION: CCW, EN, SNH)

5.5.3 Encourage research to compare the taxonomy and ecology of these species with related species outside the UK and use the information and expertise towards the conservation of species within the UK. (ACTION: CCW, EN, JNCC, SNH)

5.5.4 Subject to confidentiality and data ownership, pass information gathered during survey and monitoring of this species to JNCC or BRC so that it can be incorporated in national databases. (ACTION: CCW, EN, SNH)

5.5.5 Provide information annually to the World Conservation Monitoring Centre on the UK status of the species to contribute to maintenance of an up-to-date global Red Data List. (ACTION: JNCC)

5.6 Communications and publicity

5.6.1 Use these species to highlight the threat to UK biodiversity from the destruction of heathland and coastal habitats. (ACTION: CCW, EN, SNH)

WESTERN RAMPING-FUMITORY (*FUMARIA OCCIDENTALIS*)

I. CURRENT STATUS

1.1 Western ramping-fumitory is endemic to the UK. It is now recorded only in Cornwall and the Isles of Scilly. A mobile and sporadic species of waste ground, hedgebanks, walls and gardens, only a proportion of the known population appear in any one year. This species is often associated with human activity and was formerly widespread in the bulb fields of the Isles of Scilly.

2. CURRENT FACTORS CAUSING LOSS OR DECLINE

2.1 Changes in horticultural practice in the Isles of Scilly.

2.2 Increase in herbicide use.

2.3 The removal of hedgebanks in west Cornwall.

2.4 Tidying of marginal land and waste areas by local councils and individuals.

3. CURRENT ACTION

3.1 The species is monitored periodically by local botanists and is included on a database of records maintained by the Cornish Biological Records Centre.

4. ACTION PLAN OBJECTIVES AND TARGETS

4.1 Protect species in current range.

4.2 Promote ecological research to ensure appropriate conservation management.

5. PROPOSED ACTION WITH LEAD AGENCIES.

5.1 Policy and legislation

5.1.1 Consider the provision of incentives through use of ESA, Countryside Stewardship, Reserve Enhancement Scheme or EU Structural Funds to maintain and expand traditional landscapes and associated wildlife in Cornwall and the Isles of Scilly, including maintaining hedgebanks, ancient field systems and horticultural land use. (ACTION: MAFF, CC, EN, Local Authorities)

5.2 Site safeguard and management

5.2.1 Seek to provide management agreements for all important sites, including bulb-fields and ensure that SSSI management agreements take into account the ecological requirements of this species where necessary. (ACTION: EN)

5.2.2 Seek to ensure that programmes to tidy marginal land and waste areas do not affect existing populations of this species and take into account the needs of the species in likely areas for colonisation. (ACTION: EN, LAs)

5.3 Species management, protection and licensing

5.3.1 None proposed.

5.4 Advisory

5.4.1 Ensure landowners and managers are aware of the presence and importance of conserving this species and appropriate methods of management for its conservation. (ACTION: EN)

5.5 Future research and monitoring

5.5.1 Promote research the ecology of this species, including establishing seed viability and investigating the extent of the seed-bank to underpin appropriate management advice. (ACTION: EN, JNCC)

5.5.2 Survey regularly to establish the precise distributional range of this species and to assess the extent of new colonisation. (ACTION: EN)

5.5.3 Pass information gathered during survey and monitoring of this species to JNCC or BRC so that it can be incorporated in national databases. (ACTION: EN)

5.5.4 Provide information annually to the World Conservation Monitoring Centre on the UK status of the species to contribute to maintenance of an up-to-date global Red Data List. (ACTION: JNCC)

5.6 Communications and publicity

5.6.1 Highlight the decline in this species, the threats it faces and the opportunities to conserve it, and consider its use as a Cornish flagship species. (ACTION: EN)

EARLY GENTIAN (GENTIANELLA ANGLICA)

I. CURRENT STATUS

1.1 Early gentian is endemic to the UK and is recorded from only forty-nine 10 km squares from Cornwall to Lincolnshire. There are two sub-species, one of which is confined to three sites in Cornwall and the other which is declining in central England and the Midlands and has become extinct at one site in north Devon.

1.2 The early gentian is listed on Appendix I of the Bern Convention, Annex II(b) and IV(b) of the EC Habitats Directive, and is protected under Schedule 4 of the Conservation (Natural Habitats, etc.) Regulations 1994 and Schedule 8 of the WCA 1981. It is also listed as vulnerable on the GB Red List.

2. CURRENT FACTORS CAUSING LOSS OR DECLINE

2.1 Loss of suitable habitats on dunes, cliffs and limestone or chalk grassland.

2.2 Inappropriate management, particularly reduction in grazing.

3. CURRENT ACTION

3.1 Survey work was carried out in 1994 in Hampshire, Dorset and the Isle of Wight by the Hampshire Wildlife Trust, funded by the EN Species Recovery Programme.

3.2 Survey work, undertaken by Plantlife, commenced in 1994 in southern, central and south-west England and East Anglia. Investigations of the Isle of Wight populations are continuing, as part of the EN SRP, to determine plant performance in relation to habitat management and use.

3.3 A number of populations occur within protected areas and seven candidate SACs have been selected for this species under the EC Habitats Directive.

4. ACTION PLAN OBJECTIVES AND TARGETS

4.1 Safeguard all surviving populations.

4.2 Where extinction has occurred recently, restore 10 populations to former sites by 2004.

4.3 Maintain population at any new or re-discovered sites.

4.4 Promote research on the ecological requirements of both sub-species to ensure appropriate conservation management.

5. PROPOSED ACTION WITH LEAD AGENCIES

5.1 Policy and legislation

5.1.1 Encourage further uptake of ESA management agreements and downland restoration to include areas of degraded, unimproved habitat on and adjacent to threatened and recently lost G. anglica sites. (ACTION: CC, EN, MAFF)

5.2 Site safeguard and management

5.2.1 Ensure that the ecological requirements of this species are taken into account on management plans for SSSIs with extant populations. (ACTION: EN)

5.2.2 Carry out restoration management at key sites and encourage restoration of calcareous grassland adjacent to extant sites to enable expansion of populations. (ACTION: EN)

5.3 Species management and protection

5.3.1 Following feasibility studies and identification of suitable sites, seek to restore ten populations to areas where they have been lost recently by 2004. (ACTION: EN)

5.4 Advisory

5.4.1 Ensure land owners and managers are aware of the presence and importance of conserving this species and appropriate methods of habitat management. (ACTION: EN)

5.5 Future research and monitoring

5.5.1 Carry out studies on the population ecology and genetics of the early gentian to assess its suitability for re-introduction or translocation. (ACTION: EN, JNCC)

5.5.2 Undertake seed germination trials to refine a management regime where populations are to be revived from seed banks. (ACTION: EN)

5.5.3 Investigate evidence of other threats, e.g. collecting, spray drift, destruction of habitat, and modify management plans accordingly. (ACTION: EN)

5.5.4 Pass information gathered during survey and monitoring of this species to JNCC or BRC so that it can be incorporated in national databases. (ACTION: EN)

5.5.5 Provide information annually to the World Conservation Monitoring Centre on the UK status of the species to contribute to maintenance of an up-to-date global Red Data List. (ACTION: JNCC)

5.6 Communications and publicity

5.6.1 Publish a leaflet on the plight and conservation importance of this species, making information available to landowners and the general public on how they can help conserve it. (ACTION: EN)

FEN ORCHID (*LIPARIS LOESELII*)

I. CURRENT STATUS

1.1 The fen orchid was formerly known from over 30 localities in the UK, but may now occur only in two sites in the Norfolk Broads and two dune systems in South Wales. The morphology of the plants differs between the South Wales and East Anglian populations, and some authorities have given them varietal or sub-species status. Plants on the South Wales dune slack are sometimes regarded as variety *ovata*, a segregate otherwise known only from Brittany. The East Anglian variety *loeselii* is rather more widespread in Europe. In Wales, the plants rely on the early successional phases of dune slack development.

1.2 This species listed on Annexes II(b) and IV(b) of the EC Habitats Directive and is protected under Schedule 4 of the Conservation (Natural Habitats, etc.) Regulations 1994 and Schedule 8 of the WCA 1981.

2. CURRENT FACTORS CAUSING LOSS OR DECLINE

2.1 Drainage of peatlands in East Anglia, and water abstraction from aquifers (which may be more significant now than drainage for agriculture).

2.2 Natural processes of succession in dune slacks on the South Wales sites and Broadland fen sites.

2.3 Work undertaken to stabilise sand dunes.

3. CURRENT ACTION

3.1 The four sites where fen orchid occur are all within nature reserves, which are SSSIs. Fen orchid is currently in EN's Species Recovery Programme.

3.2 The Welsh populations occur on two NNRs and recovery work began during 1994. A *Liparis* Working Group has been established and is co-ordinated by CCW. A major management scheme supported by CCW is being implemented for the conservation of this species in its South Wales sites.

3.3 The Broadland fen management strategy, in which fen orchid management will be incorporated, will be completed by March 1996.

4. ACTION PLAN OBJECTIVES AND TARGETS

4.1 Maintain existing populations.

4.2 Where feasible, re-establish at 4 sites where it has recently become extinct.

5. PROPOSED ACTION WITH LEAD AGENCIES

5.1 Policy and legislation

5.1.1 Encourage uptake of incentives in agri-environment programmes for wetland restoration adjacent to extant populations, particularly where these could contribute to the restoration of water quality and quantity. (ACTION: MAFF, WOAD)

5.2 Site safeguard and management

5.2.1 Provide suitable management for this species at all sites where it occurs. (ACTION: CCW, EN)

5.2.2 Consider restoration management to encourage regeneration from seed banks or seedlings at four former sites. (ACTION: CCW, EN)

5.3 Species management and protection

5.3.1 Continue to implement the recovery strategies for the existing populations. (ACTION: CCW, EN)

5.3.2 Consider translocation of material to these sites if restoration management is unsuccessful. (ACTION: CCW, EN)

5.4 Advisory

5.4.1 No new action proposed.

5.5 Future research and monitoring

5.5.1 Research further seed-bank viability and dormancy, and habitat requirements to help conserve the species *in situ*. (ACTION: CCW, EN, JNCC)

5.5.2 Investigate the feasibility of translocation to dune systems within forests, including the potential of rotational tree felling to provide appropriate successional stages. (ACTION: CCW, EN, FA, JNCC)

5.5.3 Encourage research on the ecology and conservation of this species on an international level and use the information and expertise gained towards it conservation both in the UK and at a European level. (ACTION: CCW, EN, JNCC)

5.5.4 Pass information gathered during survey and monitoring of this species to JNCC or BRC so that it can be incorporated in national databases. (ACTION: CCW, EN)

5.5.5 Provide information annually to the World Conservation Monitoring Centre on the UK status of the species to contribute to maintenance of an up-to-date global Red Data List. (ACTION: JNCC)

5.6 Communications and publicity

5.6.1 As it is possible that the management required for recovery in South Wales may cause some concern with other users of the sites, including the public, information boards should be provided and public meetings held to dispel any misunderstandings that may occur. (ACTION: CCW)

FLOATING WATER-PLANTAIN (*LURONIUM NATANS*)

I. CURRENT STATUS

I.1 Floating water plantain is found only in Europe. It occurs in a range of freshwater situations but thrives best in open areas with a moderate degree of disturbance, where the growth of emergent vegetation is held in check. Populations of this species fluctuate greatly in size, often increasing when water levels drop to expose the bottom or in part-dredged canals removing plant competition.

I.2 The distribution of this plant is localised in the UK, with recent records from Wales, the West Midlands and northern England. It also occurs as an introduction to ditches in the Norfolk Broads and a few localities in Scotland. Since 1980 it has been recorded from 35 ten km squares, approximately half of them from canals and appears to have spread eastwards from the "core" natural habitat in the lakes of Snowdonia and mid-Wales, via the canal system in the nineteenth century.

I.3 Floating water plantain is listed on Annexes II and IV of the Habitats Directive and Appendix I of the Bern Convention. It is protected under Schedule 4 of the Conservation (Natural Habitats, etc.) Regulations 1994 and Schedule 8 of the WCA 1981.

2. CURRENT FACTORS CAUSING LOSS OR DECLINE

2.1 The main threat to canal populations is from the re-opening of waterways, with subsequent high levels of motorised recreational boat traffic. This can directly suppress growth of the plant through increased turbidity of the water.

2.2 Water acidification.

3. CURRENT ACTIONS

3.1 CCW carried out a survey of lakes in North Wales in 1994 which confirmed the presence of this species at a number of sites.

3.2 CCW and EN are liaising with British Waterways to produce management guidelines for canals containing this plant.

3.3 Two sites containing this species have been proposed as SACs under the EC Habitats Directive.

3.4 Recent genetic studies have indicated the importance of Welsh Lakes as source sites for this plant.

3.5 British Waterways has undertaken the relocation of individual plants to refuge sites as part of the restoration of the Montgomery Canal.

4. ACTION PLAN OBJECTIVES AND TARGETS

4.1 Maintain the present range.

4.2 Where the potential exists, increase the size of individual populations .

4.3 Develop a strategy to safeguard the species, wherever possible, in its canal habitats.

4.4 Ascertain the importance of the UK population in a European context.

5. PROPOSED ACTION WITH LEAD AGENCIES

5.1 Policy and legislation

5.1.1 Seek to develop and implement a Code of Practice to protect and enhance populations of floating water plantain in canals, to include management of disused and navigable sections of canal, and the amelioration of the effects of canal restoration. (ACTION: British Waterways, CCW, EN)

5.1.2 Seek to minimise the effects of acidification on waters containing the plantain in acid-sensitive areas. (ACTION: British Waterways, CCW, EN, FE, NRA)

5.2 Site safeguard and management

5.2.1 Ensure the needs of the species are taken into account in management plans for any SAC, National Park, NNR or SSSI where it occurs, including prevention of encroaching emergent vegetation likely out-compete this plant.. (ACTION: CCW, EN)

5.2.2 Seek to develop management agreements with the owners of disused and little used canals to include a programme of dredging and other maintenance work to produce the open habitat necessary for this plant. (ACTION: British Waterways, CCW, EN)

5.3 Species management and protection

5.3.1 Where high volumes of boat traffic may damage beds of this species, seek to develop 'refuges' near the banks protected barriers such as piling. (ACTION: British Waterways, CCW, EN)

5.3.2 Where canals containing this plant are subject to unavoidable restoration schemes, consider creating reserves and manage them to maintain healthy colonies of the species. (ACTION: British Waterways, CCW, EN)

5.3.3 Seek to dissuade planting of coniferous forests in sensitive lake catchments and around river headwaters important for this species. Where such forests already exist, encourage the creation of buffer zones around lake shores and river margins to allow deciduous woodland to develop. For proposed new plantings in areas containing the water plantain, carry out catchment assessments to determine the potential threat and any ameliorative treatment which would be necessary. (ACTION: CCW, FA, NRA, Snowdonia NPC)

5.3.4 In nature reserves with records of the species, but where it is no longer apparently present, experiment with dredging small areas of water bodies to give any remaining seed a chance to germinate. (ACTION: CCW, EN)

5.4 Advisory

5.4.1 No action proposed.

5.5 Future research and monitoring

5.5.1 In England and Wales complete the baseline survey of known sites for floating water plantain and develop a method of quantitative assessment for colonies of the plant. (ACTION: CCW, EN)

5.5.2 Encourage ecological studies of this species to support site management and translocation programmes. (ACTION: CCW, EN, JNCC)

5.5.3 Encourage research into the effects of acidification of water bodies on the survival of this species in acid-sensitive areas. (ACTION: CCW, EN, JNCC)

5.5.4 Encourage research on the ecology and distribution of this species on a European level and use the information and expertise gained towards its conservation in the UK. (ACTION: CCW, EN, JNCC)

5.5.5 Pass information gathered during survey and monitoring of this species to JNCC or BRC so that it can be incorporated in national databases. (ACTION: CCW, EN)

5.5.6 Provide information annually to the World Conservation Monitoring Centre on the UK status of the species to contribute to maintenance of an up-to-date global Red Data List. (ACTION: JNCC)

5.6 Communication and publicity

5.6.1 Ensure that any published guidelines for canal management take account of the conservation of this species. (ACTION: British Waterways, CCW, EN)

SLENDER NAIAD (NAJAS FLEXILIS)

1. CURRENT STATUS

1.1 This aquatic plant occurs in clear lowland waterbodies with low to medium concentrations of plant nutrients. These often have underlying shell and sand or limestone outcrops making the water rich in lime. It is seldom found in water less than 1 m in depth.

1.2 In the UK, this species is now found exclusively in Scotland, where it has been recorded from 34 lochs within 18 ten km squares since 1980 . The majority of sites are on islands off the west coast, although it is also recorded from one site in Central Region and in a cluster of lochs in Tayside. The only known site in England was in Esthwaite Water in the Lake District where, despite a survey in 1994, it has not been recorded since 1982. This plant also occurs in a number of sites in Ireland, but is absent from Northern Ireland.

1.3 Slender naiad is listed under Annexes II and IV of the EC Habitats Directive and Appendix I of the Bern Convention. It is protected under Schedule 4 of the Conservation (Natural Habitats, etc.) Regulations 1994 and Schedule 8 of the WCA 1981.

2. CURRENT FACTORS CAUSING LOSS OR DECLINE

2.1 Restrictions on light penetration due to heavy weed growth and nutrient enrichment from sources such as sewage effluent and fertiliser run-off from fish farms.

3. CURRENT ACTION

3.1 SNH carried out surveys in 1994 and 1995 and increased the number of known Scottish sites from 24 to 34. The status of previously known populations was also assessed.

3.2 Three SSSIs containing this species have been proposed for SAC designation under the EC Habitats Directive.

4. ACTION PLAN, OBJECTIVES AND TARGETS

4.1 Clarify the status of the species in the UK.

4.2 Safeguard remaining populations.

4.3 If feasible, restore to former site in the Lake District by 2004.

5. PROPOSED ACTIONS AND LEAD AGENCIES

5.1 Policy and legislation

5.1.1 At the sites containing this species, identify and implement water quality which will benefit the species. (ACTION: FA, RPB, SNH)

5.1.2 Establish a strategy for monitoring and maintaining the natural distribution of this species in Scotland. (ACTION: SNH)

5.2 Site safeguard and management

5.2.1 Where necessary within SSSIs, negotiate management agreements to maintain sympathetic low intensity agricultural and forestry works in the catchment of lakes containing this species. (ACTION: FA, SNH)

5.2.2 Maintain the present programme of phosphorus stripping for treated sewage effluent entering Esthwaite Water to create suitable conditions for re-introduction. (ACTION: NW Water)

5.2.3 Where appropriate within SSSIs, negotiate management agreements to prevent damaging fish management or fish farming activities. (ACTION: SNH)

5.3 Species management and protection

5.3.1 Collect seed from a range of Scottish sites and (if the plant is still present) also from Esthwaite Water, for preservation at RBG Kew's seed bank. (ACTION: RBGs Edinburgh and Kew, EN, SNH).

5.3.2 If found to be absent but conditions are suitable, consider restoring population to former site in the Lake District by 2004. (ACTION: EN)

5.4 Advisory

5.4.1 Maintain a flow of information between statutory conservation agencies and agencies responsible for water quality over the location of Najas flexilis and its requirements. (ACTION: SEPA, JNCC, SNH)

5.5 Future research and monitoring

5.5.1 Survey former and potential sites to ascertain the precise distribution of this species in Britain, including the use of underwater survey techniques where necessary. (ACTION: EN, JNCC, SNH)

5.5.2 Promote ecological studies on population dynamics and the habitat requirements of this species to underpin management advice and assess the feasibility of restoring it to the Lake District. (ACTION: EN)

5.5.3 Encourage research on the distribution and ecology of this species on an international level and use the information and expertise towards its conservation in the UK. (ACTION: JNCC, SNH)

5.5.4 Subject to confidentiality and data ownership, pass information gathered during survey and monitoring of this species to JNCC or BRC so that it can be incorporated in national databases. (ACTION: EN, SNH)

5.5.5 Provide information annually to the World Conservation Monitoring Centre on the UK status of the species to contribute to maintenance of an up-to-date global Red Data List. (ACTION: JNCC)

5.6 Communication and publicity

5.6.1 No action proposed.

HOLLY-LEAVED NAIAD (*NAJAS MARINA*)

1. CURRENT STATUS

1.1 This aquatic plant is found in shallow, slightly brackish, open water within fens and reed swamps. In the UK it has only been found in the Norfolk Broads and is now known to occur regularly only in three Broads, with transient populations in several other areas.

1.2 The holly-leaved naiad is protected under Schedule 8 of the WCA 1981.

2. CURRENT FACTORS CAUSING LOSS OR DECLINE

2.1 Eutrophication of waterbodies caused by agricultural run off and sewage discharge.

2.2 Turbulence and pollution associated with boat traffic on the Broads.

3. CURRENT ACTION

3.1 The three known permanent sites are nature reserves in SSSIs. The Norfolk Broads are within an ESA.

3.2 Work is continuing at the RBG Kew to determine optimum conditions for seed storage.

4. ACTION PLAN OBJECTIVES AND TARGETS

4.1 Maintain at its known sites.

4.2 Survey to confirm the status of the species in the UK.

4.3 Re-colonise five waterways adjacent to existing sites by 2004.

5. PROPOSED ACTION WITH LEAD AGENCIES

5.1 Policy and legislation

5.1.1 Identify and encourage water quality standards in occupied waters which will favour this species. (ACTION: Broads Authority, EN, NRA)

5.2 Site safeguard and management

5.2.1 Provide optimum conditions for growth and colonisation by this species, including removal of mud selectively on the larger Broads, and excavation of new sites. (ACTION: Broads Authority, EN)

5.3 Species management and protection

5.3.1 Re-establish colonies as sites become available after habitat restoration, seeking to re-colonise five waterways adjacent to existing colonies. (ACTION: EN)

5.4 Advisory

5.4.1 No action proposed.

5.5 Future research and monitoring

5.5.1 Continue to research ecological requirements, in particular seedling establishment and interspecific competition and determine the water quality requirements of the species. (ACTION: EN)

5.5.2 Ensure regular monitoring of the three permanent populations and identify any further threats to the species. (ACTION: EN)

5.5.3 Encourage research on the ecology and distribution of this species with other countries experiencing the same threats to the species, and use the information and expertise gained towards its conservation in the UK. (ACTION: JNCC)

5.5.4 Pass information gathered during survey and monitoring of this species to JNCC or BRC so that it can be incorporated in national databases. (ACTION: EN)

5.5.5 Provide information annually to the World Conservation Monitoring Centre on the UK status of the species to contribute to maintenance of an up-to-date global Red Data List. (ACTION: JNCC)

5.6 Communications and publicity

5.6.1 Develop a strategy to educate Broads users and adjacent land managers about the effect of their activities on the Broads' wildlife, particularly the holly-leaved naiad. (Broads Authority, EN, NRA)

SHETLAND PONDWEED (*POTAMOGETON RUTILUS*)

I. CURRENT STATUS

1.1 Shetland pondweed is endemic to northern Europe, where it appears to be under threat in many areas. In the UK it is found in lochs in Easter Ross, east Inverness-shire, Tiree, the Western Isles and Shetland. The lochs in which it occurs are often situated on calcareous rocks or sand. Shetland pondweed has been located in 12 ten km squares since 1970 but, as it is difficult to identify and occurs between one and two metres below the water surface, it may be under-recorded.

2. CURRENT FACTORS CAUSING LOSS OR DECLINE

2.1 Eutrophication of the lochs, particularly due to nutrient enrichment at sites adjacent to intensively used agricultural land.

2.2 Increased housing pressure currently threatens at least one site in Shetland.

3. CURRENT ACTION

3.1 SNH are currently undertaking research on Shetland into potential eutrophication problems at one site.

3.2 The Botanical Society of the British Isles, under contract to SNH, is gathering data to establish more accurately the distribution of this species.

3.3 Several sites for Shetland pondweed are notified as SSSIs.

4. ACTION PLAN OBJECTIVES AND TARGETS

4.1 Safeguard the species at its known, and any re-discovered, sites.

4.2 Investigate the ecological requirements of this species to aid more effective conservation management.

5. PROPOSED ACTIONS WITH LEAD AGENCIES

5.1 Policy and legislation

5.1.1 Seek to ensure that local planning policies take into account the requirements and vulnerability of this species. (ACTION: LAs)

5.2 Site safeguard and management

5.2.1 Seek to ensure that SSSIs containing this species are protected from detrimental activities outside their perimeter, especially eutrophication from agricultural run-off. (ACTION: SNH)

5.2.2 Seek to ensure existing ESAs in Scotland including or adjacent to water bodies containing this species take into account the ecological requirements of this species. (ACTION: SNH, SOAEFD)

5.3 Species management and protection

5.3.1 If after survey, the species is found to be endangered, consider for addition to Schedule 8 of the WCA 1981. (ACTION: JNCC, SNH, SOAEFD)

5.4 Advisory

5.4.1 Ensure land owners, land managers, local authorities, development agencies, water authorities and other statutory agencies are aware of the presence and importance of conserving this species in order to avoid damaging or inappropriate practices. (ACTION: SEPA, SNH)

5.4.2 Ensure landowners and managers are aware of appropriate methods of habitat management for the conservation of this species. (ACTION: SNH)

5.5 Future research and monitoring

5.5.1 Undertake a survey of former or potential sites, where feasible, to ascertain current status in the UK. (ACTION: SNH)

5.5.2 Encourage ecological studies to assess the habitat requirements of this species and identify potential threats to sites, including water quality. (ACTION: SNH)

5.5.3 Encourage research on the ecology and distribution of this species with partners in France, Germany, Scandinavia, Poland and western Russia to determine the global status of the species and use the information obtained towards conservation of the species in the UK. (ACTION: SNH, JNCC)

5.5.4 Subject to confidentiality and data ownership, pass information gathered during survey and monitoring of this species to JNCC or BRC so that it can be incorporated in national databases. (ACTION: SNH)

5.5.5 Provide information annually to the World Conservation Monitoring Centre on the UK status of the species to contribute to maintenance of an up-to-date global Red Data List. (ACTION: JNCC)

5.6 Communications and publicity

5.6.1 Use this species to highlight loch ecosystems, in particular their relation to the surrounding land and the potential impact of the use of adjacent land uses. (ACTION: SNH)

THREE-LOBED CROWFOOT (*RANUNCULUS TRIPARTITUS*)

I. CURRENT STATUS

I.I Three-lobed crowfoot is found in shallow, seasonal water bodies on heaths, especially in shallow ditches, ponds, ruts in tracks and gateways which dry out in Summer. It is intolerant of competition and thrives best where open spaces are maintained by fluctuating water levels, grazing and poaching by livestock or disturbance by vehicles.

I.2 Formerly recorded from 57 ten km squares in the UK, it has suffered a severe decline throughout its former range and is now restricted to the south and south-west of England. It has recently been recorded in 19 ten km squares in Cornwall, south Devon, south Wales, Herefordshire, Kent, Sussex and Surrey, but only occurs in any significant quantity on the Lizard Peninsula in Cornwall. Elsewhere is distributed from south-west Spain to northern Germany, and in Greece and Morocco. It is declining throughout the northern part of its range.

I.3 The species is listed as vulnerable on the GB Red List.

2. CURRENT FACTORS CAUSING LOSS OR DECLINE

2.1 Loss of heathland.

2.2 Draining or infilling of temporary pools.

2.3 Cessation of grazing allowing other vegetation to dominate.

3. CURRENT ACTION

3.1 Three-lobed crowfoot is being considered for addition to the WCA 1981.

4. ACTION PLAN OBJECTIVES AND TARGETS

4.1 Maintain all remaining populations.

4.2 If feasible, restore to ten suitable former sites by 2004.

5. PROPOSED ACTIONS WITH LEAD AGENCIES

5.1 Policy and legislation

5.1.1 Following further survey and assessment, review the need for international protection. (ACTION: DoE, JNCC)

5.2 Site safeguard and management

5.2.1 Consider protection for major populations through SSSI notification where this is necessary to secure appropriate management. (ACTION: CCW)

5.2.2 Encourage land management promoting open ground habitats suitable for this species, especially appropriate grazing and maintenance of temporary pools. (ACTION: CCW, EN)

5.2.3 Encourage positive habitat management at suitable former sites to aid germination of dormant seed in the seed bank. (ACTION: CCW, EN)

5.2.4 Seek to maintain water levels in the winter and prevent drainage of the surrounding area. (ACTION: CCW, EN)

5.3 Species management and protection

5.3.1 If feasible, seek to restore to ten suitable former sites by 2004. (ACTION: CCW, EN)

5.3.2 Collect and deposit seed in the national seed bank at Wakehurst Place and ensure that plants are kept in cultivation. (ACTION: CCW, EN)

5.4 Advisory

5.4.1 Ensure that landowners and managers are aware of the presence and importance of conserving this species and appropriate methods of habitat management for its conservation. (ACTION: CCW, EN)

5.5 Future research and monitoring

5.5.1 Survey to assess seed banks at former sites to determine the extent and feasibility of regeneration programmes. (ACTION: CCW, EN, JNCC)

5.5.2 Promote research into the ecology and habitat requirements of this species to underpin management advice and identify its suitability for re-introduction or translocation. (ACTION: CCW, EN, JNCC)

5.5.3 If found to be necessary, survey to determine whether suitable sites exist for regeneration or re-introduction of this species. (ACTION: CCW, EN, JNCC)

5.5.4 Encourage research on the ecology and conservation of this species on an international level, seeking to determine the reasons for its decline in northern Europe and using the information and expertise gained towards its conservation in the UK. (ACTION: CCW, EN, JNCC)

5.5.5 Monitor extant populations regularly and seek to identify any potential threats to the species. (ACTION: CCW, EN)

5.5.6 Pass information gathered during survey and monitoring of this species to JNCC or BRC so that it can be incorporated in national databases. (ACTION: CCW, EN)

5.5.7 Provide information annually to the World Conservation Monitoring Centre on the UK status of the species to contribute to maintenance of an up-to-date global Red Data List. (ACTION: JNCC)

5.6 Communications and publicity

5.6.1 None proposed.

SHORE DOCK (*RUMEX RUPESTRIS*)

1. CURRENT STATUS

1.1 The shore dock is a maritime plant found in Anglesey, South Devon, Cornwall and the Isles of Scilly. It also grows in the Channel Islands, Normandy, Brittany, Bordeaux and Galicia and is rare and declining throughout its range. During the last century, the number of mainland UK sites has declined by over 80% and the species is now found in ten $10km^2$ squares. The largest British population has no more than 50 individuals.

1.2 The shore dock is listed on Annexes II(b) and IV(b) of the EC Habitats Directive, and is protected under Schedule 4 of the Conservation (Natural Habitats, etc.) Regulations 1994 and Schedule 8 of the WCA 1981.

2. CURRENT FACTORS CAUSING LOSS OR DECLINE

2.1 Loss of habitat for recreational and sea defence purposes.

2.2 "Coastal squeeze" caused by sea-level rise and increased storminess.

2.3 Competition from the Hottentot fig (*Carpobrotus edulis*), an established non-native species; also from bramble and other invasive species.

3. CURRENT ACTION

3.1 A species recovery programme began in 1994, undertaken by Plantlife, ITE and EN.

3.2 SSSI notification of sites continues, though six populations still occur outside SSSIs. Six sites have been proposed as candidate SACs under the EC Habitats Directive.

4. ACTION PLAN OBJECTIVES AND TARGETS

4.1 Ensure the restoration of Favourable Conservation Status by 2004.

4.2 Ensure that developments on the coastline do not adversely affect this species or its environment.

4.3 If feasible, restore the species to at least two former sites by 2004.

5. PROPOSED ACTION WITH LEAD AGENCIES

5.1 Policy and legislation

5.1.1 Seek to ensure that proposals for coastal defence development do not damage further the existing sites for this species. (ACTION: CCW, EN, LAs)

5.2 Site safeguard and management

5.2.1 Seek to ensure that all major colonies are notifyied as SSSIs. (ACTION: EN)

5.2.2 Seek to integrate the needs of this species into shoreline management plans and encourage sympathetic management to enable natural re-colonisation at all sites. (ACTION: CCW, EN)

5.2.3 Develop zoning of sites where populations may be threatened by excessive recreational use. (ACTION: CCW, EN)

5.3 Species management and protection

5.3.1 Continue the species recovery project, and re-survey previously occupied sites to assess the feasibility of restoring at least two populations by 2004. (ACTION: CCW, EN, JNCC)

5.4 Advisory

5.4.1 Ensure that land managers realise the importance of conserving this species and are advised on management requirements. (ACTION: CCW, EN)

5.5 Future research and monitoring

5.5.1 Survey potential locations in SW England, and encourage further survey in Ireland, to locate any undiscovered populations. (ACTION: EN, DoE(NI), JNCC)

5.5.2 Encourage ecological research on this species to underpin conservation management and to assess the suitability of the species for re-introduction or translocation. (ACTION: CCW, EN, JNCC)

5.5.3 Encourage research on the ecology and conservation of this declining species with French and Spanish counterparts and use the information and expertise gained towards its conservation in the UK. (ACTION: CCW, DoE(NI), EN, JNCC)

5.5.4 Pass information gathered during survey and monitoring of this species to JNCC or BRC so that it can be incorporated in national databases. (ACTION: CCW, DoE(NI), EN)

5.5.5 Provide information annually to the World Conservation Monitoring Centre on the UK status of the species to contribute to maintenance of an up-to-date global Red Data List. (ACTION: JNCC)

5.6 Communications and publicity

5.6.1 Use this species to publicise the threat to coastal habitats. (ACTION: CCW, EN)

YELLOW MARSH SAXIFRAGE (*SAXIFRAGA HIRCULUS*)

1. CURRENT STATUS

1.1 Yellow marsh saxifrage is a perennial plant occurring in base-rich flushes and mires. It is threatened and declining throughout much of Europe. Formerly recorded from 13 vice-counties in the UK, it is now restricted to approximately 20 localities in about 10 ten km squares in Northern Ireland, Scotland and northern England. The main population concentration is now in the northern Pennines, which holds 80-90% of the UK population. The size of yellow marsh saxifrage populations have been under-estimated as the flower heads are grazed off, making recognition difficult.

1.2 This plant is listed on Annexes II and IV of the EC Habitats Directive and Appendix I of the Bern Convention. It is protected in the UK under Schedule 4 of the Conservation (Natural Habitats, etc.) Regulations 1994 and Schedule 8 of the WCA 1981.

2. CURRENT CAUSES OF LOSS OR DECLINE

2.1 Loss and degradation of habitat through afforestation, drainage and over-grazing.

3. CURRENT ACTION

3.1 A survey of known sites in Scotland has been undertaken for SNH and a species action plan is being prepared for Scottish populations.

3.2 Three sites have been proposed for SAC designation under the EC Habitats Directive.

4. ACTION PLAN OBJECTIVES AND TARGETS

4.1 Safeguard populations at all known sites and ensure that all key sites are legally protected.

4.2 If feasible, expand range by restoring to ten former sites by 2004.

4.3 Investigate the ecological requirements of this species to ensure efficient conservation management.

5. PROPOSED ACTION WITH LEAD AGENCIES

5.1 Policy and legislation

5.1.1 No action proposed.

5.2 Site safeguard and management

5.2.1 Seek to avoid damage by afforestation to both present and former sites and to land adjacent to populations, and undertake restoration where damage has occurred. (ACTION: DoE(NI), EN, FA, FE, SNH)

5.2.2 Where a site containing the species is considered to be overgrazed, consider measures to reduce the intensity of grazing. (ACTION: DANI, MAFF, SOAEFD, WOAD)

5.2.3 Consider protection for all sites through ASSI notification where this is necessary to secure appropriate management. (ACTION: DoE(NI))

5.2.4 Seek to ensure that appropriate levels of grazing are maintained for the benefit of the species. (ACTION: DANI, EN, National Parks Authorities, MAFF, SNH, SOAEFD, WOAD)

5.2.5 Ensure that the requirements of this species are taken into account in management plans for National Parks containing this species. (ACTION: National Parks Authorities)

5.2.6 Seek to ensure that no drainage work is carried out which will affect the hydrology of known sites. (ACTION: FA, NRA, RPBs)

5.3 Species management and protection

5.3.1 Following feasibility assessment and identification of suitable sites, seek to restore ten populations to sites within the former range. (ACTION: DoE(NI), EN, SNH)

5.4 Advisory

5.4.1 Ensure landowners and managers are aware of the presence, legal status and importance of conserving this species, and appropriate methods of habitat management for its conservation. (ACTION: DoE(NI), EN, SNH)

5.5 Future research and monitoring

5.5.1 Survey all former, current and potential sites to confirm the current status of the species in the UK. (ACTION: DoE(NI), EN, JNCC, SNH)

5.5.2 Promote ecological research to understand the habitat requirements of this species, particularly the impact of grazing, to underpin management advice and to assess the suitability of this species for re-introduction or translocation. (ACTION: DoE(NI), EN, JNCC, SNH)

5.5.3 If sustainable, collect and deposit seed with the seed bank at Wakehurst Place, and keep plants in cultivation at a number of botanic gardens if *ex-situ* flowering can be prevented. (ACTION: RBGs, DoE(NI), EN, SNH)

5.5.4 Encourage research on the ecology and conservation of this species on an international level, including the reasons for its decline, and use the information and expertise gained towards its conservation in the UK. (ACTION: DoE(NI), EN, JNCC, SNH)

5.5.5 Monitor extant populations regularly and seek to identify further threats to the species. (ACTION: EN, JNCC, SNH)

5.5.6 Subject to confidentiality and data ownership, pass information gathered during survey and monitoring of this species to JNCC or BRC so that it can be incorporated in national databases. (ACTION: DoE(NI), EN, SNH)

5.5.7 Provide information annually to the World Conservation Monitoring Centre on the UK status of the species to contribute to maintenance of an up-to-date global Red Data List. (ACTION: JNCC)

5.6 Communication and publicity

5.6.1 Use this species to promote the conservation and importance of moorland habitats, especially mires and flushes. (ACTION: DoE(NI), EN, SNH)

FERNS

NEWMAN'S LADY FERN (*ATHYRIUM FLEXILE*)

1. CURRENT STATUS

1.1 This fern has been recorded from a number of high altitude locations in Scotland, but can now only be found in four sites. The plant is morphologically and genetically distinct but, although it has been considered an endemic, the precise taxonomic rank is disputed with some experts considering it to be only a variety of Alpine lady fern.

2. CURRENT FACTORS CAUSING LOSS OR DECLINE

2.1 Botanical collection.

3. CURRENT ACTION

3.1 Newman's lady fern is the subject of research by the Institute of Ecology and Resource Management at Edinburgh University, proposed and supported by SNH.

4. ACTION PLAN OBJECTIVES AND TARGETS

4.1 Safeguard populations at the known sites.

4.2 Investigate the taxonomic status of this plant through the use of genetic techniques.

4.3 If found to be endemic, re-introduce to two former sites by 2004.

5. PROPOSED ACTION WITH LEAD AGENCIES

5.1 Policy and legislation

5.1.1 No action proposed.

5.2 Site safeguard and management

5.2.1 Ensure protected site management considers the maintenance of this species. (ACTION: SNH)

5.2.2 Monitor known sites for potential impacts from land management. (ACTION: SNH)

5.3 Species management and protection

5.3.1 If taxonomic status is verified, consider adding this species to Schedule 8 of the WCA 1981. (ACTION: JNCC, SNH)

5.3.2 If found to be endemic, establish a population in cultivation. (ACTION: SNH)

5.3.3 Attempt re-introduction of species to two former sites, where suitable habitat still occurs. (ACTION: SNH)

5.4 Advisory

5.4.1 Ensure landowners at last remaining sites are aware of the presence and importance of conserving this species. (ACTION: SNH)

5.5 Future research and monitoring

5.5.1 Attempt to clarify the taxonomy of this species through genetic techniques. (ACTION: SNH)

5.5.2 Survey former sites to assess whether the species still occurs at any of them, and to establish whether any suitable habitat remains. (ACTION: SNH)

5.5.3 Investigate the ecology of the species in order to be able to provide advice on management for its conservation. (ACTION: SNH)

5.5.4 Subject to confidentiality and data ownership, pass information gathered during survey and monitoring of this species to JNCC or BRC so that it can be incorporated in national databases. (ACTION: SNH)

5.5.5 Provide information annually to the World Conservation Monitoring Centre on the UK status of the species to contribute to maintenance of an up-to-date global Red Data List. (ACTION: JNCC)

5.6 Communications and publicity

5.6.1 The location of sites should not be publicised due to the risk from collectors.

KILLARNEY FERN (TRICHOMANES SPECIOSUM)

1. CURRENT STATUS

1.1 Although primarily a species of the UK, Ireland, Brittany and the Atlantic Islands (Canaries, Madeira and the Azores), the Killarney fern is also found in Europe at scattered locations in other parts of France, Spain, Portugal and Italy.

1.2 In the UK, the asexual form (sporophyte) has been recorded from at least 14 localities in Northern Ireland, England, south-west Scotland and Wales. These populations contain only 16 separate colonies, varying greatly in size from a few to over a thousand fronds and cover areas from 0.25 m² to 4m² of damp, deeply-shaded caves and stream ravines. In contrast, the sexual form (gametophyte) is much more widespread in the UK, but appears to exist in a state of arrested development, unable to produce the mature form under present conditions.

1.3 The Killarney fern is listed on Annexes II and IV of the Habitats Directive and Appendix I of the Bern Convention. It is listed as vulnerable on the GB and Irish Red Lists and rare on the IUCN global RDL. In the UK it is protected under Schedule 4 of the Conservation (Natural Habitats, etc.) Regulations 1994 and Schedule 8 of the WCA 1981.

2. CURRENT FACTORS CAUSING LOSS OR DECLINE

2.1 Botanical collection, including trampling and vegetation removal associated with photography.

2.2 Human activities which alter ambient humidity, for example tree-felling, stream water abstraction and changes in catchment run-off from drainage and afforestation.

2.3 Pollution and physical damage caused by sewage, fertilisers, mine and quarry spoil and human activities such as gill-scrambling.

2.4 Natural processes, for example stream-scouring from cloudburst, wind-blow of sheltering trees, land-slips and rock-falls, plant competition, prolonged frost and drought.

3. CURRENT ACTION

3.1 Sporophyte populations are monitored regularly in Scotland and Cornwall.

3.2 EN is currently determining the present status of the fern at known sites.

4. ACTION PLAN OBJECTIVES AND TARGETS

4.1 Maintain and monitor existing sporophyte populations.

4.2 Assess current distribution and status of the gametophyte.

4.3 Investigate the genetic diversity and population ecology of the species to aid effective conservation management.

4.4 If feasible, restore colonies to four former locations by 2004.

5. PROPOSED ACTION WITH LEAD AGENCIES

5.1 Policy and legislation

5.1.1 No action proposed.

5.2 Site safeguard and management

5.2.1 Seek to ensure the requirements of the species are taken into account in site management plans and attempt to secure favourable management agreements for sites containing this species which are not protected through designation. (ACTION: CCW, DoE(NI), EN, FA, FE, SNH)

5.2.2 Consider the protection of additional sites through SSSI/ASSI notification where this is necessary to secure appropriate management and does not compromise the security of the site. (ACTION: CCW, DoE(NI))

5.3 Species management and protection

5.3.1 Consider re-introduction to four localities, in Merioneth, Cumbria, Arran and Argyll, where the precise site of previous occurrence is known, and the fern was lost either by collecting or through exceptional conditions. Use only cultivated material of known provenance to the four localities. (ACTION: CCW, EN, JNCC, SNH)

5.4 Advisory

5.4.1 Ensure that landowners are aware of the importance and legal status of this species, appropriate methods of habitat management for its conservation and the threats currently facing known populations. (ACTION: CCW, DoE(NI), EN, SNH)

5.4.2 Ensure the relevant societies are aware of the legal and ecological implication of collecting this species. (ACTION: CCW, DoE(NI), EN, SNH)

5.5 Future research and monitoring

5.5.1 Continue experimental studies on the gametophyte, and seek to determine the conditions required for the production of sporophytes. (ACTION: NERC)

5.5.2 Consider research needs to clarify the taxonomy of the species, including the relationship between the gametophyte and sporophyte forms, and the suitability of the species for re-introduction or translocation. (ACTION: CCW, DoE(NI), EN, JNCC, SNH)

5.5.3 Compile an inventory of all sporophyte populations in cultivation, in botanic gardens and private collections, and establish provenances if possible. Consider the feasability of using material of known provenance in re-introduction experiments. (ACTION: CCW, DoE(NI), EN, JNCC, SNH)

5.5.4 Monitor all sporophyte colonies regularly to assess status of the species in the UK. (ACTION: CCW, DoE(NI), EN, JNCC, SNH)

5.5.5 Subject to confidentiality and data ownership, pass information gathered during survey and monitoring of this species to JNCC or BRC so that it can be incorporated in national databases. (ACTION: CCW, DoE(NI), EN, SNH)

5.5.6 Provide information annually to the World Conservation Monitoring Centre on the UK status of the species to contribute to maintenance of an up-to-date global Red Data List. (ACTION: JNCC)

5.6 Communications and publicity

5.6.1 Publicity is not recommended for this species due to the risk from collectors.

FUNGI

SANDY STILT PUFFBALL (*BATTARRAEA PHALLOIDES*)

I. CURRENT STATUS

1.1 Very little is known of this fungus, which requires a dry, sunny habitat, possibly facing towards the light inside hollow trees. It was first described from Britain and has a scattered distribution in western Europe. Although it was formerly known from much further north, its main areas of distribution became confined to sites in southern and eastern England. The fungus is only known now from three sites, and only predictably in one hedge-bank in Suffolk. Although the population at this site fluctuates from year to year, it appears to be stable.

1.2 This species is listed as endangered on the GB Red List.

2. CURRENT FACTORS CAUSING LOSS OR DECLINE

2.1 Overgrowth of hedge-bank in Suffolk.

2.2 Loss of hollow trees which provided its former habitat.

2.3 Road-widening or re-surfacing of road at Suffolk site.

3. CURRENT ACTION

3.1 The hedge-bank where this fungus grows is monitored regularly and is managed by the Suffolk Wildlife Trust for the benefit of the species (as far as its requirements are known).

4. ACTION PLAN OBJECTIVES AND TARGETS

4.1 Maintain and protect all currently known populations.

4.2 Establish a survey of suitable sites to determine the status of the species in the UK.

4.3 Encourage research into the ecological requirements of the species.

5. PROPOSED ACTIONS WITH LEAD AGENCIES

5.1 Policy and legislation

5.1.1 Consider adding the species to Schedule 8 of the WCA. (ACTION: DoE, EN, JNCC)

5.2 Site safeguard and management

5.2.1 Continue management at the Suffolk site and apply experience gained at this site to any other extant sites. (ACTION: EN)

5.2.2 Encourage hollow trees, or other suitable habitat, to be retained in areas adjacent to known sites. (ACTION: EN, FA, FE)

5.2.3 Seek to protect the Suffolk population from road-widening or re-surfacing activities which may damage the population. (ACTION: DoT, Local Highways Authorities)

5.2.4 Consider notifying sites for the species as SSSI. (ACTION: EN)

5.3 Species management and protection

5.3.1 None proposed.

5.4 Advisory

5.4.1 Ensure relevant landowners, managers and conservation agencies are aware of the presence and importance of conserving this species and any appropriate methods for its management. (ACTION: EN)

5.5 Future research and monitoring

5.5.1 Promote the survey of all previously known sites to establish the change in distribution and status of this species. (ACTION: EN)

5.5.2 Encourage research into the ecological requirements of this species to underpin management advice. (ACTION: EN, JNCC)

5.5.3 Continue monitoring populations regularly at present known sites. (ACTION: EN)

5.5.4 Encourage research on the ecology and conservation of this species on an international level and use the information and expertise gained towards its conservation in the UK. (ACTION: EN, JNCC)

5.5.5 Pass information gathered during survey and monitoring of this species to JNCC or BRC so that it can be incorporated in national databases. (ACTION: EN)

5.5.6 Provide information annually to the World Conservation Monitoring Centre on the UK status of the species to contribute to maintenance of an up-to-date global Red Data List. (ACTION: JNCC)

5.6 Communications and publicity

5.6.1 Discourage the collection of this fungi in restricted areas where it occurs. (ACTION: EN)

DEVIL'S BOLETE (BOLETUS SATANAS)

1. CURRENT STATUS

1.1 This is a distinctive, brightly coloured fungus which is found only in association with beech trees. Populations appear to be declining rapidly throughout its range in Europe, and southern England may now hold the largest viable population in Europe.

1.2 The distribution of Devil's bolete in the UK is not fully known but it appears to be confined to two beech woods on chalk on the South Downs, where it has been recorded with decreasing frequency in recent years. However, sightings are dependent on the production of the distinctive fruiting body and the species may still persist in other sites. Records have also decreased since the 1987 hurricane, which destroyed many trees.

1.3 The species is listed as vulnerable on the GB Red List.

2. CURRENT FACTORS CAUSING LOSS OR DECLINE

2.1 Loss of suitable beech trees in current range.

2.2 Trampling.

2.3 Acid deposition affecting beech hosts.

2.4 Botanical collection.

3. CURRENT ACTION

3.1 None known.

4. ACTION PLAN OBJECTIVES AND TARGETS

4.1 Maintain known populations.

4.2 Undertake a survey of suitable and former sites to assess the current status of this species.

5. Proposed action with lead agencies

5.1 Policy and legislation

5.1.1 Consider adding this species to Schedule 8 of the WCA 1981. (ACTION: DoE, EN, JNCC)

5.2 Site safeguard and management

5.2.1 Seek to avoid the effects of trampling, using public access restrictions in the immediate vicinity of this species where necessary. (ACTION: EN)

5.2.2 Promote suitable woodland management to maintain optimum conditions for this species in the current range and the vicinity. (ACTION: EN, FA, FE)

5.3 Species management and protection

5.3.1 No specific action proposed.

5.4 Advisory

5.4.1 Ensure landowners, local naturalists, wildlife trusts, and relevant authorities are aware of the presence and importance of conserving this species, and appropriate methods of management for its conservation. (ACTION: EN, FA)

5.4.2 Ensure the relevant societies and organisations are aware of the ecological implications of collecting this species. (ACTION: EN)

5.5 Future research and monitoring

5.5.1 Determine the current distribution of this species through a survey of all known and suitable sites. (ACTION: EN)

5.5.2 Promote research into the ecological requirements of this species to underpin management advice. (ACTION: EN, JNCC)

5.5.3 Encourage monitoring of former sites to observe for fruiting bodies and the persistence of the species. (ACTION: EN)

5.5.4 Pass information gathered during survey and monitoring of this species to JNCC or BRC so that it can be incorporated in national databases. (ACTION: EN)

5.5.5 Provide information annually to the World Conservation Monitoring Centre on the UK status of the species to contribute to maintenance of an up-to-date global Red Data List. (ACTION: JNCC)

5.6 Communications and publicity

5.6.1 Ensure local botanists and societies are aware of the impact and dangers of collecting this species. (ACTION: EN)

5.6.2 Consider the species for inclusion in a UK Red Data Book for fungi. (ACTION: JNCC)

NAIL FUNGUS (*PORONIA PUNCTATA*)

I. CURRENT STATUS

1.1 Nail fungus is possibly the rarest fungus in Europe. It occurs in the dung of horses and ponies which have fed on unimproved pasture or hay. Formerly widespread in the UK, it is now confined to the New Forest, and is otherwise found only in a few places in south-east Europe.

1.2 The fungus is listed on the GB Red List as endangered and in the IUCN/WCMC RDL as indeterminate.

2. CURRENT FACTORS CAUSING LOSS OR DECLINE

2.1 Changes in agricultural practices, particularly the decline in use of horses and the loss of unimproved grasslands (particularly hay meadows)

3. CURRENT ACTION

3.1 None known.

4. ACTION PLAN OBJECTIVES AND TARGETS

4.1 Survey to confirm the status of the species in the UK.

4.2 Maintain the population at viable levels in the New Forest.

4.3 If feasible, restore to ten former sites by 2004.

4.4 Investigate ecological requirements to aid more effective conservation management.

5. PROPOSED ACTION WITH LEAD AGENCIES

5.1 Policy and legislation

5.1.1 No action proposed.

5.2 Site safeguard and management

5.2.1 Encourage positive management for this species at remaining sites, especially the traditional practice of pony grazing in the New Forest and the maintenance of improved grassland, particularly hay meadows. (ACTION: EN, FE)

5.2.2 Seek to ensure the needs of this species are taken into account for any SSSI management plan where it occurs. (ACTION: EN)

5.3 Species management and protection

5.3.1 If feasible, restore to ten former sites by 2004. (ACTION: EN)

5.4 Advisory

5.4.1 Ensure landowners and managers of re-discovered sites are aware of the presence and importance of this species, and appropriate methods of habitat management for its conservation. (ACTION: EN)

5.5 Future research and monitoring

5.5.1 Carry out a survey in the New Forest to establish current status of this species. (ACTION: EN)

5.5.2 Consider research into the ecological requirements of this species to assess whether it is a suitable candidate for re-introduction or translocation. (ACTION: EN)

5.5.3 Promote research on the effects of veterinary products used for horses on the ecology of this species. (ACTION: EN, JNCC)

5.5.4 Pass information gathered during survey and monitoring of this species to JNCC or BRC so that it can be incorporated in national databases. (ACTION: EN)

5.5.5 Provide information annually to the World Conservation Monitoring Centre on the UK status of the species to contribute to maintenance of an up-to-date global Red Data List. (ACTION: JNCC)

5.6 Communications and publicity

5.6.1 No action proposed.

TULOSTOMA NIVEUM (A GASTEROMYCETE FUNGUS)

I. CURRENT STATUS

I.I This fungus occurs in very specific habitat conditions on clumps of moss on limestone boulders. It is known only from one site in Finland, seven sites in Sweden and a single colony in Scotland, where it grows on large boulders in limestone scree under humid conditions created by a nearby waterfall. This site has been monitored closely for the past five years and, in 1994, the population increased substantially above that recorded for previous years. A survey of suitable sites in the area has been carried out, but no additional sites have been found.

I.2 The species is listed as critically endangered on the GB Red List and vulnerable on the IUCN/WCMC RDL.

2. CURRENT FACTORS CAUSING LOSS OR DECLINE

2.1 A major road improvement scheme could potentially affect peripheral parts of the population.

3. CURRENT ACTION

3.1 The population is monitored regularly to identify changes.

3.2 The species will be studied as part of SNH's Action Plans for Lower Plants project.

3.3 The only known site for this species is protected within an NNR.

4. ACTION PLAN OBJECTIVES AND TARGETS

4.1 Safeguard only known population.

4.2 Establish true status of this species, both in Britain and Europe.

4.3 Continue to monitor the population regularly to assess population size, fluctuations and to identify any potential threats.

5. PROPOSED ACTIONS WITH LEAD AGENCIES

5.1 Policy and legislation

5.1.1 Attempt to ensure that local development or changes in land-use do not adversely affect the host plants. (ACTION: SNH, SOAEFD)

5.2 Site safeguard and management

5.2.1 Attempt to ensure that any road improvements do not impinge upon the site. (ACTION: SOAEFD, LA, SNH)

5.2.2 Ensure that the NNR management plan takes into account the requirements of this species. (ACTION: SNH)

5.3 Species management and protection

5.3.1 If found to be threatened in Europe, review the need for international protection. (ACTION: JNCC, SOAEFD)

5.4 Advisory

5.4.1 No action proposed.

5.5 Future research and monitoring

5.5.1 Continue to survey other suitable habitats for this species. (ACTION: SNH)

5.5.2 Maintain annual monitoring of this site to identify any significant changes and potential threats to the species. (ACTION: SNH)

5.5.3 Pass information gathered during survey and monitoring of this species to JNCC or BRC so that it can be incorporated in national databases. (ACTION: SNH)

5.5.4 Provide information annually to the World Conservation Monitoring Centre on the UK status of the species to contribute to maintenance of an up-to-date global Red Data List. (ACTION: JNCC)

5.6 Communications and publicity

5.6.1 Consider species for addition to a Red Data Book on fungi. (ACTION: JNCC)

LICHENS

STARRY BRECK-LICHEN (*BUELLIA ASTERELLA*)

I. CURRENT STATUS

I.I The starry breck-lichen grows in turf which is calcareous, sandy, lichen- dominated and grazed by rabbits. It is found in the UK, Germany, France, Norway, and Switzerland. In the UK, it is restricted to one site in the Brecklands of Suffolk, where only a few individuals remain.

I.2 The species is listed as critically endangered on the GB Red List, and is protected under Schedule 8 of the WCA.

2. CURRENT FACTORS CAUSING LOSS OR DECLINE

2.1 Threats to this species are not fully understood, but are thought to include lack of rabbit grazing, encroachment of scrub and soil acidification from conifer seedlings on nearby plantations. Spray drift and nitrogen deposition may also pose a threat.

3. CURRENT ACTION

3.1 This species is the subject of an EN Pre-recovery Programme project investigating the success of transplanting the lichen between Breckland sites.

4. ACTION PLAN, OBJECTIVES AND TARGETS

4.1 Maintain and protect the population at its current site.

4.2 If feasible, re-introduce to four formerly occupied sites by 2005.

5. PROPOSED ACTION WITH LEAD AGENCIES

5.1 Policy and legislation

5.1.1 Continue to encourage the uptake of ESA agreements in the Brecklands which promote the use of grazing and trampling, and seek to prevent the establishment of seedlings, and seek to enhance these further through more closely tailoring these to individual cases. (ACTION: MAFF, EN)

5.2 Site safeguard and management

5.2.1 Encourage habitat management techniques to control coarse vegetation, encroachment by scrub and conifer seedlings and the maintenance of lichen-dominated communities. (ACTION: EN)

5.2.2 Consider notifying the site as an SSSI. (ACTION: EN)

5.3 Species management and protection

5.3.1 Following feasibility assessment and identification of suitable sites, seek to re-introduce populations to five sites within the former range of this species. (ACTION: EN)

5.4 Advisory

5.4.1 Ensure relevant local landowners, naturalists, Wildlife Trusts and LAs are aware of the presence, legal status and importance of conserving of this species. (ACTION: EN)

5.4.2 Provide advice to land managers on appropriate methods of management for this species. (ACTION: EN)

5.5 Future research and monitoring

5.5.1 Survey potential present and former sites to ascertain their suitability for re-introduction. (ACTION: EN)

5.5.2 If suitable habitat remains, undertake research to identify the most appropriate methods and carry out re-introductions of the species to five suitable, unoccupied sites. (ACTION: EN, JNCC)

5.5.3 Continue to monitor all extant sites on a regular basis. (ACTION: EN)

5.5.4 Encourage research into the ecological requirements of this species at other European sites and use the information gained to enhance the opportunities for the survival of the species in the UK. (ACTION: EN, JNCC)

5.5.5 Pass information gathered during survey and monitoring of this species to JNCC or BRC so that it can be incorporated in national databases. (ACTION: EN)

5.5.6 Provide information annually to the World Conservation Monitoring Centre on the UK status of the species to contribute to maintenance of an up-to-date global Red Data List. (ACTION: JNCC)

5.6 Communications and publicity

5.6.1 None proposed.

ORANGE-FRUITED ELM-LICHEN (*CALOPLACA LUTEOALBA*)

I. CURRENT STATUS

I.I Orange-fruited elm-lichen used to be relatively widespread in the UK, with a distributional bias towards eastern, lowland Britain. However, it has suffered a severe decline in the last century and is now largely confined to the dry bark of mature elm trees in areas of parkland, old pasture or roadside locations with less than 75 mm of rainfall per annum. It may occasionally also occur on other tree species in dry, well-lit situations and on soft calcareous rocks. The decline was attributed initially to agricultural intensification but was compounded in the 1960s by the loss of the host plant through Dutch Elm disease.

I.2 Orange-fruited elm-lichen is found mainly in western Europe where it has undergone a decline and now appears to be extinct in the Netherlands, Denmark and northern Germany. It has also been reported from North America.

I.3 This species is listed as vulnerable on the GB Red List and is protected under Schedule 8 of the WCA 1981.

2. CURRENT FACTORS CAUSING LOSS OR DECLINE

2.1 Felling of host trees.

2.2 Loss of habitat due to Dutch elm disease.

2.3 Pollution from intensive agricultural practices and sulphur dioxide emissions.

3. CURRENT ACTION

3.1 Scottish sites for this species are being surveyed as part of the SNH lower plants project.

4. ACTION PLAN OBJECTIVES AND TARGETS

4.1 Establish current status and distribution of the species.

4.2 Maintain all known populations.

4.3 Restore five populations to former sites by 2005.

5. PROPOSED ACTION WITH LEAD AGENCIES

5.1 Policy and legislation

5.1.1 None proposed.

5.2 Site safeguard and management

5.2.1 Seek to establish favourable management for all sites occupied by this species, ensuring all SSSI management agreements take into account its requirements. (ACTION: CCW, EN, SNH)

5.2.2 Consider the protection of all key sites for this species through SSSI notification where this is necessary to secure appropriate management. (ACTION: CCW)

5.2.3 Develop a scheme to restore disease-resistant elms to their area of former distribution. (ACTION: FA, MAFF, SOAEFD, WOAD)

5.3 Species management and protection

5.3.1 Ensure that, wherever possible, host trees are not felled. (ACTION: CCW, EN, SNH)

5.3.2 Once suitable methods have been determined and sites identified, seek to restore five populations to former sites. (ACTION: CCW, EN, JNCC, SNH)

5.3.3 Attempt to provide mechanisms to reduce the impact of agrochemicals on surviving populations. (ACTION: CCW, EN, JNCC, SNH)

5.4 Advisory

5.4.1 Ensure that local landowners, managers, naturalists and Wildlife Trusts are aware of the presence and importance of conserving this species, its legal protection and suitable methods of management for its conservation. (ACTION: CCW, EN, SNH)

5.5 Future research and monitoring

5.5.1 Promote a survey of all known and potential sites to determine the current distribution of the species. (ACTION: CCW, EN, JNCC, SNH)

5.5.2 Promote research into the ecological requirements of this species, including the suitability of host trees other than elm as a substrate for this lichen, and determine the most suitable methods for re-introduction or translocation. (ACTION: CCW, EN, JNCC, SNH)

5.5.3 Investigate potentially harmful effects of sulphur dioxide pollution and agricultural chemical sprays on this species and its host. (ACTION: CCW, EN, JNCC, SNH)

5.5.4 Encourage research on the ecology and conservation of this species on an international level and use the knowledge and expertise gained towards its conservation within the UK. (ACTION: CCW, EN, JNCC, SNH)

5.5.5 Establish periodic monitoring of sites to assess population size and identify potential threats. (ACTION: CCW, EN, JNCC, SNH)

5.5.6 Subject to confidentiality and data ownership, pass information gathered during survey and monitoring of this species to JNCC or BRC so that it can be incorporated in national databases. (ACTION: CCW, EN, SNH)

5.5.7 Provide information annually to the World Conservation Monitoring Centre on the UK status of the species to contribute to maintenance of an up-to-date global Red Data List. (ACTION: JNCC)

5.6 Communications and publicity

5.6.1 None proposed.

RIVER JELLY LICHEN (*COLLEMA DICHOTOMUM*)

1. CURRENT STATUS

1.1 This aquatic lichen grows on submerged rocks in partial shade in fast-flowing intermediate and upland streams. It is rare in the UK and has been declining since 1960, and is now known only from eleven 10 km squares in mid-Wales, northern England, Scotland and Northern Ireland. Its distribution also extends into northern Europe and Russia.

1.2 It is listed as vulnerable on both the IUCN/WCMC and GB Red Lists, and is protected under Schedule 8 of the WCA 1981.

2. CURRENT FACTORS CAUSING LOSS OR DECLINE

2.1 Eutrophication of streams leading to the species being replaced by algae.

2.2 Increased silt loads in rivers and streams.

2.3 Water acidification.

2.4 Reduced water levels caused by water abstraction, for example from small-scale hydroelectric schemes.

3. CURRENT ACTION

3.1 Survey work has been carried out in Snowdonia, as a result of impact assessment studies related to proposals for small-scale hydroelectric developments. No sites were found as a result of this survey.

3.2 All Scottish sites for this species were surveyed in 1994 as part of SNH's lower plant conservation project.

4. ACTION PLAN OBJECTIVES AND TARGETS

4.1 Establish the current status of the species in the UK.

4.2 Safeguard known populations.

4.3 Undertake research to ensure efficient conservation management.

4.4 If feasible, re-establish populations at five former sites by 2005.

5. PROPOSED ACTIONS WITH LEAD AGENCIES

5.1 Policy and legislation

5.1.1 Seek to eliminate the risk of water pollution, for example through the provision of advice on farm waste management where this species occurs. (ACTION: MAFF, NRA, RPBs, SOAEFD WOAD)

5.1.2 Seek to include river catchments supporting this species within existing and any new ESA designations. (ACTION: DANI, MAFF, SOAEFD, WOAD)

5.2 Site safeguard and management

5.2.1 Consider notifying key sites for this species as SSSIs/ASSIs where this is necessary to secure appropriate management. (ACTION: CCW, DoE(NI))

5.2.2 Ensure river catchment management plans adequately reflect the water quality and quantity requirements for the river jelly lichen. (ACTION: LAs, NRA, RPBs, SEPA)

5.2.3 Ensure careful woodland management in riparian areas compatible with FA's Forest and Water Guidelines to remove additional problems caused by removal of shade along rivers. (ACTION: FA, FE)

5.3 Species management and protection

5.3.1 Following feasibility studies and identification of appropriate sites, seek to restore five populations to unoccupied sites when suitable conditions have been provided. (ACTION: CCW, DoE(NI), EN, JNCC, NRA, RPBs, SNH)

5.4 Advisory

5.4.1 Ensure land managers adjacent to extant sites, local planning authorities and Water Management Authorities are aware of the presence, legal status and threats to the species and its community, and the importance of its conservation. (ACTION: CCW, DoE(NI), EN, FA, NRA, RPBs, SNH)

5.5 Future research and monitoring

5.5.1 Undertake survey of potential sites to establish the distribution of the species. (ACTION: CCW, DoE(NI), EN, SNH)

5.5.2 Encourage research into the ecological requirements of the species to determine the optimum conditions for growth and the feasibility of re-introduction. (ACTION: CCW, DoE(NI), EN, SNH)

5.5.3 Investigate further the effects of eutrophication and acidification of streams on this species and seek to reverse the impacts. (ACTION: NRA, RPBs, SEPA)

5.5.4 Establish a protocol for regular monitoring of this species and the water quality in the vicinity of known sites. (ACTION: CCW, DoE(NI), EN, JNCC, NRA, RPBs, SNH)

5.5.5 Encourage research on the ecology and conservation of this species on an international level and use the information and expertise gained towards its conservation in the UK. (ACTION: CCW, EN, JNCC, SNH)

5.5.6 Pass information gathered during survey and monitoring of this species to JNCC or BRC so that it can be incorporated in national databases. (ACTION: CCW, DoE(NI), EN, SNH)

5.5.7 Provide information annually to the World Conservation Monitoring Centre on the UK status of the species to contribute to maintenance of an up-to-date global Red Data List. (ACTION: JNCC)

5.6 Communications and publicity

5.6.1 Use the river jelly lichen to highlight threats from eutrophication to the ecology of streams. (ACTION: CCW, DoE(NI), EN, JNCC, SNH)

ELM'S GYALECTA (*GYALECTA ULMI*)

1. CURRENT STATUS

1.1 Formerly more widespread in Britain, this species is now confined to six sites in Scotland and one in England (Northumberland), all of which are on calcareous rock outcrops. It was formerly also known as an epiphyte on elms. The European distribution of the species is widespread but scattered, including Iceland and Caucasia.

1.2 Elm's gyalecta is listed as endangered on the GB Red List, and is protected under Schedule 8 of the WCA 1981.

2. CURRENT FACTORS CAUSING LOSS OR DECLINE

2.1 Loss of habitat due to Dutch Elm disease.

2.2 Agricultural spray drift.

2.3 Collection by botanists.

3. CURRENT ACTION

3.1 The six Scottish sites have been surveyed by SNH to establish the status of the population.

3.2 All except one of the sites are on SSSIs.

4. ACTION PLAN OBJECTIVES AND TARGETS

4.1 Establish the current distribution of this species, and verify population status at the one remaining site in England.

4.2 Safeguard the remaining populations.

4.3 Restore the species to five former sites by 2004.

4.4 Promote ecological research to ascertain the reasons for the restricted distribution of the species.

5. PROPOSED ACTION WITH LEAD AGENCIES

5.1 Policy and legislation

5.1.1 Encourage low intensity farming practices on land adjacent to this species to minimise agricultural spray drift. (ACTION: EN, MAFF, SNH, SOAEFD)

5.2 Site safeguard and management

5.2.1 Seek to ensure that management agreements for SSSIs take into account the ecological requirements of this species, where appropriate. (ACTION: EN, SNH)

5.3 Species management and protection

5.3.1 Following further research on the suitability of elm restoration to the conservation of this species, consider planting additional disease-resistant elm trees in vicinity of current and former colonies to aid regeneration and expansion of populations. (ACTION: EN, FA, SNH)

5.3.2 Discourage illegal collecting of this species and seek to ensure offenders are prosecuted. (ACTION: DoE, EN, Police Forces, Fiscal/CPS offices, SNH)

5.4 Advisory

5.4.1 Ensure landowners and managers are aware of the presence, legal status and importance of conserving this species, and of appropriate methods of habitat management. (ACTION: EN, SNH)

5.4.2 Ensure local botanical groups and other interested organisations are aware of the ecological and legal implications of collecting this species. (ACTION: EN, SNH)

5.5 Future research and monitoring

5.5.1 Undertake a survey of all existing and potential sites for this species to verify its current status and to identify suitable sites for translocation. (ACTION: EN, SNH)

5.5.2 Encourage studies on the ecology of this species to identify best methods, and the suitability of introduced elms, for translocation or re-introduction. (ACTION: EN, JNCC, SNH)

5.5.3 Establish regular monitoring of the extant populations and identify potential threats to the species. (ACTION: EN, SNH)

5.5.4 Encourage research on the ecology and distribution of this species at an international level and use the information and expertise gained towards its conservation in the UK. (ACTION: JNCC)

5.5.5 Pass information gathered during survey and monitoring of this species to JNCC or BRC so that it can be incorporated in national databases. (ACTION: EN, SNH)

5.5.6 Provide information annually to the World Conservation Monitoring Centre on the UK status of the species to contribute to maintenance of an up-to-date global Red Data List. (ACTION: JNCC)

5.6 Communications and publicity

5.6.1 No publicity on the locations of this species is advised because of the risk from botanical collection.

PSEUDOCYPHELLARIA AURATA (A LICHEN)

I. CURRENT STATUS

I.I This lichen occurs on trees, rocks and heather stems. It formerly occurred in the UK in southern and south-west England and also on the Channel Islands, but was last recorded from the south-west on the Isles of Scilly in 1967. It is still known from Sark and from one site - the Blasket Islands, County Kerry - in Ireland. It is a strongly oceanic species which is at the northern end of its European range in the UK, and is widespread in tropical and temperate regions of the southern hemisphere.

I.2 It is listed on the GB Red List as critically endangered.

2. CURRENT FACTORS CAUSING LOSS OR DECLINE

2.1 Burning of heathland.

2.2 Trampling, nutrient enrichment and over-grazing by livestock.

2.3 Collection by botanists.

3. CURRENT ACTION

3.1 None known.

4. ACTION PLAN OBJECTIVES AND TARGETS

4.1 Confirm whether species is extinct on mainland Britain through survey of potential habitats.

4.2 Safeguard former sites from damage until status is clarified.

4.3 Consider protection for sites if re-discovered.

5. PROPOSED ACTION WITH LEAD AGENCIES

5.1 Policy and legislation

5.1.1 No action proposed.

5.2 Site safeguard and management

5.2.1 Seek to secure favourable management agreements in the vicinity of re-discovered sites, including discouraging the use of agricultural fertilisers where necessary. (ACTION: EN)

5.2.2 If re-discovered, protect species from burning and trampling, nutrient enrichment and over-grazing by livestock. (ACTION: EN)

5.3 Species management and protection

5.3.1 Investigate the feasibility and desirability of re-introducing the species to the UK if it is not re-discovered at any of its former sites. (ACTION: EN)

5.4 Advisory

5.4.1 Ensure landowners and planning authorities are notified of the presence and importance of conserving this species at any re-discovered sites, and on appropriate methods of habitat management for its conservation. (ACTION: EN)

5.4.2 Ensure the relevant societies are aware of the ecological implications of collecting this species. (ACTION: EN)

5.5 Future research and monitoring

5.5.1 Survey all former and current sites to establish whether it is still present in the UK. (ACTION: EN)

5.5.2 If re-discovered, consider research to understand the lichen's ecological requirements and identify any potential threats. (ACTION: EN, JNCC)

5.5.3 If re-discovered, monitor populations regularly to assess population and identify any potential threats to the species. (ACTION: EN)

5.5.4 Pass information gathered during survey and monitoring of this species to JNCC or BRC so that it can be incorporated in national databases. (ACTION: EN)

5.5.5 Provide information annually to the World Conservation Monitoring Centre on the UK status of the species to contribute to maintenance of an up-to-date global Red Data List. (ACTION: JNCC)

5.6 Communications and publicity

5.6.1 Consider publicity needs of the species if it is re-discovered. (ACTION: EN, JNCC)

PSEUDOCYPHELLARIA NORVEGICA (A LICHEN)

1. CURRENT STATUS

1.1 This lichen is found on sheltered tree trunks in ancient woodland, willow carr and old hazel stands, and occasionally on old heather bushes. It is now considered extinct in Wales and is known from only one site in England. The distribution is very localised in Scotland. Elsewhere it is found in south-west and north-west Ireland, south-west Norway, Madeira, the Azores and Chile.

2. CURRENT FACTORS CAUSING LOSS OR DECLINE

2.1 Loss of suitable habitat due to changes in management.

2.2 Air pollution leading to acid deposition.

2.3 Alterations to watercourses affecting willow carr habitats may be a threat at some sites.

3. CURRENT ACTION

3.1 SNH will be surveying for this species in 1995/97.

3.2 FE are being encouraged to manage their Ardnamurchan sites for this species.

4. ACTION PLAN OBJECTIVES AND TARGETS

4.1 Maintain populations at all known current sites.

4.2 If feasible, restore species to five former sites by 2004.

4.3 Investigate the ecological requirements of this species to aid more effective conservation management of the species and its community.

4.4 Clarify the status of the species in Europe.

5. PROPOSED ACTION WITH LEAD AGENCIES

5.1 Policy and legislation

5.1.1 No action proposed.

5.2 Site safeguard and management

5.2.1 Consider notification of known sites for this species as SSSI/ASSI if this is necessary to secure appropriate management. (ACTION: DoE(NI))

5.2.2 Seek to secure favourable management for woodland supporting this species. (ACTION: DoE(NI), EN, FA, FE, SNH)

5.3 Species management and protection

5.3.1 Consider adding to Schedule 8 of the WCA 1981. (ACTION: DoE, DoE(NI), EN, JNCC, SNH, SOAEFD)

5.3.2 If feasible following survey and assessment, seek to restore species to five former sites by 2004. (ACTION: CCW, DoE(NI), EN, SNH)

5.3.3 Ensure that wherever possible in selected areas host trees are identified and protected to allow the expansion of existing populations. (ACTION: DoE(NI), EN, FA, FE, SNH)

5.3.4 Following further assessment of the impact of acid deposition on this species, seek to reduce acid emissions in the vicinity of known sites. (ACTION: DoE, DoE(NI), EN, SNH, SOAEFD)

5.3.5 If found to be threatened in Europe, review the need for international protection. (ACTION: DoE, JNCC, SOAEFD)

5.4 Advisory

5.4.1 Ensure landowner and managers are aware of the presence and locations of this species and the importance of its conservation, including the provision of advice on suitable methods of habitat management. (ACTION: DoE(NI), EN, SNH)

5.5 Future research and monitoring

5.5.1 Encourage research into the ecological requirements of this species to ensure appropriate management advice and assess the suitability of the species for re-introduction or translocation. (ACTION: DoE(NI), EN, SNH)

5.5.2 Encourage research into the impact of acid deposition on this species and seek to identify other potential threats to its survival. (ACTION: DoE(NI), EN, SNH)

5.5.3 Survey potential sites to assess the suitability of host trees and opportunities for expanding existing populations. (ACTION: DoE(NI), EN, FA, SNH)

5.5.4 Pass information gathered during survey and monitoring of this species to JNCC or BRC so that it can be incorporated in national databases. (ACTION: DoE(NI), EN, SNH)

5.5.5 Provide information annually to the World Conservation Monitoring Centre on the UK status of the species to contribute to maintenance of an up-to-date global Red Data List. (ACTION: JNCC)

5.6 Communications and publicity

5.6.1 No action proposed.

SCHISMATOMMA GRAPHIDIOIDES (A LICHEN)

1. CURRENT STATUS

1.1 This lichen is restricted to slightly nutrient-enriched bark on the trunks of beech, ash or oak trees in ancient parkland or open woodland. It is very rare in the UK and is now recorded from only five to ten sites in eastern Scotland and south-west England. Elsewhere it occurs across continental Europe, but is not found east of Germany or Italy.

1.1 It is listed as vulnerable in the GB Red List and rare in the IUCN global RDL.

2. CURRENT FACTORS CAUSING LOSS OR DECLINE

2.1 Felling of ancient trees in ancient woodland or parkland.

2.2 Pollution of parkland trees through agricultural intensification, e.g. from fertiliser dust and spray drift.

3. CURRENT ACTION

3.1 Scottish sites for this species will be surveyed in 1995-97 as part of SNH's Action Plans for Lower Plants project.

4. ACTION PLAN OBJECTIVES AND TARGETS

4.1 Safeguard populations at all known sites.

4.2 Confirm the current status and distribution of species in the UK and Europe.

4.3 If feasible, restore to five former sites by 2004.

4.4 Investigate the ecological requirements of this species to aid conservation management.

5. PROPOSED ACTION WITH LEAD AGENCIES

5.1 Policy and legislation

5.1.1 Continue development of a strategy for the protection of ancient woodland and parkland supporting this species throughout the UK, including the ameliorating the effects of agricultural spray drift and the importance of this habitat in an international context. (ACTION: DoE, FC, JNCC, SNH)

5.2 Site safeguard management

5.2.1 Attempt to secure positive management for known sites to ensure appropriate management for the species, including discouraging the use of agrochemical sprays on areas adjacent to sites where this is been proven to have adverse effect on host trees. (ACTION: EN, FA, SNH)

5.2.2 Ensure any management plans for ancient parklands and woodlands where this species occurs take into account the requirements of the species and its community. (ACTION: EN, FA, SNH)

5.3 Species management and protection

5.3.1 Consider the species for addition to Schedule 8 of the WCA 1981. (ACTION: DoE, EN, JNCC, SNH, SOAEFD)

5.3.2 If, after further survey and assessment, the species is found to be threatened in Europe, review the need for international protection. (ACTION: DoE, JNCC, SOAEFD)

5.3.3 Wherever possible, protect individual host trees at remaining and former sites with a view to providing sites for re-introduction/translocation. (ACTION: FA, EN, LAs, SNH)

5.3.4 Where feasible, seek to restore populations to five former sites by 2004. (ACTION: EN, SNH)

5.4 Advisory

5.4.1 Ensure landowners and managers are aware of the presence and importance of conserving this species and appropriate methods of habitat management for its conservation. (ACTION: EN, SNH)

5.5 Future research and monitoring

5.5.1 Encourage research into the ecological and habitat requirements of this species and its community, to underpin management advice, and assess its suitability for re-introduction or translocation. (ACTION: EN, JNCC, SNH)

5.5.2 Encourage further research to assess the impact of acid deposition and agrochemicals on the species and its host plants, to help understand its limited distribution, and identify other potential threats to its survival. (ACTION: EN, JNCC, SNH)

5.5.3 Encourage research on the ecology and conservation of this species on an international level, including the reasons for its decline, and use the information and expertise gained towards its conservation in the UK. (ACTION: EN, JNCC, SNH)

5.5.4 Pass information gathered during survey and monitoring of this species to JNCC or BRC so that it can be incorporated in national databases. (ACTION: EN, SNH)

5.5.5 Provide information annually to the World Conservation Monitoring Centre on the UK status of the species to contribute to maintenance of an up-to-date global Red Data List. (ACTION: JNCC)

5.6 Communications and publicity

5.6.1 No action proposed.

MOSSES

GREEN SHIELD-MOSS (*BUXBAUMIA VIRIDIS*)

I. CURRENT STATUS

1.1 Green shield-moss is a short-lived, ephemeral species which occurs on decaying conifer wood in sheltered and shaded situations. It grows as scattered individuals and occurs sparsely throughout most of Europe. It also occurs in south-west Asia, China and North America. In the UK, since 1950 it has been recorded from two sites in Scotland, but has only been recorded in one site recently.

1.2 This species is considered critically endangered on the GB Red List and vulnerable on the European Red Data List. It is protected under Schedule 8 of the WCA 1981 and is listed on Appendix I of the Bern Convention and Annex II of the EC Habitats Directive.

2. CURRENT FACTORS CAUSING LOSS OR DECLINE

2.1 The removal of dead wood.

2.2 Botanical collection.

3. CURRENT ACTION

3.1 SNH has recently surveyed the both the current and some former sites for this species under their lower plant conservation project. Monitoring is programmed for 1995.

3.2 The only known site is notified as a SSSI and is proposed as a SAC under the EC Habitats Directive.

4. ACTION PLAN OBJECTIVE AND TARGETS

4.1 Survey to confirm status of this species in the UK.

4.2 Maintain the population at the only remaining site, and any newly discovered sites, through the maintenance of suitable habitat conditions.

4.3 If found to have been lost, re-introduce to former site in Scotland if conditions remain suitable.

4.4 Promote further research into the ecological requirements of this species to underpin appropriate management advice.

5. PROPOSED ACTION WITH LEAD AGENCIES

5.1 Policy and legislation

5.1.1 None proposed.

5.2 Site safeguard and management

5.2.1 Ensure the needs of this species are taken into account in the management plan for the known site. (ACTION: FE, SNH)

5.2.2 Encourage the provision of suitable dead conifer wood in woodland management for areas containing this species. (ACTION: FE, SNH)

5.3 Species management and protection

5.3.1 Discourage illegal collecting of this species and seek to ensure offenders are prosecuted. (ACTION: JNCC, SNH, SOAEFD, Police Force)

5.4 Advisory

5.4.1 Ensure that land owners and the relevant authorities responsible for the extant, or newly located sites, are aware of the presence, legal status and importance of conserving this species. (ACTION: SNH)

5.4.2 Advise land owners and managers on methods of woodland management considered to be beneficial to this species, including the provision of deadwood habitats. (ACTION: FA, SNH)

5.5 Future research and monitoring

5.5.1 Assess the feasibility of *ex-situ* cultivation as a necessary precursor to any recovery attempts. (ACTION: SNH)

5.5.2 Survey former and potential sites for this species to determine whether suitable habitat exists for re-introduction or translocation programmes, and assess the feasibility of such programmes. (ACTION: SNH)

5.5.3 Promote research into the ecological requirements of this species to underpin management advice. (ACTION: SNH)

5.5.4 Promote research into this species on an international level and use the information and expertise gained towards conserving the species in the UK. (ACTION: JNCC, SNH)

5.5.5 Subject to confidentiality and data ownership, pass information gathered during survey and monitoring of this species to JNCC or BRC so that it can be incorporated in national databases. (ACTION: SNH)

5.5.6 Provide information annually to the World Conservation Monitoring Centre on the UK status of the species to contribute to maintenance of an up-to-date global Red Data List. (ACTION: JNCC)

5.6 Communications and publicity

5.6.1 The location of sites for this species should not be made public because of the risk from collection.

5.6.2 Ensure that the relevant societies are aware of the ecological and legal implications of collecting this species. (ACTION: JNCC, SNH)

DERBYSHIRE FEATHER-MOSS (*THAMNOBRYUM ANGUSTIFOLIUM*)

I. CURRENT STATUS

I.I Derbyshire feather-moss is endemic to the UK and is found at only one site on a seasonally-inundated, shaded limestone rock-face alongside a calcareous spring in Derbyshire.

I.2 The species is listed as critically endangered on the GB Red List and as endangered on the IUCN/WCMC global list. It is protected under Schedule 8 of the WCA 1981.

2. CURRENT FACTORS CAUSING LOSS OR DECLINE

2.1 Botanical collection.

2.2 Recreational activities, such as rock climbing and pot-holing.

3. CURRENT ACTION

3.1 This site is currently protected as an SSSI and a NNR.

3.2 The species and the water quality of the site are monitored regularly.

4. ACTION PLAN OBJECTIVES AND TARGETS

4.1 Safeguard at its only known site.

4.2 Safeguard at any other sites at which it is found.

4.3 Promote ecological research on this species to aid effective conservation management.

5. PROPOSED ACTIONS WITH LEAD AGENCIES

5.1 Policy and legislation

5.1.1 No action proposed.

5.2 Site safeguard and management

5.2.1 No action proposed.

5.3 Species management and protection

5.3.1 Discourage illegal collecting of this species and ensure offenders are prosecuted. (ACTION: EN, LA)

5.4 Advisory

5.4.1 Ensure visitors to the NNR are aware of the presence and vulnerability of the species. Encourage local climbers and caving societies to use alternative rock faces and cave entrances. (ACTION: EN)

5.4.2 Ensure the relevant societies are aware of the ecological and legal implications of collecting this species. (ACTION: EN)

5.5 Future research and monitoring

5.5.1 Investigate the ecological and habitat requirements of this species to help underpin management advice and identify potential threats to the survival of the population. (ACTION: EN)

5.5.2 Monitor extant population regularly and seek to identify any further, or undue, threats to this species. (ACTION: EN)

5.5.3 Survey similar habitats in the area to determine if the plant occurs elsewhere. (ACTION: EN)

5.5.4 Establish a number of *ex-situ* populations in culture. (ACTION: RBGs, EN)

5.5.5 Pass information gathered during survey and monitoring of this species to JNCC or BRC so that it can be incorporated in national databases. (ACTION: EN)

5.5.6 Provide information annually to the World Conservation Monitoring Centre on the UK status of the species to contribute to maintenance of an up-to-date global Red Data List. (ACTION: JNCC)

5.6 Communications and publicity

5.6.1 Use the presence and ecology of this species to highlight the importance of rock habitats for UK biodiversity and the threats posed by human activities. (ACTION: EN)

WEISSIA MULTICAPSULARIS (A MOSS)

1. CURRENT STATUS

1.1 This small, patch-forming, ephemeral moss grows on damp, non-calcareous muddy or sandy clay soils. It is found in a variety of situations from northern France and the UK, where it is now restricted to the south-west of England and south Wales. It has been recorded from eleven sites since 1950, mainly in Cornwall, but also in Devon, Gwent and Oxfordshire. In Cornwall it grows typically on banks and tracksides on sea cliffs and inland field banks, but has also been recorded from wayside banks, woodland rides, banks in old quarries and fallow fields.

1.2 The moss is listed as vulnerable on the GB Red List.

2. CURRENT FACTORS CAUSING LOSS OR DECLINE

2.1 Lack of periodic disturbance required to maintain open conditions and control competing vegetation.

3. CURRENT ACTION

3.1 None known.

4. ACTION PLAN OBJECTIVES AND TARGETS

4.1 Clarify the current distribution of this species in the UK.

4.2 Maintain populations at viable levels throughout its range.

4.3 Investigate the ecological requirements of this species to ensure appropriate conservation management.

5. PROPOSED ACTION WITH LEAD AGENCIES

5.1 Policy and legislation

5.1.1 No action proposed.

5.2 Site safeguard and management

5.2.1 Consider notification of key sites through SSSIs where this is necessary to achieve appropriate management. (ACTION: CCW)

5.2.2 Encourage positive management for this species on all sites, especially periodic disturbance to maintain open soils. (ACTION: CCW, EN, FA, LAs, MAFF)

5.3 Species management and protection

5.3.1 No action proposed.

5.4 Advisory

5.4.1 Ensure conservation bodies, landowners and managers are aware of the presence and importance of conserving this species, and appropriate methods of management. (ACTION: ADAS, CCW, EN, FA, LAs)

5.5 Future research and monitoring

5.5.1 Collate available information on occurrence at former and current sites to establish the status of this moss, and attempt to assess the most favourable localities for long-term survival in the UK. (ACTION: CCW, EN, JNCC)

5.5.2 Promote research into the ecological and habitat requirements of this species to underpin appropriate management advice and assess the suitability of the species for re-introduction or translocation. (ACTION: CCW, EN, JNCC)

5.5.3 Encourage research on the ecology and conservation of this species in northern France, to establish the current conservation status, and use the information and expertise gained towards its conservation in the UK. (ACTION: JNCC)

5.5.4 Pass information gathered during survey and monitoring of this species to JNCC or BRC so that it can be incorporated in national databases. (ACTION: CCW, EN)

5.5.5 Provide information annually to the World Conservation Monitoring Centre on the UK status of the species to contribute to maintenance of an up-to-date global Red Data List. (ACTION: JNCC)

5.6 Communications and publicity

5.6.1 No action proposed.

GLAUCOUS BEARD-MOSS (*DIDYMODON GLAUCUS* - FORMERLY *BARBULA GLAUCA*)

1. CURRENT STATUS

1.1 This moss grows in dry crevices on bare chalk and limestone faces. It occurs throughout Europe, from the UK to Romania and from Italy to Scandinavia, where it is now very rare. It has also been recorded in the Canary Islands. Always rare in the UK, this species is now confined to a single site in Wiltshire, where the largest colony covers approximately 266 cm². A few smaller colonies have been recorded nearby, within the same site.

1.2 The glaucous beard-moss is listed as critically endangered on the GB Red List and is protected under Schedule 8 of the WCA 1981.

2. CURRENT FACTORS CAUSING LOSS OR DECLINE

2.1 Lack of site management, especially over-shading by encroaching scrub.

2.2 Rubbish dumping.

3. CURRENT ACTION

3.1 EN have cleared scrub from the site, which is within a SSSI.

3.2 A monitoring programme has been established.

3.3 Specimens of the plant are currently held in culture at Cambridge University.

4. ACTION PLAN OBJECTIVES AND TARGETS

4.1 Safeguard populations at the remaining site.

4.2 Provide suitable habitat in adjacent areas including cliff exposure and scrub management to encourage the spread of this species.

4.3 Research the ecological requirements of this species to ensure appropriate conservation management and to determine the feasibility of re-introduction.

5. PROPOSED ACTION WITH LEAD AGENCIES

5.1 Policy and legislation

5.1.1 No action proposed.

5.2 Site safeguard and management

5.2.1 Continue to ensure SSSI management plan takes account of the requirements of this species, including scrub management to prevent over-shading and prohibiting rubbish dumping. (ACTION: EN)

5.3 Species management and protection

5.3.1 Discourage illegal collecting of the species and ensure offenders are prosecuted. (ACTION: EN, JNCC, DoE)

5.4 Advisory

5.4.1 Ensure local botanical groups and other interested organisations are aware of the legal and ecological implications of collecting this species. (ACTION: EN)

5.5 Future research and monitoring

5.5.1 Encourage research on the population ecology and habitat requirements of this species to establish the optimum conditions for growth, and the feasibility of re-introduction. (ACTION: EN, JNCC)

5.5.2 Encourage research on the ecology and conservation of this species on an international level, including the reasons for its decline, particularly in Scandinavia, and use the information and expertise gained towards its conservation in the UK. (ACTION:EN, JNCC)

5.5.3 Pass information gathered during survey and monitoring of this species to JNCC or BRC so that it can be incorporated in national databases. (ACTION: EN)

5.5.4 Provide information annually to the World Conservation Monitoring Centre on the UK status of the species to contribute to maintenance of an up-to-date global Red Data List. (ACTION: EN, JNCC, SNH)

5.6 Communications and publicity

5.6.1 Publicity for this species is not advised because of the risk from collection.

CORNISH PATH-MOSS (*DITRICHUM CORNUBICUM*)

I. CURRENT STATUS

I.I Cornish path moss is endemic to the UK and has been confined to only one site in Cornwall since 1963. It is a pioneer species characteristic of path and track edges and is unable to compete with larger plants. The moss occurs in three locations within a site covering approximately three square metres of old mine spoil, which is enriched with copper minerals.

I.2 The moss is listed as endangered by the IUCN and critically endangered by the GB Red List. It is protected under Schedule 8 of the WCA 1981.

2. CURRENT FACTORS CAUSING LOSS OR DECLINE

2.1 Encroachment by coarse vegetation.

2.2 Loss of habitat through re-surfacing and disturbance by vehicles.

2.3 Development of the site for tourism or housing.

3. CURRENT ACTION

3.1 The only remaining site is due for notification as a SSSI in 1995/96.

3.2 The plant has been taken into cultivation.

4. ACTION PLAN OBJECTIVES AND TARGETS

4.1 Maintain at the only remaining site in Cornwall.

4.2 Promote research into the ecological requirements of this species to ensure optimum conditions and to investigate the possibility of re-introduction.

4.3 If a suitable receptor site is found, introduce at least one population to Cornwall by 2004.

5. PROPOSED ACTION WITH LEAD AGENCIES

5.1 Policy and legislation

5.1.1 No action proposed.

5.2 Site safeguard and management

5.2.1 Ensure that development proposals in the vicinity of the remaining site takes into account the requirements of this species. (ACTION: EN, LA)

5.2.2 Ensure appropriate management of local habitat to encourage the colony to spread, including the control of vehicles in and around the extant site. (ACTION: EN, LA)

5.3 Species management and protection

5.3.1 Continue to keep stocks of this plant in cultivation, including collection and cultivation of material from the current site. (ACTION: EN, RBG Kew)

5.3.2 Following feasibility studies and identification of suitable sites, seek to restore at least one population to Cornwall by 2004. (ACTION: EN)

5.4 Advisory

5.4.1 Ensure landowner is aware of the presence, legal status and importance of conserving this species, and appropriate methods of habitat management for its conservation. (ACTION: EN, LA)

5.5 Future research and monitoring

5.5.1 Survey potential sites for this species, to establish its current status and to identify suitable sites for possible introduction or translocation. (ACTION: EN)

5.5.2 Promote research into the ecological requirements of this species to assess the potential for introduction or translocation. (ACTION: EN, JNCC)

5.5.3 Monitor extant population regularly and investigate potential threats to this species. (ACTION: EN)

5.5.4 Pass information gathered during survey and monitoring of this species to JNCC or BRC so that it can be incorporated in national databases. (ACTION: EN)

5.5.5 Provide information annually to the World Conservation Monitoring Centre on the UK status of the species to contribute to maintenance of an up-to-date global Red Data List. (ACTION: JNCC)

5.6 Communications and publicity

5.6.1 No action proposed.

SLENDER GREEN FEATHER-MOSS (*HAMATOCAULIS VERNICOSUS* FORMERLY *DREPANOCLADUS VERNICOSUS*)

1. CURRENT STATUS

1.1 Slender green feather-moss is reported to occur in base-rich lowland sedge fens and upland flushes. It has been recorded from 70 ten km squares throughout Britain since 1950, although recent research has indicated that much of the British material is in fact the closely-related, and recently described *Scorpidium cossonii* (microscopic examination of the stem is required to clarify the taxonomy). It has also been recorded in two 10 km squares in Northern Ireland.

1.2 This moss is a circumpolar species, widespread in the boreal zone but scarce in the arctic. It is currently listed as data deficient on the GB Red List pending further clarification of historical specimens. It is also listed on Annex II of the EC Habitats Directive; Appendix I of the Bern Convention, and is protected under Schedule 8 of the WCA 1981.

2. CURRENT FACTORS CAUSING LOSS OR DECLINE

2.1 Lowland habitat degradation due to lowering of the water table, water pollution and lack of active management leading to scrub and coarse vegetation encroachment. Afforestation and quarrying also pose a threat to former sites in Northern Ireland.

2.2 Upland flushes are less vulnerable but suitable habitat is often over-run by coarse vegetation if grazing pressure is reduced.

3. CURRENT ACTION

3.1 The taxonomic status of this species is currently being assessed by Royal Botanical Gardens, Edinburgh using available herbarium samples as part of SNH's lower plant conservation project.

3.2 Many sites currently receive statutory protection.

4. ACTION PLAN OBJECTIVES AND TARGETS

4.1 Clarify the current status of *D. vernicosus* in the UK. No further conservation action should be undertaken until this is done.

4.2 Retain current levels of protection for *D. vernicosus* until its status in clarified.

5. PROPOSED ACTIONS WITH LEAD AGENCIES

5.1 Policy and legislation

5.1.1 No action proposed.

5.2 Site safeguard and management

5.2.1 No action proposed.

5.3 Species management and protection

5.3.1 No action proposed.

5.4 Advisory

5.4.1 If species is found to be genuinely threatened, ensure land owners, land managers and local authorities are aware of its presence, legal status and importance of its conservation, and appropriate methods of habitat management. (ACTION: CCW, DoE(NI), EN, SNH)

5.5 Future research and monitoring

5.5.1 Herbarium specimens from all sites at which *D. vernicosus* has been recorded should be examined to determine the true status and distribution of the species (and *S. cossonii*). (ACTION: CCW, DoE(NI), EN, JNCC, SNH)

5.5.2 If following herbarium work, *D. vernicosus* is found to be genuinely rare, known sites should be surveyed to determine its current status. (ACTION: CCW, DoE(NI), EN, JNCC, SNH)

5.5.3 If species is found to be genuinely threatened, encourage research to determine the ecological requirements of the species to underpin appropriate advice on habitat management. (ACTION: CCW, DoE(NI), EN, JNCC, SNH)

5.5.4 Pass information gathered during survey and monitoring of this species to JNCC or BRC so that it can be incorporated in national databases. (CCW, DoE(NI), EN, SNH)

5.5.5 Provide information annually to the World Conservation Monitoring Centre on the UK status of the species to contribute to maintenance of an up-to-date global Red Data List. (ACTION: JNCC)

5.6 Communications and publicity

5.6.1 No publicity necessary at present. Statutory agency staff should be made aware of the necessity to clarify the status of the plant. (ACTION: CCW, DoE(NI), EN, JNCC, SNH)

LIVERWORTS

MARSH EARWORT (JAMESONIELLA UNDULIFOLIA)

1. CURRENT STATUS

1.1 This is a leafy liverwort of wet mineral-rich bog (*Sphagnum* mires). It was formerly widespread in the UK, with a number of sites in Cornwall, Gloucestershire, Cumbria and Argyll, but has recently been recorded from only one site in Cornwall and another in Argyll, both of which are small and vulnerable to destruction. However, it is easily confused with the superficially similar species *Odontoschisma sphagni* and may be under-recorded.

1.2 Marsh earwort appears to be rare worldwide, occurring in eastern Asia, North America and Greenland. It is listed as endangered in the GB Red List, and is protected under Schedule 8 of the WCA 1981.

2. CURRENT FACTORS CAUSING LOSS OR DECLINE

2.1 Changes in hydrological conditions, particularly through drainage and flooding for reservoirs.

2.2 Loss of mires due to afforestation.

2.3 Eutrophication of mire habitat, including pollution from agricultural run-off.

2.4 Poaching by livestock.

3. CURRENT ACTION

3.1 The Argyll site was surveyed to establish the population status in 1994 as part of SNH's lower plant conservation project.

3.2 The Cornish site is notified as a SSSI.

4. ACTION PLAN OBJECTIVES AND TARGETS

4.1 Maintain and protect populations at known sites.

4.2 Survey potential sites in Argyll to determine whether other populations exists in the Region.

4.3 Survey former and potential sites in Cornwall to assess the distributional status.

4.4 Undertake ecological research to underpin effective conservation management.

4.5 Restore to five former sites in the UK by 2004, if feasible.

5. PROPOSED ACTIONS WITH LEAD AGENCIES

5.1 Policy and legislation

5.1.1 No action proposed.

5.2 Site safeguard and management

5.2.1 Seek to protect the Argyll site by notification as SSSI, positive management agreement or NGO reserve acquisition, with the aim of maintaining an intact hummock-hollow structure in the *Sphagnum* mire. (ACTION: SNH)

5.2.2 Discourage adverse land-use change in the vicinity of this species. (ACTION: EN, SNH)

5.2.3 Encourage favourable management of mires and adjacent areas where marsh earwort has been recorded formerly to establish suitable conditions for re-generation or re-introduction of the species. (ACTION: EN, SNH)

5.3 Species management and protection

5.3.1 Following feasibility assessment and identification of suitable sites, seek to restore five populations to sites within the former range.

5.4 Advisory

5.4.1 Ensure land managers are aware of the presence, legal protection and importance of conserving this species, and provide information on appropriate management. (ACTION: EN, SNH, JNCC)

5.5 Future research and monitoring

5.5.1 Survey potential sites in Cornwall and Argyll (and if possible, sites on the west coast of Scotland) to identify if the earwort is present elsewhere. (ACTION: EN, JNCC, SNH)

5.5.2 Encourage ecological research on this species, including the dispersal and population dynamics, to help understand its limited distribution and identify threats to the survival of the plant. (ACTION: EN, JNCC, SNH)

5.5.3 Investigate the possibility of rehabilitating some of the sites from which the marsh earwort has disappeared (particularly in Cornwall), and translocating plants back to those sites. (ACTION: EN)

5.5.4 Encourage research on the ecology and conservation of this species on an international level and use the information and expertise gained towards its conservation in the UK. (ACTION: EN, JNCC, SNH)

5.5.5 Pass information gathered during survey and monitoring of this species to JNCC or BRC so that it can be incorporated in national databases. (ACTION: EN, SNH)

5.5.6 Provide information annually to the World Conservation Monitoring Centre on the UK status of the species to contribute to maintenance of an up-to-date global Red Data List. (ACTION: JNCC)

5.6 Communications and publicity

5.6.1 Use the decline in species to highlight the importance of mosses and liverworts and the importance of appropriate management of mire habitats for their survival. (ACTION: EN, SNH, JNCC)

NORFOLK FLAPWORT (*LOPHOZIA RUTHEANA* FORMERLY *LEIOCOLEA RUTHEANA*)

I. CURRENT STATUS

1.1 The Norfolk flapwort occurs in very wet, calcareous fens with other plants of the 'brown moss' community. Since 1950 it has been recorded from only five sites in the UK, four in Norfolk and one in Berkshire, but recently has only been recorded from one of the Norfolk sites, where the survival of the population is at risk due to a proposed road-widening scheme. A record also exists of a site in Cumbria, but this was not found during a cursory study in 1993. Elsewhere the species occurs in Europe, where populations are declining, and in North America.

1.2 The flapwort is listed as critically endangered on the GB Red List, and is protected under Schedule 8 of the WCA 1981.

2. CURRENT FACTORS CAUSING LOSS OR DECLINE

2.1 Lack of fen management allowing encroachment of coarse vegetation.

2.2 Pollution from agricultural run-off.

2.3 Road-widening at the Norfolk site.

3. CURRENT ACTION

3.1 The known extant site is an NNR which is managed with the aim of keeping the fen open and wet.

3.2 Recent survey work was not successful in finding the species at any former sites.

4. ACTION PLAN OBJECTIVES AND TARGETS

4.1 Maintain the existing population at its known site.

4.2 Survey to establish the current distribution of the species in the UK.

4.3 Re-establish the flapwort in at least five of its former sites by 2004.

5. PROPOSED ACTIONS WITH LEAD AGENCIES

5.1 Policy and legislation

5.1.1 Seek to ensure that conservation mechanisms such as SACs, ESAs, Countryside Stewardship take account of the conservation needs of the Norfolk flapwort, where appropriate. (ACTION: EN, MAFF)

5.1.2 Identify and encourage water quality standards and levels which will favour the species at any newly discovered sites. (ACTION: EN, NRA)

5.2 Site safeguard and management

5.2.1 Encourage favourable management on land adjacent to sites which have, or once contained, the flapwort with a view to providing suitable conditions for re-establishment or re-introduction. (ACTION: EN)

5.2.2 Ensure management of newly discovered sites take into account the requirements of this species. (ACTION: EN)

5.3 Species management and protection

5.3.1 None proposed.

5.4 Advisory

5.4.1 Ensure land managers are aware of the presence, legal protection and importance of conserving this species, and the importance of maintaining appropriate fen conditions. (ACTION: EN)

5.5 Future research and monitoring

5.5.1 Further survey the Cumbria site to establish the status of plant there. (ACTION: EN)

5.5.2 Promote further survey of all former sites in Norfolk to establish the status of the species in the area and to identify suitable sites for possible re-introductions. (ACTION: EN)

5.5.3 Encourage research on the ecology and conservation of this species on an international level and use the information and expertise gained towards its conservation in the UK. (ACTION: EN, JNCC)

5.5.4 Monitor extant population regularly and identify any threats to the species. (ACTION: EN)

5.5.5 Pass information gathered during survey and monitoring of this species to JNCC or BRC so that it can be incorporated in national databases. (ACTION: EN)

5.5.6 Provide information annually to the World Conservation Monitoring Centre on the UK status of the species to contribute to maintenance of an up-to-date global Red Data List. (ACTION: JNCC)

5.6 Communications and publicity

5.6.1 No action proposed.

ATLANTIC LEJEUNEA (*LEJEUNEA MANDONII*)

I. CURRENT STATUS

1.1 This liverwort is very rare and recorded only from the UK, Ireland, Spain, Portugal, the Canary Islands and Madeira. It occurs on shaded, basic, dry habitat on rocks, trees or rotting logs in humid Atlantic woods, ravines or sheltered coastal sites. Since 1950, it has been recorded in only six 10 km squares in the UK: three in Scotland and three in Cornwall. However, since 1970 it has been recorded in only one site in Cornwall and its current status in Scotland is unknown.

1.2 It is listed as endangered on the GB Red List and rare on the IUCN/WCMC global RDL.

2. CURRENT FACTORS CAUSING LOSS OR DECLINE

2.1 Decline in water quality in ravines.

2.2 Rhododendron colonisation in woods and ravines.

2.3 Recreational activities.

3. CURRENT ACTION

3.1 SNH will be surveying Scottish sites during 1995/97.

3.2 Plantlife are to produce a detailed Species Action Plan during 1995.

4. ACTION PLAN OBJECTIVES AND TARGETS

4.1 Survey to establish the status of the species in the UK.

4.2 Maintain at all known, new or re-discovered sites.

4.3 Promote research into the ecology of the species to ensure effective conservation management.

4.4 Review the need for SSSI notification.

5. PROPOSED ACTIONS WITH LEAD AGENCIES

5.1 Policy and legislation

5.1.1 Identify water quality standards which will favour this species and seek to ensure that these are taken into account in the management of occupied watercourses. (ACTION: EN, NRA, RPBs, SNH)

5.2 Site safeguard and management

5.2.1 Encourage landowners to carry out positive management of important habitats for this species, paying particular attention to the problems caused by public access. (ACTION: EN, FA, SNH)

5.2.2 Review the need for notification of sites as SSSI pending the completion of surveys designed to discover whether the species still occurs at other sites. (ACTION: EN, SNH)

5.2.3 Seek to remove *Rhododendron* from affected sites. (ACTION: EN, FA, FE, SNH)

5.3 Species management, protection and licensing

5.3.1 Consider addition of species to Schedule 8 of the WCA 1981. (ACTION: DoE, JNCC)

5.4 Advisory

5.4.1 Ensure land owners and managers at newly discovered, or re-discovered sites, are aware of the presence and international importance of conserving this species, and provide information on appropriate methods of management. (ACTION: EN, SNH)

5.5 Future research and monitoring

5.5.1 Survey all former and potential sites to determine the distribution of this species. (ACTION: EN, JNCC, SNH)

5.5.2 Encourage ecological research on this species, including population dynamics, to help identify the reasons for its disappearance from former sites. (ACTION: EN, JNCC, SNH)

5.5.3 Encourage research on the ecology and conservation of this species on an international level, particularly with others on the Atlantic fringe, and use the information and expertise gained towards its conservation in the UK. (ACTION: EN, JNCC, SNH)

5.5.4 Monitor population at extant site regularly and identify any threats to the species. (ACTION: EN)

5.5.5 Pass information gathered during survey and monitoring of this species to JNCC or BRC so that it can be incorporated in national databases. (ACTION: EN, SNH)

5.5.6 Provide information annually to the World Conservation Monitoring Centre on the UK status of the species to contribute to maintenance of an up-to-date global Red Data List. (ACTION: JNCC)

5.6 Communications and publicity

5.6.1 Raise awareness among landowners along the Atlantic fringe of the uniqueness of Atlantic bryophyte flora and the need for its protection. (ACTION: CCW, EN, FA, SNH)

WESTERN RUSTWORT (*MARSUPELLA PROFUNDA*)

1. CURRENT STATUS

1.1 Formerly recorded from three sites in Cornwall, this small, rare liverwort is now known to be present at only one site, where it grows on crumbling clay and mica-rich granite in disused china clay workings. It is otherwise known from Portugal, the Canaries, Azores and Madeira, but is rare throughout its range.

1.2 It is also listed as critically endangered in the GB Red List and is protected under Schedule 8 of the WCA 1981. It is also listed on Appendix I of the Bern Convention and Annex II of the EC Habitats Directive.

2. CURRENT FACTORS CAUSING LOSS OR DECLINE

2.1 Overgrowth of coarse vegetation.

2.2 Overgrazing leading to mechanical damage (abrasion).

2.3 Botanical collection.

3. CURRENT ACTION

3.1 All three Cornish sites where this plant has been recorded were surveyed in 1993.

3.2 The extant site has been proposed as an SAC under the EC Habitats Directive.

4. ACTION PLAN OBJECTIVES AND TARGETS

4.1 Safeguard at the only known extant site in Cornwall.

4.2 Survey other potentially suitable sites in Cornwall and maintain populations if found.

4.3 Promote research into the ecological and habitat requirements of this species to ensure effective conservation management.

4.4 Restore to at least one former Cornish site, if feasible, by 2004, if the species is not rediscovered at other sites after survey.

5. PROPOSED ACTION WITH LEAD AGENCIES

5.1 Policy and legislation

5.1.1 No action proposed.

5.2 Site safeguard and management

5.2.1 Encourage positive habitat management for this species where it occurs. (ACTION: EN)

5.3 Species management and protection

5.3.1 Discourage illegal collecting of this species and ensure offenders are prosecuted. (ACTION: EN, LA)

5.3.2 Following feasibility studies and identification of suitable sites, seek to restore at least one population to Cornwall by 2004. (ACTION: EN)

5.4 Advisory

5.4.1 Ensure landowners and managers are aware of the presence and international importance of conserving this plant, and appropriate methods of habitat management for its conservation. (ACTION: EN)

5.4.2 Ensure local botanical groups and other interested organisations are aware of the legal and ecological implications of collecting this species. (ACTION: EN)

5.5 Future research and monitoring

5.5.1 Undertake further survey work to confirm the current status of this species in the UK. (ACTION: EN)

5.5.2 Promote research on this species, including population size and the impact of vegetation management, and identify whether it is a suitable candidate for re-introduction or translocation. (ACTION; EN)

5.5.3 Maintain and study a small amount of this plant *ex-situ* within a botanical gardens or institute with expertise in bryophtye culture. (ACTION: EN)

5.5.4 Monitor extant population regularly and seek to identify threats to the species. (ACTION: EN)

5.5.5 Pass information gathered during survey and monitoring of this species to JNCC or BRC so that it can be incorporated in national databases. (ACTION: EN)

5.5.6 Provide information annually to the World Conservation Monitoring Centre on the UK status of the species to contribute to maintenance of an up-to-date global Red Data List. (ACTION: JNCC)

5.6 Communications and publicity

5.6.1 Publicity for this species is not advised because of its vulnerability to botanical collection.

PETALWORT (PETALOPHYLLUM RALFSII)

1. CURRENT STATUS

1.1 Petalwort is predominantly found on damp calcareous dune slacks and can vary in abundance from year to year, probably depending on weather conditions. It may disappear from view in the summer, surviving as tubers underground. It is widely but sparsely distributed in the UK, Mediterranean countries, Portugal, Ireland and North America but is restricted to nineteen sites in Britain, in south-west England, Merseyside, Northumberland, Ross and Cromarty, and Wales where it is known to have large populations in Anglesey. It is also recorded from Northern Ireland.

1.3 Petalwort is listed on Appendix I of the Bern Convention and Annex II of the Habitats Directive. It is also listed as vulnerable on the GB Red List and is protected under Schedule 8 of the WCA 1981.

2. CURRENT FACTORS CAUSING LOSS OR DECLINE

2.1 Loss of habitat due to development, dune stabilisation and natural succession.

2.2 Drainage.

2.3 Recreation.

2.4 Construction of golf courses.

2.5 Botanical collection.

3. CURRENT ACTION

3.1 SNH surveyed the Scottish site as part of their lower plant conservation project, and CCW have assessed a number of populations in a number of Welsh dune systems.

3.2 Many populations lie within SSSIs and some are managed as NNRs. One site in NI is an ASSI.

3.3 Six sites have been proposed as SACs under the EC Habitats Directive.

4. ACTION PLAN OBJECTIVES AND TARGETS

4.1 Maintain populations throughout its UK range.

4.2 Assess the viability of translocation.

4.3 Seek to protect all remaining sites from further habitat deterioration and review SSSI coverage.

4.4 Investigate the ecological requirements of this species to aid more effective conservation management.

5. PROPOSED ACTION WITH LEAD AGENCIES

5.1 Policy and legislation

5.1.1 Seek to ensure that local planning policies take into account the requirements of this species. (ACTION: CCW, DoE(NI), EN, LAs, SNH)

5.2 Site safeguard and management

5.2.1 Review the existing SSSI/ASSI coverage for this species, to determine whether it is sufficient. (ACTION: CCW, DoE(NI), EN, SNH)

5.2.2 Develop management plans for occupied dune slacks, including measures to maintain or, if necessary, increase wetness and prevent deterioration through human recreational pressure and development. (ACTION: CCW, DoE(NI), EN, IDBs, NRA, SNH)

5.2.3 Maintain moist partially colonised and open dune slack habitats. (ACTION: CCW, DoE(NI), EN, SNH)

5.3 Species management and protection

5.3.1 Discourage illegal collecting of this species and seek to ensure offenders are prosecuted. (ACTION: CCW, DoE(NI), EN, JNCC, SNH)

5.4 Advisory

5.4.1 Wherever practicable, ensure that landowners and managers are aware of the presence, legal status and importance of conserving this species and its habitat, and appropriate methods of management. (ACTION: CCW, DoE(NI), EN, SNH)

5.4.2 Ensure that relevant societies are aware of the legal and ecological implications of collecting this species. (ACTION: CCW, DoE(NI), EN, JNCC, SNH)

5.5 Future research and monitoring

5.5.1 Encourage research to assess changes in populations size in response to human recreational activities, and to identify any potential threats from other sources. (ACTION: CCW, DoE(NI), EN, SNH)

5.5.2 Consider research needs to better characterise reproductive biology and microhabitat requirements, and assess the suitability of the species for ex-situ cultivation and translocation, if appropriate. (ACTION: CCW, DoE(NI), EN, SNH)

5.5.3 Undertake a survey of all former and potential sites to determine the current distribution of this species in the UK. (ACTION: CCW, DoE(NI), EN, JNCC, SNH)

5.5.4 Encourage research on the ecology and distribution of this species on an international level, particularly the reasons for its decline throughout the current range, and use the information and expertise gained towards its conservation in the UK. (ACTION: CCW, DoE(NI), EN, JNCC, SNH)

5.5.5 Seek to monitor extant populations and identify further threats to this species. (ACTION: CCW, DoE(NI), EN, JNCC, SNH)

5.5.6 Pass information gathered during survey and monitoring of this species to JNCC or BRC so that it can be incorporated in national databases. (ACTION: CCW, DoE(NI), EN, SNH)

5.5.7 Provide information annually to the World Conservation Monitoring Centre on the UK status of the species to contribute to maintenance of an up-to-date global Red Data List. (ACTION: JNCC)

5.6 Communications and publicity

5.6.1 Use this species to highlight the importance of dune systems and the threats facing them. (ACTION: CCW, DoE(NI), EN, SNH, JNCC)

STONEWORTS

MOSSY STONEWORT (*CHARA MUSCOSA*)

1. CURRENT STATUS

1.1 This plant is a small, tufted stonewort which grows on sand in the shallow margins of water bodies. It is endemic to the Britain and Ireland but may be extinct in the latter. In Britain, it is known only from one site in Orkney and one in the Outer Hebrides, although it has not been recorded in these since the 1920s and 1930s respectively. A recent search at the Orkney site did not reveal the plant but the water quality was found to be deteriorating due to agricultural run-off from surrounding fields. As charophyte oospores are relatively long-lived, it is possible that the species may persist and would re-establish if the water quality was improved.

1.2 This species is listed as data deficient (possibly extinct) in the GB Red List and as globally threatened by WCMC/IUCN.

2. CURRENT FACTORS CAUSING LOSS OR DECLINE

2.1 The status of this species is not clear and the ecological requirements are not fully understood. However, factors impacting on the species are thought to include water pollution caused by fertiliser run-off from surrounding fields at the Orkney site, in addition to siltation and reed growth.

3. CURRENT ACTION

3.1 The Orkney site was surveyed in 1994 as part of SNH's lower plant conservation project; the Outer Hebrides site is scheduled for survey in 1995/97.

4. ACTION PLAN OBJECTIVES AND TARGETS

4.1 Survey to establish the status of the species in the UK.

4.2 Safeguard any populations which are discovered or re-discovered, possibly by way of notifying sites as SSSI.

4.3 Where feasible, re-establish populations at the former sites in Orkney and the Outer Hebrides, by 2005.

5. PROPOSED ACTIONS WITH LEAD AGENCIES

5.1 Policy and legislation

5.1.1 If re-discovered, consider species for addition to Schedule 8 of the WCA 1981 and Appendix I of the Bern Convention. (ACTION: DoE, JNCC, SNH)

5.2 Site safeguard and management

5.2.1 Seek to establish favourable management at known sites, taking into account the needs of the species to prevent silting or reed growth at margins. (ACTION: LAs, SEPA, SNH)

5.2.2 Encourage the improvement of water quality at the Orkney site to provide optimum conditions for recovery. (ACTION: Island Councils, SEPA)

5.2.3 Consider notifying sites for this species as SSSI. (ACTION: SNH)

5.3 Species management and protection

5.3.1 If charophyte oospores are available from former sites and, following feasibility investigations, seek to re-establish populations at the recent sites on Orkney and the Outer Hebrides once suitable conditions are established. (ACTION: SNH)

5.4 Advisory

5.4.1 Ensure landowners, managers and the relevant authorities are aware of the potential presence and importance of conserving this species. (ACTION: SNH)

5.5 Future research and monitoring

5.5.1 Undertake a thorough survey of all potential sites in the vicinity of former recorded sites to determine the status of the species in the UK. (ACTION: SNH)

5.5.2 If re-discovered, encourage ecological research to establish the requirements and appropriate methods of monitoring this species. (ACTION: JNCC, SNH)

5.5.3 If charophyte oospores are found at former sites, investigate the feasibility of extraction and *ex-situ* propagation prior to a re-establishment programme. (ACTION: SNH)

5.5.4 Pass information gathered during survey and monitoring of this species to JNCC or BRC so that it can be incorporated in national databases. (ACTION: SNH)

5.5.5 Provide information annually to the World Conservation Monitoring Centre on the UK status of the species to contribute to maintenance of an up-to-date global Red Data List. (ACTION: JNCC)

5.6 Communications and publicity

5.6.1 None proposed.

COSTED HABITAT ACTION PLANS

REEDBEDS
A COSTED HABITAT ACTION PLAN

1. CURRENT STATUS

Reedbeds are wetlands dominated by stands of the common reed *Phragmites australis*, wherein the water table is at or above ground level for most of the year. They tend to incorporate areas of open water and ditches, and small areas of wet grassland and carr woodland may be associated with them. There are about 5000 ha of reedbeds in the UK, but of the 900 or so sites contributing to this total, only about 50 are greater than 20 ha, and these make a large contribution to the total area. Reedbeds are amongst the most important habitats for birds in the UK. They support a distinctive breeding bird assemblage including 6 nationally rare Red Data Birds the bittern *Botaurus stellaris*, marsh harrier, *Circus aeruginosus*, crane *Grus grus*, Cetti's warbler *Cettia cetti*, Savi's warbler *Locustella luscinioides* and bearded tit *Panurus biarmicus*, provide roosting and feeding sites for migratory species (including the globally threatened aquatic warbler *Acrocephalus paludicola*) and are used as roost sites for several raptor species in winter. Five GB Red Data Book invertebrates are also closely associated with reedbeds including red leopard moth *Phragmataecia castanaea* and a rove beetle *Lathrobium rufipenne*.

2. CURRENT FACTORS AFFECTING THE HABITAT

- Small total area of habitat and critically small population sizes of several key species dependent on the habitat.
- Loss of area by excessive water extraction and, in the past, land drainage and conversion to intensive agriculture.
- Lack of or inappropriate management of existing reedbeds leading to drying, scrub encroachment and succession to woodland.
- Most of the important reedbeds are found on the coast of eastern England, where relative sea-level rise is predicted to lead to the loss of significant areas of habitat.
- Pollution of freshwater supplies to the reedbed: siltation may lead to drying; toxic chemicals may lead to loss of fish and amphibian prey for key species; accumulation of poisons in the food chain and eutrophication may cause reed death.

3. CURRENT ACTION

3.1 Legal status

Most of the more significant reedbeds are notified as SSSI/ASSI and many are notified as Wetlands of International Importance under the Ramsar Convention and as SPAs under EC Birds Directive. Several of the larger reedbeds are managed as NNRs by EN and CCW, and as reserves of the RSPB and County Wildlife Trusts.

3.2 Management, research and guidance

EN's 3 year, £200,000 *Action for Bittern* project, part of its Species Recovery Programme, provides funding for reedbed rehabilitation and extension in England.

The RSPB has a priority programme for reedbed rehabilitation on their reserves and are creating new reedbeds on land of low nature conservation interest purchased by the society.

The Broads Authority conducts a reedbed management programme within their executive area in association with EN, who provide management agreements to owners/occupiers for reedbed management.

The Suffolk river valleys and Broads ESAs require farmers to maintain and manage reedbeds, and capital grants are available for restoration work. Payments are also available under Countryside Stewardship for the management, creation and restoration of reedbeds.

The statutory conservation agencies have negotiated several management agreements on SSSIs to help secure sympathetic reedbed management and have worked with key partners using EU Life funding to create an extensive reedbed on former peat workings in the Somerset Levels.

RSPB/EN/Broads Authority/British Reedgrowers' Association published a leaflet 'Reedbed Management for Bitterns' and the management guide 'Reedbed Management for Commercial and Wildlife Interests Handbook' to encourage the management and creation of reedbeds.

Statutory conservation agency and RSPB staff provide advice to a range of reedbed owners on appropriate management, rehabilitation, extension and creation.

Voluntary and statutory agency staff monitor (and license the monitoring of) the population size and productivity of key reedbed species.

The NRA has been encouraged to incorporate reedbed protection, management or creation in its catchment and shoreline management plans.

Many reedbeds are subject to, or will soon be subject to, water-level management plans as prepared under a MAFF and Welsh Office initiative.

4. ACTION PLAN OBJECTIVES AND PROPOSED TARGETS

- Identify and rehabilitate by the year 2000 the priority areas of existing reedbed (targeting those of 2ha or more) and maintain this thereafter by active management.

This target should provide habitat for 40 pairs of bitterns and provide optimum conditions for other reedbed species and should be targeted primarily in the south-east.

- Create 1,200 ha of new reedbed on land of low nature conservation interest by 2010.

The creation of new reedbed should be in blocks of at least 20 ha with priority for creation in areas near to existing habitat, and linking to this wherever possible. The target should provide habitat for an estimated 60 breeding pairs of bitterns boosting numbers to previous levels. It should be targeted in the south-east of Britain.

5. PROPOSED ACTION WITH LEAD AGENCIES

5.1 Policy and legislation

- Continue to notify nationally important sites as SSSI/ASSI by 1998. (ACTION: CCW, DoE(NI), EN, SNH)
- Continue the existing programme of designations of internationally important sites as SPA and/or Ramsar and SAC by 2004. (ACTION: DoE, DoE(NI), SO, WO)
- Develop a clear national strategy for reedbed creation and management by 1997, cross-relating to coastal

management plans, ESAs, set-aside and mineral extraction plans, and ensuring that an effective level of monitoring and inventory is maintained. (ACTION: CCW, DoE, DoE(NI), EN, JNCC, SNH, SO, WO)

- Consider modifying or expanding existing habitat schemes such as Wildlife Enhancement Schemes (WES), Tir Cymen, ESAs, Countryside Stewardship, Nitrate Sensitive Areas and Habitat Scheme to encourage and allow for the creation of 1,200 ha of reedbed. Priority should be given also to reedbed creation as a preferred condition of after-use for mineral extraction sites. (ACTION: CCW, DoE, DoE(NI), EN, LAs, MAFF, SOAEFD, SNH, WOAD)

- Encourage the development of both sympathetic water abstraction, water level management policies and of appropriate coastal zone management plans in order to protect existing reedbeds. (ACTION: NRA, IDBs, LAs)

5.2 Site safeguard and management

- Ensure that development schemes do not affect the integrity or the conservation interest of reedbeds. (ACTION: LAs)

- Acquire, in appropriate circumstances, or grant-aid acquisition of, land of low nature conservation interest for the creation of new reedbeds. (ACTION: CCW, EN, SNH)

- Ensure favourable management of key reedbeds by 2010, offering, where appropriate, long-term, targeted management agreements for reedbed management on important sites. (ACTION: CCW, EN, SNH)

5.3 Advisory

- Ensure the favourable management of key reedbeds by providing advice based on the most recently available prescriptions. (ACTION: CCW, DoE(NI), EN, SNH)

- Ensure that authorities creating new reedbeds for effluent treatment and other primary purposes receive up-to-date advice on reedbed creation for wildlife. (ACTION: CCW, DoE(NI), EN, SNH)

- Initiate training courses for land managers and countryside land management advisors on techniques of reedbed creation and management. (ACTION: CCW, DoE(NI), EN, SNH)

5.4 International

- Promote pan-European co-operation on research, conservation and management of reedbeds and reedbed species. (ACTION: CCW, EN, JNCC, SNH)

5.5 Future research and monitoring

- Promote research into the ecology of key GB reedbed species, particularly in relation to management such as cutting regimes, burning and mere and dyke management. (ACTION: CCW, EN, SNH)

- Ensure the continued surveillance of population distribution, size and productivity for key GB reedbed species and of water levels, water quality and current reedbed management for all significant reedbeds. (ACTION: CCW, NRA, EN, SEPA, SNH)

- Encourage necessary research to inform and monitor attempts to restore and re-establish *Phragmites* swamp. (ACTION: CCW, EN, SNH)

- Begin large-scale trials of the use of reedbeds for reducing point and diffuse source agricultural pollution by 1998. Trials should include the study of the most effective means of reedbed establishment, management and their benefits to wildlife. (ACTION: MAFF, NRA)

5.6 Communications and publicity

- Provide material which promotes the importance of reedbeds and their conservation by end of 1997. (ACTION: CCW, EN, SNH)

- Launch a campaign to enhance the market for UK reed by 1997. (ACTION: DoE, LAs)

COSTINGS

The successful implementation of the action plan will have resource implications for both the private and public sectors. The data in Table 1 below provide a preliminary estimate of the likely resource costs to the public sector in the years 1997, 2000 and 2010, in addition to existing public expenditure commitments in 1995. Figures are provided for central estimates of costs and also for a range of alternative costs (low and high). These alternative figures reflect different payment (and cost) levels and different scheme coverage assumptions. The costings also take account of revenue from reed production.

The data are based on targets whereby 5,000 hectares of existing reedbed habitat will be appropriately maintained and improved and 1200 hectares of reedbed will be re-established through to 2010. This results in a central estimate of about £100 per hectare per year (including existing commitments in 1995) required for management and enhancement costs (by 2010). This figures is also based on the assumption that the proportion of private land under management schemes will increase from 22% in 1995 to 78% in the year 2010.

In order to re-establish 1200 hectares of reedbed habitat additional costs will be shown in Table 1. It is assumed that about half the area can be re-established by 2000 at an average (central) expenditure of approximately £620 per hectare per year (including existing commitments) in 2000. On-going costs to 2010 will comprise a higher proportion of management expenditure relative to new establishment costs.

It should be noted that the above figures will not necessarily be the net cost to the public sector. While significant increases in environmentally based payment schemes would be required to make payments to land managers there could, be some savings in terms of reduced agricultural support payments.

COSTINGS

Habitat Type: Reedbed (£000 per annum)

Total Area to be maintained and enhanced (Ha)	1997			2000			2010		
	Low	Central	High	Low	Central	High	Low	Central	High
5,000	40	90	110	90	180	230	190	310	420

Area to be re-established (Ha)	1997			2000			2010		
	Low	Central	High	Low	Central	High	Low	Central	High
1,200	50	100	170	110	200	340	130	230	410

SALINE LAGOONS
A COSTED HABITAT ACTION PLAN

I. CURRENT STATUS

Lagoons in the UK are essentially bodies, natural or artificial, of saline water partially separated from the adjacent sea. They retain a proportion of their sea water at low tide and may develop as brackish, full saline or hyper-saline water bodies. The largest lagoon in the UK is in excess of 450 ha although the rest are much smaller and some may be less than 1 ha. Lagoons contain soft sediments which often support tasselweeds and carophytes as well as filamentous green and brown algae. In addition lagoons contain invertebrates rarely found elsewhere. They also provide important habitat for waterfowl, marshland birds and seabirds. The invertebrate fauna present can be divided into three main components: those that are essentially freshwater in origin, those that are marine / brackish species and those that are more specialist lagoonal species. The presence of certain indigenous and specialist plants and animals make this habitat important to the UK's overall biodiversity.

There are several different types of lagoons, ranging from those separated from the adjacent sea by a barrier of sand, or shingle ('typical lagoons') to those arising as ponded waters in depressions on soft sedimentary shores to those separated by a rocky sill or artificial construction such as a sea wall. Sea-water exchange in lagoons occurs through a natural or man-modified channel or by percolation through or overtopping of the barrier. The salinity of the systems is determined by various levels of fresh water input from ground or surface waters. The degree of separation and the nature of the material separating the lagoon from the sea are the basis for the distinguishing several different physiographic types of lagoon.

2. CURRENT FACTORS AFFECTING THE HABITAT

The processes which lead to the natural development of some types of lagoons are generally inhibited by human coastal activities. It is probable that the formation of new lagoons will not keep pace with the process of lagoon loss. Current factors affecting this habitat type include:

a Lagoons are naturally transient; salinity regimes change as succession leads to freshwater conditions and eventually to vegetation such as fen carr. Some formerly saline sites are now freshwater.

- The bar-built sedimentary barriers of 'typical' coastal lagoons tend to naturally move landwards with time. Lagoons behind them will eventually be in-filled as bar sediments approach the shore.

- Pollution, in particular nutrient enrichment leading to eutrophication, can have major detrimental effects. This may result from direct inputs to the lagoon or from water supply to the lagoon.

- Artificial control of water (sea and fresh) to lagoons can have profound influences on the habitat.

- Many lagoons are often seen as candidates for in-filling or land claim as part of coastal development.

- Some coastal defence works can prevent the movement of sediments along the shore and lead to a gradual loss of the natural coastal structures within which many coastal lagoons are located.

- The impact of coastal defences will be compounded by the effects of sea level rise. It has been estimated that about 120 ha of coastal lagoons in England alone (10% of the existing resource) will be lost in the next 20 years, mainly as a consequence of sea level rise.

- Sea level rise also presents an opportunity for the reinstatement of saline waters to freshwater lakes which once were coastal lagoons, thereby allowing the creation of new lagoonal habitat.

3. CURRENT ACTION

3.1 Legal status

In Great Britain 10 species of invertebrate and plant associated with lagoons are protected under the Wildlife and Countryside Act 1981. No lagoon species are listed for protection under the Wildlife (Northern Ireland) Order 1985.

Of the 177 lagoon sites surveyed in England, just over 50 % occur within existing SSSIs and about 10% occur within NNRs and as many in LNRs. Fewer examples are found in Wales where only about four lagoons are recognised (there remain some un-surveyed potential sites in Clwyd). A survey currently under way in Scotland is expected to identify about 130 lagoons. A preliminary study suggests that there may be 30 lagoonal habitat sites in Northern Ireland (of these only a few small perched salt marsh pools are thought to be natural in origin). In Northern Ireland they will all eventually fall within the ASSI/SPAs network.

Internationally important lagoons have been designated, for their bird interest, as SPAs under EC Birds Directive. Coastal lagoons are also listed as a priority habitat on Annex I of the EC Habitats Directive and the UK Government has recently set out its proposals for sites which it could merit designation as SACs under this Directive.

3.2 Management research and guidance

Coastal groups are currently preparing shoreline management plans for defined lengths of coast. The production of these plans will require identification of key habitats, including coastal lagoons, and confirmation of their management requirements.

Certain lagoons have an established research base and study group.

4. ACTION PLAN OBJECTIVES AND PROPOSED TARGETS

- The current number, area and distribution of coastal lagoons should be maintained and enhanced. There are at present only about 1,300 ha of known saline lagoonal habitats in the UK.

- Create, by the year 2010, sufficient lagoon habitat to offset losses over the last 50 years.

Recent evaluations estimated that 38 English lagoons were lost in the later half of the eighties. Within the next 20 years the creation of at least 120 ha of lagoon habitat is considered attainable and necessary within England just to keep pace with projected losses.

Farmers can meet their set-aside requirements by setting-aside field margins of a minimum 20 metre width. The scheme literature advises them on how best to manage the margins to benefit wildlife. For 1996, the set-aside requirement for rotational and other forms of set-aside (including field margins) will be the same. This may encourage more farmers to set-aside their land as field margins.

Some 1,530 km (185 ha) of conservation headlands have also been established by some 100 farmers under initiatives encouraged by the Game Conservancy Trust. Most farms are outside ESAs and receive no payment, although the DoE provides support to the Game Conservancy Trust to employ a Field Adviser to oversee deployment and efficacy.

4. ACTION PLAN OBJECTIVES AND TARGETS

- Maintain, improve and restore by management the biodiversity of some 15,000 ha of cereal field margins on appropriate soil types in the UK by 2010.

The target of 15,000 ha represents the consensus of expert opinion of the area necessary for the maintenance, improvement and restoration of biodiversity. The figure covers the conservation management of rare arable flowers (which generally occur on drier less fertile soils) and also grass margins which occur on a much wider range of soils (including heavy and fertile soils).

Plants that would benefit include pheasant's eye, lambs succory *Arnoseris minima*, cornflower, corn gromwell, corn parsley, corn buttercup, shepherd's needle, narrow fruited corn salad and red hemp nettle *Galeopsis angustifolium*. Many invertebrates would benefit directly and indirectly: butterflies such as the orange-tip *Anthocaris cardamines* and 16 other species which selectively use cereal field margins but do not breed in the crop; and many species of Orthoptera, Hemiptera, Hymenoptera and Coleoptera (especially Chrysomelidae such as *Gastrophysa polygoni*). The plants and invertebrate populations which could be expected to inhabit such strips could benefit a range of birds such as grey partridge *Perdix perdix*, quail *Coturnix coturnix*, corn bunting *Milaria calandra*, and possibly mammals such as brown hare *Lepus europaeus*. Grass margins also bring additional conservation benefits such as acting as pollution buffers between arable land and watercourses.

5. PROPOSED ACTION WITH LEAD AGENCIES

5.1 Policy and legislation

- Assess in terms of ecology, pedology and value for money, the most appropriate geographical areas to target cereal field margin options (i.e. wildlife strips, conservation headlands and grass margins) under environmental schemes and consider developing and extending cereal field margin options in appropriate ESAs and under Countryside Stewardship and Tir Cymen. (ACTION: MAFF, SOAEFD, WOAD)

- Review payment rates for cereal field margin options to assess whether they provide an adequate incentive for take-up on small areas on any one farm. (ACTION: MAFF, SOAEFD, WOAD)

- Review management guidelines for wildlife strips and conservation headlands in the light of research findings and advance in pesticides. (ACTION: MAFF, SOAEFD, WOAD)

- Consider the costs and benefits associated with promoting environmental management of field margins for crops other than cereals. (ACTION: MAFF, SOAEFD, WOAD)

- Ensure that any findings from research programmes on pesticides which are relevant to the management of cereal field margins are reflected in future policy and are communicated to interested bodies. (ACTION: MAFF, SOAEFD, WOAD)

5.2 Site safeguard and management

- Promote management favourable to cereal field margins through appropriate environmental schemes. (ACTION: CCW, DANI, EN, MAFF, SNH, SOAEFD, WOAD)

- Consider extending the current advisory network by providing at least two full-time skilled BASIS-trained advisors nationally to assist the Field Advisors currently employed by the Game Conservancy Trust.

5.3 Advisory

- Review existing guidance on conservation management of cereal field margins and promote new guidelines where appropriate. (ACTION: MAFF, SOAEFD, WOAD)

- Consider options for a network of field advisors who can provide up-to-date information on favourable conservation management practices. (ACTION: DoE, SO, WO, MAFF, SOAEFD, WOAD)

- Develop training courses on cereal field margin management and target these on land management advisers (e.g. ADAS, ELMS staff, Agricultural College and University Staff) groups of farmers, and major landowners (e.g. National Trust), and pesticide spray contractors. (ACTION: CCW, EN, SNH)

5.4 International

- Take account of experience with cereal field margin schemes in all German Lander, Austria, Switzerland, Denmark, Sweden, Finland and the Netherlands in developing UK policy and practice. (ACTION: MAFF, SOAEFD, WOAD)

- Encourage the European Environment Agency to develop networks of interested groups and research data on cereal field margins. (ACTION: DoE, JNCC)

5.5 Monitoring and research

- Continue to develop more specific pesticides, especially insecticides and target their use instead of broad spectrum pesticides in cereal field margins. (ACTION: Agrochemical industry)

- Monitor how effectively the prescriptions in ELMS are contributing towards the conservation of key indicator species of this habitat. (ACTION: CCW, EN, SNH)

- Assess existing research on the practicalities and benefits of undersown conservation headlands and consider testing such a management option under ELMS. (ACTION: MAFF, SOAEFD, WOAD)

5.6 Communications and publicity

- No action proposed.

COSTINGS

The successful implementation of the action plan will have resource implications for both the private and public sectors. The data in Table 1 below provide a preliminary estimate of the likely resource costs to the public sector in the years 1997, 2000 and 2010, in addition to existing public expenditure commitments in 1995.

The data are based on targets whereby 15,000 ha of cereal field margins will be appropriately maintained and improved through to 2010.

HABITAT TYPE: Cereal Field Margins (£000 per annum)

Area to be maintained and enhanced (Ha)	1997	2000	2010
15,000	500	1,100	2,100

CHALK RIVERS
A COSTED HABITAT ACTION PLAN

I. CURRENT STATUS

There are approximately 35 chalk rivers and major tributaries ranging from 20 to 90 kilometres in length. They are located in south and east England - from the Frome in Dorset to the Hull in Humberside.

Chalk rivers have a characteristic plant community, often dominated in mid-channel by river water crowfoot *Ranunculus penicillatus* var *pseudofluitans* and starworts *Callitriche obtusangula* and *C. platycarpa*, and along the edges by watercress *Rorippa nasturtium-aquaticum* and lesser water-parsnip *Berula erecta*. They have low banks which support a range of water-loving plants. This plan considers action required for the river channel and banks but not for the whole catchment or floodplain.

All chalk rivers are fed from groundwater aquifers, producing clear waters and a generally stable flow and temperature regime. These are conditions which support a rich diversity of invertebrate life and important game fisheries, notably for brown trout *Salmo trutta*. Brook lamprey *Lampetra planeri*, salmon *Salmo salar*, crayfish *Austropotamobius pallipes* and otter *Lutra lutra* are among the species listed on Annex II of the EC Habitats Directive which chalk rivers support.

Most chalk rivers have 'winterbourne' stretches in their headwaters. These often run dry, or partially dry, in late summer because of lack of rainfall recharging the aquifer. A characteristic range of invertebrates has adapted to these conditions, as has the brook water crowfoot *Ranunculus peltatus*.

Where the river corridor (approximately 50m either side of the river) is not affected by intensive agriculture, fisheries or urban development, rich fen vegetation has developed. This is maintained by extensive cattle grazing or naturally progresses to carr woodland. These areas are particularly rich in insect life and breeding birds.

2. CURRENT FACTORS AFFECTING THE HABITAT

- *Abstraction*: Excessive abstraction mainly for public water supply from the chalk aquifer has contributed to low flows on a number of chalk rivers. This has led not only to drying out of upper sections and riparian zones, but also to accumulation of silt and changes in the aquatic vegetation structure. Artificial measures to counter these effects, such as sealing of the bed with concrete and narrowing of the channel, can themselves have negative ecological consequences.

- *Physical modification*: Like most lowland rivers, many chalk rivers have had their beds dredged and lowered and have been confined to specific channels for flood defence, drainage, navigation, and other purposes. As 'low energy' systems, chalk rivers have been less able than other river types to reassert their channel structure. Some have side channels, created during much higher flows after the last ice age. These have sometimes been modified to create lakes for ornamental or fishery purposes. The management of water meadows from a mill head was also a familiar practice in recent centuries. The full extent of these modifications on the animal and plant communities of chalk rivers is not known.

- *Pollution*: In common with most lowland rivers, chalk rivers are significantly affected by sewage discharges and in times of low flow, de-oxygenation may occur. This has caused the upper reaches of at least one SSSI river to be classified in the lowest water quality category. High levels of nitrates (leaching from ploughed land into groundwater) and phosphate (from sewage effluent) are found in many chalk rivers. Because of this enrichment, excessive growths of blanket-weed have been observed on what were previously crystal-clear waters. Changes in plant communities have occurred, including loss of water crowfoot beds from some river stretches. Effluent from fish farms, water-cress beds and light industry can have similar effects.

- *Catchment land use:* This is often dominated by arable cultivation for wheat and barley. Prior to the 1940s, many of these chalk downland areas were in extensive grazing regimes or under woodland. Land use change adjacent to rivers has led to conversion of permanent grassland to intensive leys and silage as well as arable crops. These have significant consequences on river nutrient loads. The ploughing up of the catchments has led to high levels of nitrate leaching into the groundwater aquifer and to the run-off of soil particles, causing siltation and concretion of river gravels, which are vital for the spawning of salmon and trout. Alongside the rivers, the land is often used for cattle pasture. Some of these areas were formerly water meadows, with the early grass production used for hay and grazing. Over-grazing can exacerbate siltation of river gravels. Light trampling also creates muddy margins of importance for a range of uncommon invertebrates. Direct destruction as a result of development pressure may also occur.

- *Fisheries management:* On many chalk rivers this is intensive, with regular 'weed' cuts in the channel; fencing off and mowing of strips along the bank; infilling and stabilisation of banks; removal of unwanted fish species (e.g. pike, grayling); and stocking with farm-reared trout. Some fisheries management practices are evidently beneficial to conservation, such as cleaning gravels, while others are neutral providing they do not either impact on characteristic plant and animal communities or are carried out in previously unmanaged areas.

3. CURRENT ACTION

3.1 Legal status

In carrying out their functions the NRA, Water Companies, Internal Drainage Bodies and local authorities in England and Wales have a statutory duty to further conservation where consistent with enactments relating to their functions. These are set out in the Water Resources Act 1991, and the Land Drainage Act 1991. River Purification Boards (RPBs) in Scotland do not have the same duties. Both the NRA and RPBs have statutory responsibilities for pollution control.

The duty to further conservation applies to the water management functions of the Environment Agency for England and Wales from April 1996, while the pollution control functions of this Agency will have a duty to have regard to the desirability of conserving and enhancing features of special interest. The establishment of the Scottish Environment Protection Agency (SEPA) and the new water authorities will strengthen conservation duties compared to the predecessor RPBs.

England has the principal resource of chalk rivers in Europe. EN has carried out surveys of river plants on 25 chalk rivers and identified eight (Avon, Frome, Hull Headwaters, Itchen, Kennet, Lambourn, Upper Nar and Test) which qualify as SSSI. These will be notified as statutory sites by 1998. The NRA, Water Companies and local authorities have a duty to further the conservation of all rivers. On SSSI chalk rivers, the NRA has agreed to prepare joint conservation strategies with EN by 1998.

EN has undertaken work to identify which chalk rivers might qualify as SACs under the EC Habitats Directive.

3.2 Management, research and guidance

The NRA is undertaking a consultation programme on Catchment Management Plans (CMP) for chalk rivers and intends to publish them by 1998. CMPs include work being undertaken or planned in relation to water pollution control, water resource management, fisheries management and in-river maintenance.

MAFF has designated ESAs in the valleys of two chalk rivers, where farmers are encouraged financially to undertake favourable management and to revert arable to pasture. The Upper Salisbury Avon has also been selected as one of the four pilot rivers for the Water Fringe option of the Habitat Scheme. The Ministry's Directorate of Fisheries Research has undertaken work demonstrating the problems caused by siltation of spawning gravels and that gravel cleaning can significantly enhance the natural production of juvenile salmonids. Further work is planned on the improvement of spawning gravels and the management of riparian vegetation.

The historical and current contribution of individual riparian landowners in undertaking small scale enhancement works, and some estates for preserving more extensive areas of natural habitat and water meadows alongside these rivers, is considerable.

4. ACTION PLAN OBJECTIVES AND PROPOSED TARGETS

- Maintain the characteristic plants and animals of chalk rivers, including their winterbourne stretches.
- Restore water quality, flows and habitat diversity where they have deteriorated on rivers designated as SSSIs.
- Review the need and potential for restoration on the remaining chalk rivers, in consultation with local communities, and plan for these where cost-effective.

The targets are not expressed as percentage of habitat because action should be directed to where it is needed and where it is cost effective. It will vary according to the extent of pollution, habitat degradation and low flows in individual rivers. It is known, for instance, that phosphate levels have increased since 1980 and exceed recommended standards on seven SSSI rivers, involving discharges from 12 sewage treatment works and one factory. The action plan includes identification of priorities and cost effective options within a phased programme, concentrating on the eight river SSSIs.

5. PROPOSED ACTION WITH LEAD AGENCIES

5.1 Policy and legislation

- Review abstraction consents and licences during catchment management plan production. Where abstraction is found to be damaging the quality of the chalk river habitat, consider revoking the licences. (ACTION: NRA)
- Review compensation provisions for abstraction licences in the Water Resources Act 1991 (to bring them more into line with those for discharge consents). (ACTION: DoE)
- Review licences for industrial/effluent discharge where these are found to damage the quality of chalk rivers. (ACTION: NRA)
- Seek to ensure that development adjacent to, or directly impacting on nationally and internationally important chalk rivers is minimised. (ACTION: LA, DoT, DTI)

5.2 Site safeguard and management

- Complete programmes for notification of chalk river SSSIs by 1998. (ACTION: EN)
- Progress programmes for chalk river SACs and aim to complete designation by 2004. (ACTION: DoE)
- Develop initial conservation strategies for chalk river SSSIs. (ACTION: EN, NRA)
- Schemes to encourage sympathetic management of catchments and river corridors should be reviewed by 2000 and extended where appropriate in order to reduce the run off of silt and enhance wildlife habitats. (ACTION: NRA, EN, MAFF).
- Water quality on SSSI rivers should be assessed against proposed Special Ecosystem Statutory Water Quality Objective targets and problem sources identified. Significant pollution on the other chalk rivers should also be assessed. A plan for remedying water quality problems should be drawn up for each SSSI river by 1998 and for the remaining chalk rivers by 2002. Where phosphate removal is required at sewage treatment works on SSSI rivers, it should be installed by 2000. (ACTION: DoE, NRA, EN, Water Companies)

5.3 Advisory

- Promote advice on the best approaches to river corridor and catchment management. (ACTION: NRA).

5.4 International

- No action proposed.

5.5 Future research and monitoring

- Assess the nature conservation value and potential for restoration of chalk rivers, other than those which are SSSI/pSAC by 2001. (ACTION: NRA, EN)
- The feasibility of channel restoration on stretches of modified small chalk rivers should be established by 2001 using an experimental approach to assess the wider applicability of physical restoration techniques. (ACTION: NRA, EN)

- Initiate a study investigating the beneficial impact of the management of chalk rivers and adjacent land use on the aquatic plants and animals. (ACTION: NRA, EN)

5.6 Communications and publicity

- No action proposed.

COSTINGS

The successful implementation of the action plan will have resource implications for both the private and public sectors. The data in Table 1 below provide a preliminary estimate of the likely resource costs to the public sector in the years 1997, 2000 and 2010, in addition to existing public expenditure commitments in 1995.

The data are based on targets whereby 7000 km of chalk river will be appropriately maintained and improved through to 2010.

HABITAT TYPE: Chalk rivers (£000 per annum)

Length to be maintained and enhanced (Km)	1997	2000	2010
700	500	1,000	1,100

FENS
A COSTED HABITAT ACTION PLAN

I. CURRENT STATUS

The UK is thought to host a large proportion of the fen surviving in the EU. As in other parts of Europe fen vegetation has declined dramatically in the past century.

Fens are peatlands which receive water and nutrients from the soil, rock and ground water as well as from rainfall: they are minerotrophic. Two types of fen can broadly be distinguished: topogenous and soligenous. Topogenous fens are those where water movements in the peat or soil are generally vertical. They include basin fens and floodplain fen. Soligenous fens, where water movements are predominantly lateral, include mires associated with springs, rills and flushes in the uplands, valley mires, springs and flushes in the lowlands, trackways and ladder fens in blanket bogs and laggs of raised bogs.

Fens can also be described as 'poor-fens' or 'rich-fens'. Poor-fens, where the water is derived from base-poor rock such as sandstones and granites occur mainly in the uplands, or are associated with lowland heaths. They are characterised by short vegetation with a high proportion of bog mosses *Sphagnum* spp. and acid water (pH of 5 or less). Rich-fens, are fed by mineral-enriched calcareous waters (pH 5 or more) and are mainly confined to the lowlands and where there are localised occurrences of base-rich rocks such as limestone in the uplands. Fen habitats support a diversity of plant and animal communities. Some can contain up to 550 species of higher plants, a third of our native plant species; up to and occasionally more than half the UK's species of dragonflies, several thousand other insect species, as well as being an important habitat for a range of aquatic beetles.

In intensively farmed lowland areas fens occur less frequently, are smaller in size and more isolated than in other parts of the UK. There are, however, exceptions to this. The UK's largest continuous area of base-poor fen, the Insh Marshes in the floodplain of the River Spey in Scotland, covers an area of 300 ha, the calcareous rich fen and swamp of Broadland covers an area of 3,000 ha and Lough Erne system in Fermanagh has extensive areas of fen and swamp. In some lowland areas such as the Scottish borders and southern Northern Ireland there are concentrations of small fens of particular importance.

2. CURRENT FACTORS AFFECTING THE HABITAT

Fens are dynamic semi-natural systems and in general, management is needed to maintain open-fen communities and their associated species richness. Without appropriate management (e.g. mowing, grazing, burning, peat cutting, scrub clearance), natural succession will lead to scrub and woodland forming. Current factors affecting this habitat type are:

- Past loss of area by drainage and conversion to intensive agriculture.
- Excessive water abstraction from aquifers has dried up or reduced spring line flows, and generally lowered water tables. Abstractions also have affected the natural balance between the differing water qualities of ground water and surface water.
- Small total area of habitat and critically small population sizes of several key species dependent on the habitat.
- Lack of or inappropriate management of existing fens leading to drying, scrub encroachment and succession to woodland.
- Valley fens are particularly susceptible to agricultural run-off and afforestation within the catchment.
- Enrichment or hypertrophication resulting in changing plant communities.

3. CURRENT ACTION

3.1 Legal status

The majority of fens are notified as SSSI/ASSIs and many are notified as Wetlands of International Importance under the Ramsar Convention and as SPAs under the EC Birds Directive. Several of the larger fens are managed as NNRs by EN and CCW, and as reserves of the RSPB and County Wildlife Trusts. Several types of fen are listed in the Habitats Directive including transition mire, poor and rich fen, alkaline fens (rich-fen). A number of fens have been proposed as SACs under the EC Habitats Directive for these types.

3.2 Management research and guidance

CCW has an active programme of positive management focused on NNRs and undertake active management to restore favourable conditions on key fen sites.

The Broads Authority conducts a fen management programme within their executive area in association with EN, who negotiate management agreements with owners/occupiers for reedbed management.

The Broads ESA and Suffolk rivers ESA both play an important role in protecting the fens.

The statutory conservation agencies have negotiated several management agreements on SSSIs to help secure sympathetic fen management and have worked with key partners using EU Life funding to create an extensive fen on former peat workings in the Somerset Levels.

Statutory conservation agency staff provide advice to a range of fen owners on appropriate management, rehabilitation, extension and creation.

Voluntary and statutory agency staff monitor the population size and productivity of key fen species.

The NRA has been encouraged to incorporate fen protection, management or creation in its catchment and shoreline management plans.

Many fens are subject to, or soon will be subject to, water-level management plans prepared by flood defence operating authorities (NRA, IDBs, LAs) under a MAFF and Welsh Office initiative.

4. ACTION PLAN OBJECTIVES AND PROPOSED TARGETS

- Identify priority fen sites in critical need of, and initiate, rehabilitation by the year 2005. All rich fen and other sites with rare communities should be considered.
- Ensure appropriate water quality and water quantity for the continued existence of all SSSI/ASSI fens by 2005.

5. ACTION REQUIRED

5.1 Policy and legislation

- Review water quality and set standards for fens by year 1998 through the appropriate government agencies and departments. Aim to meet these targets by year 2010. (ACTION: NRA, Water Companies, DoE, RPBs, LAs).

- Review water resource uses by 1998 and aim to meet these targets where they affect fens by year 2010. (ACTION: NRA, SO).

- Consider modifying or expand existing habitat schemes and countryside schemes such as the Wildlife Enhancement Scheme (WES). Tir Cymen, ESA's, Countryside Stewardship and Nitrate Sensitive Areas to encourage the protection of fens from agricultural contaminants (ACTION: CCW, DoE, NRA, EN, MAFF, SNH)

- Prepare and implement water level management plans. (ACTION: NRA, IDBs, LAs, MAFF)

5.2 Site safeguard and management

- Continue to notify important sites as SSSI/ASSIs by 1998. (ACTION: CCW, DoE(NI) EN, SNH)

- Progress with the existing programme for designation as Ramsar, SPA and SACs by year 2004. (ACTION: DoE, DoE(NI), SO, WO).

- Ensure that development schemes do not affect the integrity or the conservation interest of fens (ACTION: LAs).

- Agree a list of fens requiring remedial treatment by 1998. (ACTION: CCW, DoE, DoE(NI) EA, EN, SNH, SO, WO, RPBs).

- Ensure that favourable management is in place for priority fen sites by 2005, by NNR establishment and SSSI/ASSI management agreement or equivalent (ACTION: CCW, DoE(NI), EN, SNH).

5.3 Advisory

- Agree conservation strategies with relevant statutory and non statutory agencies. (ACTION: CCW, NRA, EN, SNH).

- Initiate or participate in training courses appropriate to the management of fens. (ACTION: CCW, EN, SNH).

5.4 International

- Promote the interchange of management techniques conservation strategies and co-operation on research affecting fens. (ACTION: CCW, EN, SNH).

5.5 Future research and monitoring

- Undertake necessary research to inform and monitor attempts to restore and re-create rich fen and related habitats. (ACTION: CCW, EN, SNH)

- Promote research into the ecology of fen species, particularly in relation to water quality, water quantity and management requirements. (ACTION: CCW, EN, SNH)

5.6 Communications and publicity

- No action proposed.

COSTINGS

The successful implementation of the action plan will have resource implications for both the private and public sectors. The data in Table 1 below provide a preliminary estimate of the likely resource costs to the public sector in the years 1997, 2000 and 2010, in addition to existing public expenditure commitments in 1995.

The data are based on targets whereby 1200 hectares of fens will be appropriately maintained and improved through to 2010.

HABITAT TYPE: Fens (£000 per annum)

Area to be maintained and enhanced (Ha)	1997	2000	2010
1,200	40	70	70

ANCIENT AND/OR SPECIES-RICH HEDGEROWS
A COSTED HABITAT ACTION PLAN

I. CURRENT STATUS

Ancient hedgerows, which tend to be those which support the greatest diversity of plants and animals, may be defined as those which were in existence before the Enclosure Acts, passed mainly between 1720 and 1840 in Britain and from the mid seventeenth century in Ireland. Species-rich hedgerows may be taken as those which contain 5 or more native woody species on average in a 30 metre length, or 4 or more in northern England, upland Wales and Scotland. Hedges which contain fewer woody species but a rich basal flora of herbaceous plants should also be included but practical criteria for identifying them have yet to be agreed. Many of the thin straight hawthorn hedges which characterise later parliamentary enclosures, as well as most hedges which consist mainly of beech, privet or yew or non-native trees, are excluded. Recently planted species-rich hedges are included.

Hedges which consist only of an earth or stone bank or wall are not covered in this action plan, which is limited to boundary lines of trees or shrubs. Where such lines of trees or shrubs are associated with features such as banks, ditches, trees or verges, these features are considered to form part of the hedgerow.

It is recognised that hedges are important not just for biodiversity, but also for farming, landscape, cultural and archaeological reasons.

Hedgerows are important habitats in their own right. They are a primary habitat for at least 47 extant species of conservation concern in the UK, including 13 globally threatened or rapidly declining ones, more than for most other key habitats. They are especially important for butterflies and moths, farmland birds, bats and dormice. Indeed, hedgerows are the most significant wildlife habitat over large stretches of lowland UK and are essential refuge for a great many woodland and farmland plants and animals. Over 600 plant species (including some endemic species such as a whitebeam *Sorbus devoniensi*), 1500 insects, 65 birds and 20 mammals have been recorded at some time living or feeding in hedgerows.

Hedgerows may also act as wildlife corridors for many species, including reptiles and amphibians, allowing dispersal and movement between other habitats, although this is difficult to prove conclusively.

Elsewhere in Europe, ancient hedged landscapes are found only in parts of France (i.e. bocage), northern Italy, the Austrian Alps, Greece and the Republic of Ireland.

In 1993 it was estimated that about 329,000 km of hedgerow remained in England and 49,000 km in Wales. In 1990, a similar estimate for Scotland was 33,000 km. Between 1986 and 1991 it was estimated that there were about 125,000 km of hedgerows in Northern Ireland. Thus the current UK total, assuming a continued overall net rate of loss due to removal and neglect of about 5% pa in all four countries, may be estimated to be about 450,000 km.

The proportion of this which is ancient and/or species-rich can only be guessed at. However, if we assume that most species-rich hedges are ancient, and *vice versa*, then some indication can be gained from an analysis, based on 1978 and 1990 data, which found that 26% of all hedges in Britain were blackthorn dominant, 5% mixed hazel, 5% mixed hawthorn and 4% elm dominant. In addition, beech dominant hedges (2%) were found to have an especially rich hedge bottom plant assemblage. From this it may be surmised that some 42% of British hedges, or about 154,000 km, are ancient and/or species-rich. Such hedges are concentrated in southern England, especially in the south-west, and in southern Wales, and are relatively scarce in Scotland. In Northern Ireland, where species-rich hedges are concentrated in Fermanagh, a sample survey in 1990/1 estimated that about 33% of hedges are species-rich, giving a length of about 41,000 km. Thus the total UK resource of ancient and/or species-rich hedges is in the order of 190,000 km.

Hedgerows adjacent to roads, green lanes, tracks and wooded ground tend to be particularly species-rich.

2. CURRENT FACTORS AFFECTING THE HABITAT

Since 1945 there has been a drastic loss of hedgerows through removal and neglect throughout the UK, especially in eastern counties of England, which continues even now. Between 1984 and 1990, the *net* loss of hedgerow length in England was estimated as 21%, in Scotland 27% and in Wales 25%. This loss was the result of a combination of outright removal (1.7% per annum) and neglect (3.5% pa). In England and Wales at least the loss continued between 1990 and 1993, with neglect becoming increasingly important and removal less so. No comparable figures are available for Northern Ireland.

- Neglect (no cutting or laying) leading to hedgerows changing into lines of trees and the development of gaps. This reflects modern high labour costs and loss of traditional skills.
- Too frequent and badly timed cutting leading to poor habitat conditions, the development of gaps and probable species changes.
- Loss of hedgerow trees through senescence and felling, without encouraging replacements
- Use of herbicides, pesticides and fertilisers right up to the bases of hedgerows leading to nutrient enrichment and a decline in species diversity.
- Increased stocking rates, particularly of sheep, leading to hedgerow damage and the need to fence fields. The presence of fences reduces the agricultural necessity for hedge maintenance and so hastens their decline. The modern practice of "ranching" (placing netting around several fields to form a grazing block) also contributes to the deterioration of internal hedges).
- Removal for agricultural and development purposes.

3. CURRENT ACTION

3.1 Legal status

The Environment Act 1995 introduces an enabling power to protect *important* hedgerows in Britain. Land managers will probably be required to consult local authorities before hedgerows can be removed. The Department of the Environment is currently drafting the criteria for determining whether a hedgerow is important or not. The hedgerow protection clauses in the Environment Act 1995 do not apply to Scotland where Government's view is that there is no evidence that loss of ancient and/or species-rich hedgerows is a problem of sufficient dimension to merit legal protection.

Article 10 of the EC Habitats Directive requires member states to encourage the management of hedges (and other linear features) in their land use planning and development policies and, in particular, with a view to improving the ecological coherence of the Natura 2000 network. This is reflected in The Conservation (Natural Habitats, etc.) Regulations, 1994, which recognises that such linear features are essential for the migration, dispersal and genetic exchange of wild species. PPG9 (Nature Conservation, 1994) further encourages the development of policies for the management of hedgerows.

3.2 Management, research and guidance

MAFF, SOAEFD and WOAD grant aid the restoration and planting of hedges in Britain under the Farm and Conservation Grant Scheme. However, in England and Wales this scheme is being phased out and is to end in its current form in February 1996: a similar decision has not yet been made for Scotland. It will be replaced by grants available under the Countryside Stewardship.

During the period 1991/2 to 1994/5, 3,161 km of hedge restoration work was agreed in England under Countryside Stewardship agreements (which include the former Hedgerow Incentive Scheme). This represents an expenditure of £700,000 per annum. The sympathetic management of at least an equal length of hedgerow has been secured as a condition of these agreements.

In Scotland, SNH provides discretionary grants for the improvement or creation of hedges and other landscape features. SNH has also recently produced a series of leaflets on the management of boundary habitats, including hedges.

In Wales, the Hedgerow Renovation Scheme administered by CCW provides funding for the renovation of selected hedgerows. Between December 1992 and March 1995, 346 schemes were agreed, covering 185 km, with a further 728 km retained as a condition of agreements. An application for EU funding for this scheme has been made, under the EU 5b programme.

Most ESAs offer payments for the restoration and creation of hedges and require the sympathetic management of all other hedges on holdings under agreement. No figures on current levels of expenditure are available. Many local schemes also exist which offer financial incentives, for example, in National Parks.

In 1993 Plantlife launched the Great Hedge Project aiming to create a network of hedges across the country and to foster public interest in hedges.

In 1994 the Devon Hedge Group was formed, aiming to promote the appreciation and management of hedges. Similar groups are now proposed in Shropshire, Norfolk and Cornwall.

Further guidance is also available from ADAS and the Institute of Terrestrial Ecology who recently produced a range of reports for DoE and MAFF on the status, management and wildlife of hedgerows in Britain. MAFF are also currently commissioning further research on hedge management and establishment. The Forestry Commission has published guidance on the establishment of trees in hedgerows. FWAG has produced a Hedge Pack to advise farmers on good hedge management practices. Because of the important role new woodlands can play in strengthening the ecological linkage provided by hedgerows, the Forestry Authority grant-aids new woodlands, in particular where they are placed next to ancient hedgerows and other features which act as relict woodland habitats.

4. ACTION PLAN OBJECTIVES AND PROPOSED TARGETS

- Halt the *net* loss of species-rich hedgerows through neglect and removal by the year 2000, and *all* loss of hedgerows which are both ancient and species-rich by 2005.

The targets for halting loss of ancient species-rich hedges are based on the need to stop the loss as a soon as possible, because they are largely irreplaceable features of the countryside, tempered by the practical difficulties of knowing where these hedges are and how their extent may be monitored.

- Achieve the favourable management of 25% (c.47,500 km) of species-rich and ancient hedges by the year 2000, and of 50% (c.95,000 km) by 2005.

The majority of hedges are likely to need some management in the long term; and if left for more than about 10 years there is a major risk that they will either change beyond a recoverable state or become so open that they cease to be hedges. Hence the need for the ambitious targets up to 50% by 2005.

- Maintain overall numbers of hedgerow trees within each county or district at least at current levels, through ensuring a balanced age structure.

Most surveys have shown that hedgerow tree numbers have been declining and that there is a shortage of younger age classes. Some hedgerow trees will continue to be lost, so new ones are needed to keep the total number steady. The target is therefore the minimum needed to allow the continuation of this important biological resource.

5. PROPOSED ACTION WITH LEAD AGENCIES

5.1 Policy and legislation

- Ensure that grant aid for the management, restoration and establishment of hedgerows is available to farmers. As part of this process, consider a standard payments for all hedge works across land management schemes, to facilitate up-take and administration. (ACTION: DANI, MAFF, SOAEFD, WOAD)
- Promote the uptake of, and consider extending the scope of, ESA, Countryside Stewardship, Tir Cymen, etc., for the management and restoration of ancient and/or species-rich hedgerows, for the planting of new hedgerows and for the establishment of hedgerow trees. When promoting the management and restoration of hedgerows, emphasise the term *important* hedgerows (to be defined under the Environment Act 1995 Regulations). (ACTION: CCW, DANI, MAFF, SOAEFD, WOAD)
- Explore the possibility of making the favourable management of ancient and/or species-rich hedgerows a condition of arable set aside payments. (ACTION: DANI, MAFF, SOAEFD, WOAD)

- Promote the use of practices that can protect hedges from fertilisers and pesticides, such as conservation headlands and set-aside strips. (ACTION: DANI, MAFF, SOAEFD, WOAD)
- Seek to extend the hedgerow protection clauses in the Environment Act to Scotland, then enforce the requirements of the Act with respect to *important* hedges once the necessary regulations have been passed. (ACTION: DoE, LAs, SOAEFD)
- Enforce the requirement for felling licences for hedgerow trees, as appropriate, and encourage the planting of replacements. (ACTION: FA)
- Ensure that development plans contain policies to promote the protection and management of hedges and seek to minimise adverse effects on hedges from planning proposals. (ACTION: DoE, DoE(NI), LAs, SO, WO)

5.2 Site safeguard and management
- Encourage the retention and favourable management of ancient and/or species-rich hedgerows that form an integral part of, enhance, or link Natura 2000 sites. (ACTION: CCW, DoE(NI), EN, SNH)
- Encourage favourable management of ancient and/or species-rich roadside hedges, especially favourable cutting practices. (ACTION: DoE(NI), DoT, LAs, Highways Agency)
- Consider the practicality of establishing registers of ancient and of species-rich hedgerows. (ACTION: CCW, DANI, DOE(NI), EN, LAs, SNH, SOAEFD, WOAD)

5.3 Advisory
- Consider the development of hedge management skills through training, especially for contractors. (ACTION: Agricultural Training Board, LAs)

5.4 International
- Liaise with relevant authorities in France and Eire to exchange information and ideas on hedge conservation, and in particular to form partnerships to gain EC funding. (ACTION: CCW, DANI, DoE(NI), EN, LAs, SNH, SOAEFD, WOAD)

5.5 Future research and monitoring
- Define *important* hedgerows which should be afforded protection through the Environment Act 1995.
- Refine the definition of species-rich hedges, and identify priority areas for conservation action, through supporting further systematic UK-wide research into the types of hedges that occur, their biodiversity, and their regional distribution. (ACTION: CCW, DANI, DoE, DoE(NI), EN, SNH, SOAEFD, WOAD)
- Carry out sample surveys at 10 year intervals in regions throughout the UK to enable trends in ancient and/or species-rich hedgerow status and in numbers of hedgerow trees to be accurately determined. (ACTION: DANI, DoE(NI), DoE, SOAEFD, WOAD)
- Consider the need for further research on economic outlets for the produce of hedge management such as biomass and fuel wood. (ACTION: CC, DANI, DoE, FA, SOAEFD, WOAD)
- Consider research on the effects on wildlife of different hedge management regimes. (ACTION: DANI, DoE, MAFF, SOAEFD, WOAD)
- Research into the colonisation of wildlife from hedges into new woodlands established next to old hedges. (ACTION: CCW, DoE(NI), EN, SNH, FA)

5.6 Communications and publicity
- Continue to promote an awareness among the public and land managers of the importance of hedgerows and their associated features for wildlife, of the continuing loss of hedgerows, and of the need for management to maintain biodiversity. (ACTION: CCW, DANI, DoE(NI), EN, LAs, MAFF, SNH, SOAEFD, WOAD)

COSTINGS
The successful implementation of the action plan will have resource implications for both the private and public sectors. The data in Table 1 below provide a preliminary estimate of the likely resource costs to the public sector in the years 1997, 2000 and 2010, in addition to existing public expenditure commitments in 1995. Current public expenditure is about £2.5 million, significantly below expenditure on hedges in 1993/94 of about £3.5 million.

It is assumed that about 10% of hedgerows (ie about 19,000km) are currently under favourable conservation management. The data in the table are based on targets whereby 47,000km of species rich and ancient hedgerows will be favourably managed by 2000 and 95,000km by 2010 (continuing through from the 2005 target). Figures are provided for central estimates of costs and also for a range of alternative costs (low and high). These alternative figures reflect different payment (and cost) levels and different scheme coverage assumptions. It is assumed for the central cost estimates that 25% of the target length will require programme assistance. The low expenditure figure reflects a 20%, and the high figure a 30%, requirement for assistance of the target length.

Providing advice to land managers on hedgerow management will require an estimated further £250k per year throughout the programme to 2010. In addition, an average of £75k will be required to carry out necessary survey work and monitoring work. These figures are incorporated in the 1997, 2000 and 2010 costings below.

Habitat Type: Ancient and/or species rich hedgerows (£000 per annum)

Total Area to be maintained and enhanced (Km)	1997			2000			2010		
	Low	Central	High	Low	Central	High	Low	Central	High
95,000	900	1,000	1,200	1,500	1,700	2,200	2,500	3,000	3,800

LIMESTONE PAVEMENTS
A COSTED HABITAT ACTION PLAN

I. CURRENT STATUS

Limestone pavements are a scarce and non-renewable resource. They were exposed by the scouring action of ice sheets during the ice age which ended some 10,000 years ago. Since then water action has widened the cracks in the pavements to form a complex pattern of crevices known as *grikes* between which are massive blocks of worn limestone called *clints*.

The habitat is widely scattered in Britain, on Carboniferous limestone in Wales, Northern England and Northern Ireland, and Durness limestone in Scotland. The total area in the UK of this habitat is less than 3,000 ha with the largest areas occurring in North Yorkshire and Cumbria, and smaller areas in Lancashire, Wales and Scotland. The UK holds a significant proportion of the resource of this habitat within the European Union.

Limestone pavements are of both geological and biological importance. The vegetation is rich in vascular plants, bryophytes and lichens and varies according to geographical location, altitude, rock type and the presence or absence of grazing animals. Limestone pavement vegetation may also contain unusual combinations of plants, with woodland and wood-edge species well-represented in the sheltered grikes. The clints support plants of rocky habitats or are often unvegetated. In the absence of grazing scrub may develop. In oceanic areas scrub over limestone pavement is important for epiphytes.

2. CURRENT FACTORS AFFECTING THE HABITAT

A comprehensive survey undertaken in 1975 estimated that 61% of the total limestone pavement area was intact but only 3% of the remaining pavements were undamaged. There have been no recent estimates of change. Some damage has, however, continued in the intervening years and, as it is irreversible, the resource has been further reduced.

The main factors affecting limestone pavement areas are:

- Illegal or incidental removal of pavements.
- Legal removal of pavements under extant planning permissions.
- Overgrazing of some upland pavements and abandonment of lowland pavements.

3. CURRENT ACTION

3.1 Legal status

Under section 34 of the Wildlife and Countryside Act 1981 limestone pavement is subject to protection measures that are additional to the normal SSSI provisions. Pavements of special interest (for wildlife, geology or physiography) can be notified to the local authority, who may then make a Limestone Pavement Order to protect the pavement. Once an LPO is in place, removal of rock becomes a criminal offence under the Wildlife and Countryside Act. ASSIs can also be declared in Northern Ireland under the Wildlife Order (Northern Ireland) 1985.

The most important limestone pavement areas have been notified as SSSIs. Limestone pavement is also listed as a priority habitat type on Annex I of the EC Habitats Directive. Exceptional examples of limestone pavement areas were recently proposed by the UK Government as areas that merit designation as SACs under this Directive.

3.2 Management, research and guidance

In 1989 the Nature Conservancy Council along with the Countryside Commission and local authorities, set up a Limestone Pavement Project. The project set out to survey all the pavements in North Yorkshire, Lancashire and Cumbria and to notify all those of special interest to relevant local planning authorities. The project was completed in 1994. EN and the Countryside Commission consider that most of the pavements of "special interest" under the terms of the Wildlife and Countryside Act should now be protected by a Limestone Pavement Order made by the Local Planning Authority. The implementation of these Orders is being monitored by the Limestone Pavement Forum, a consortium of local authority and statutory agencies.

Voluntary sector organisations, concerned at the continued damage (both legal and illegal) to limestone pavements established the Limestone Pavement Action Group in 1994, to highlight the issue of the damage caused to this irreplaceable habitat by demand for the use of water-worn stone in rockeries, and to campaign for better protection for pavements.

4. ACTION PLAN OBJECTIVES AND PROPOSED TARGETS

- Ensure that there is no further loss to the extent or quality of limestone pavement areas.
- Maintain the balance between features of geological importance and a characteristic assemblage of native plant species.

Limestone pavements are a non-renewable resource and the UK holds a significant proportion of the resource of the habitat within the European Union. The objectives will help us to meet our international responsibility to conserve the remaining pavements.

5. PROPOSED ACTION WITH LEAD AGENCIES

5.1 Policy and legislation

- Review the operation of section 34 of the Wildlife and Countryside Act to ensure that this legislation is effective in preventing illegal damage to limestone pavements. (ACTION: DoE, LAs, SO, WO)
- Review existing planning permissions for potential revocation or to facilitate negotiation of an end to extraction or incidental destruction by 2000. All legal extraction to have ceased by 1998. No new planning permissions should be granted for any legal or incidental destruction, nor should any further extensions to existing permission be granted. (ACTION: DoE, LAs, SO, WO)
- All new development proposals should have a "no use" clause, relating to limestone pavement as rockery stone, inserted into the landscaping conditions by the end of 1996. (ACTION: DoE, LAs, SO, WO)
- Continue existing programmes to notify nationally important sites as SSSI/ASSI by 1998. (ACTION: CCW, DoE(NI), EN, SNH)
- Continue the existing programme to designate exceptional examples of limestone pavement as SACs by 2004. (ACTION: DoE, SO, WO)

5.2 Site safeguard and management

- Seek to ensure that any threatened limestone pavements notified by CCW, EN and SNH under section 34 of the 1981 Act receive the protection of Limestone Pavement Order designations. (ACTION: CCW, EN, SNH)
- Submit to the relevant Secretary of State for direction, all development proposals likely to affect protected limestone pavements, where the local authority wishes to consent but the appropriate conservation agency has objected. (ACTION: DoE, SO, WO)
- Encourage the management of grazing activities on overgrazed limestone pavements such that the visibility of features of geological importance is in balance with the maintenance of a characteristic assemblage of native plant species. (ACTION: CCW, DoE(NI), EN, SNH).

5.3 Advisory

- Promote an awareness amongst the public, garden centre owners and landscape architects about the effects of removal of limestone pavement for rockery stone. (ACTION: DoE)

5.4 International

- Establish the extent of trade in water-worn limestone pavements between Member States in the EU and propose methods for control. Liaison with overseas agencies dealing with limestone pavement is essential. (ACTION: DoE)

5.5 Future research and monitoring

- Consider the need for and scale of a repeat of the 1975 national survey (to include Northern Ireland) of limestone pavement. Assess the requirement for an information system for maintaining data on the extent and quality of limestone pavements. (ACTION: DoE(NI), JNCC)

5.6 Communications and publicity

- Encourage the production of a booklet which highlights the environmental damage caused by the removal of limestone pavement for rockery stone. (ACTION: CCW, EN, SNH)

COSTINGS

The successful implementation of the action plan will have resource implications for both the private and public sectors. The data in Table 1 below provide a preliminary estimate of the likely resource costs to the public sector in the years 1997, 2000 and 2010, in addition to existing public expenditure commitments in 1995.

There are currently less than 3,000ha of limestone pavement and only about 60% of this area could be assisted in order to achieve favourable conservation management schemes. The data for current expenditure (1995) are based on there being about 700ha under appropriate conservation management. In order to achieve potential revocation of planning permissions on two limestone pavement sites a total expenditure of £500k has been allocated over the years 1996-2000. By 2010 new capital works will be required on many areas and expenditure of £40k is incorporated to reflect this requirement.

The costings are specifically for limestone pavement sites. However, the resource may often require management of a larger area and this would require an increase in expenditure several times greater than indicated below.

COSTINGS

HABITAT TYPE: Limestone pavement (£000 per annum)

Area to be maintained and enhanced (Ha)	1997	2000	2010
1,600	130	130	100

LOWLAND HEATHLAND
A COSTED HABITAT ACTION PLAN

I. CURRENT STATUS

Lowland heathland is characterised by the presence of plants such as heather, dwarf gorses, and cross-leaved heath and is generally found below 300 metres in altitude. Areas of good quality heathland should consist of an ericaceous layer of varying heights and structures, some areas of scattered trees and scrub, areas of bare ground, gorse, wet heaths, bogs and open water. The presence and numbers of characteristic birds, reptiles, invertebrates, vascular plants, bryophytes and lichens are important indicators of habitat quality.

Lowland heathland is a priority for nature conservation because it is a rare and threatened habitat. In England only one sixth of the heathland present in 1800 now remains. The UK has some 58,000 ha of lowland heathland of which the largest proportion (55%) is found in England. The most significant areas for lowland heathland include the counties of Hampshire, Cornwall, Dorset, Surrey, Devon, Staffordshire, Suffolk, Norfolk, Pembrokeshire, West Glamorgan and west Gwynedd. The UK has an important proportion (about 20%) of the international total of this habitat.

2. CURRENT FACTORS AFFECTING THE HABITAT

In the past heathland was lost primarily to agriculture, forestry, mineral extraction and development. Uncontrolled burning has also been a particular threat to bryophyte and lichen-rich heathland. The main factors affecting the habitat at present are:

* Encroachment of trees and scrub and the simplification of vegetation structure due to a lack of conservation management such as light grazing, controlled burning and cutting.
* Nutrient enrichment, particularly deposition of nitrogen compounds emitted from intensive livestock farming, or from other sources.
* Fragmentation and disturbance from developments such as housing and road constructions.
* Agricultural improvement including reclamation and overgrazing, especially in Northern Ireland.

3. CURRENT ACTION

3.1 Legal status

Through the Wildlife and Countryside Act 1981, a large proportion of the lowland heathland habitat has been notified as SSSI.

3.2 Management, research and guidance

The Countryside Stewardship scheme included 9,413 ha of lowland heathland in England by March 1994. This is the only country-wide heathland management and re-creation scheme. A number of counties in England, however, have heathland management projects which receive financial support through EN's National Lowland Heathland Programme. A number of other bodies including the National Trust, MoD, County Wildlife Trusts and RSPB are also actively involved in heathland management and the Forestry Authority is promoting heathland regeneration within woodlands.

The CCW is carrying out a lowland heathland survey in Wales to identify all the remaining important sites and improve management and protection. A survey of the distribution, extent and condition of lowland heathland in Scotland is required.

Management of lowland heathland is carried out through EN's Wildlife Enhancement Scheme which is expected to cover 9,000 ha of heathland by 1997; management agreements are negotiated with SNH over SSSIs containing lowland heathland and also through MAFF's ESAs, notably in Breckland and West Penwith in Cornwall. In Northern Ireland some lowland heath is managed within DANI's ESAs.

4. ACTION PLAN OBJECTIVES AND PROPOSED TARGETS

* Maintain, and improve by management, all existing lowland heathland (58,000 ha).
* Encourage the re-establishment by 2005 of a further 6,000 ha of heathland with the emphasis on the counties of Hampshire, Cornwall, Dorset, Surrey, Devon, Staffordshire, Suffolk and Norfolk in England and Pembrokeshire, Glamorgan and west Gwynedd in Wales, particularly where this links separate heathland areas.

Through the Change in Key Habitats Project (CKH) it has been estimated that there is 67,000 ha of recently modified heathland with the potential for restoration. The figure of 6,000 ha therefore represents a modest attempt to recreate approximately 10% of the existing lowland heathland resource. This target could be realistically met using existing Countryside Management Schemes. The careful targeting of 6,000 ha of lowland heathland recreation will also make a modest contribution to reversing the effects of past fragmentation of the resource.

5. PROPOSED ACTION WITH LEAD AGENCIES

5.1 Policy and legislation

* Where significant gaps in the SSSI/ASSI coverage of lowland heathland are identified the appropriate SSSI/ASSI procedure should be implemented by 1998. (Action: CCW, DoE(NI) EN, SNH)
* Consider expanding Countryside Stewardship, Tir Cymen, Environmentally Sensitive Area (ESA) and Wildlife Enhancement Schemes (WES) to meet the targets for heathland management and re-creation. Determine the applicability of a new scheme similar to Countryside Stewardship for Scotland. (ACTION: CCW, DANI, EN, MAFF, SNH, SO, WOAD)
* Take account of the conservation requirements of lowland heathland in developing and adjusting agri-environment schemes. (ACTION: DANI, MAFF, SOAEFD, WOAD)
* Simplify the process for submission of applications to the Secretary of State to fence lowland heathland that is common land for grazing, to maintain its wildlife interest. (ACTION: DoE, WO)
* In areas that support lowland heathland, there should be a presumption in favour of re-establishing heathland on derelict land or land that has been used for mineral extraction. (ACTION: DoE, SO, WO)
* Encourage Forest Enterprise and the MoD to agree action plans with specific targets for heathland restoration or management for all heathland sites in their ownership with the statutory nature conservation agencies by the end of 2000. (ACTION: Forest Enterprise, MoD)

5.2 Site safeguard and management

- The long term funding of county heathland management projects, most of which have full time project officers and which play a key role in delivering heathland management needs to be addressed. Consideration should be given to establishing county heathland projects in Wales. (ACTION: EN, CCW).
- Relevant local authorities should incorporate heathland Wildlife Site protection policies in development plans by 2000. (ACTION: LAs)

5.3 Advisory

- Organisations with experience of heathland management should continue to provide advice on how to manage and restore lowland heathland. (ACTION: CCW, EN, LAs, SNH).
- Continue existing training courses on heathland management and conservation and target these at land management advisors and officers running countryside management schemes. (ACTION: RSPB)
- Produce county lowland heathland re-creation plans identifying areas with a high potential for heathland re-establishment by 2000 for all lowland heathland counties. (ACTION: EN, CCW, SNH)
- Seek to disseminate lowland heathland inventories to key organisations involved in heathland management for all counties in England by 1997. Seek to complete the Welsh national survey of lowland heathland so that inventories can be published to guide the targeting of countryside management schemes. Consider the need for a survey and subsequent inventory project in Scotland. Inventories will need periodic updating (see the requirements of the information sub group). (ACTION: CCW, EN, RSPB, SNH)

5.4 International

- Continue to develop contacts between international experts in heathland conservation, through mechanisms such as the European Heathland Workshop. This is essential to exchange experience and avoid duplication of effort. (ACTION: CCW, EN, SNH)
- The European Environment Agency should be encouraged to develop an inventory of lowland heathland to support EU policy development. (ACTION: DoE)

5.5 Future research and monitoring

- Develop a rapid monitoring method to be used at a sample of sites to ensure that heathland management schemes are meeting their objectives. (ACTION: CCW, EN, SNH)
- Seek to ensure that appropriate studies to evaluate new labour saving technologies for heathland restoration especially for techniques such as turf cutting and rotovation are implemented. (ACTION: CCW, DoE, EN, SNH, SO, WO)
- Establish a baseline survey for monitoring the extent, condition and restoration of lowland heathland in England. (ACTION: DoE)

5.6 Communications and publicity

- Undertake a publicity campaign to raise awareness of the importance of lowland heathland by 1998. (ACTION: CCW, EN).

COSTINGS

The successful implementation of the action plan will have resource implications for both the private and public sectors. The data in Table 1 below provide a preliminary estimate of the likely resource costs to the public sector in the years 1997, 2000 and 2010, in addition to existing public expenditure commitments in 1995. Figures are provided for central estimates of costs and also for a range of alternative costs (low and high). These alternative figures reflect different payment (and cost) levels and different scheme coverage assumptions.

The data are based on targets whereby 58,000 hectares of existing heathland habitat will be appropriately maintained and improved and 6,000 hectares of heathland will be re-established through to 2010. This results in a central estimate of about £95 per hectare per year (including existing commitments) required for management and enhancement costs (by 2010). The figures also are based on the assumption that the area of land under management schemes will increase from 48% in 1995 to 92% of private sector land by 2010. The figures also include a public sector land purchase component of 50 hectares each year, and a 50% grant to private sector land purchases of 120 hectares each year, through to 2010.

In order to re-establish 6,000 hectares of lowland heathland additional costs will be as shown in Table 1. This results in an average expenditure of about £300 per hectare established per year (including existing commitments) by 2010, as the proportion of ongoing management relative to new establishment increases.

It should be noted that the above figures will not necessarily be the net cost to the public sector. While significant increases in environmentally based payment schemes would be required to make payments to land managers there could be some savings in terms of reduced agricultural support payments. On the other hand, there may be additional opportunity costs that are excluded from this analysis. An example would be lost timber revenue for public sector landowners such as Forest Enterprise.

COSTINGS

Habitat Type: Lowland Heathland (£000 per annum)

Total Area to be maintained and enhanced (Ha)	1997			2000			2010		
	Low	Central	High	Low	Central	High	Low	Central	High
58,000	300	900	1,800	500	1,700	3,600	1,800	2,600	4,700

Area to be re-established (Ha)	1997			2000			2010		
	Low	Central	High	Low	Central	High	Low	Central	High
6,000	200	200	400	300	400	700	700	800	1,200

COASTAL AND FLOODPLAIN GRAZING MARSH
A COSTED HABITAT ACTION PLAN

1. CURRENT STATUS

Grazing marsh is defined as periodically inundated pasture, or meadow with ditches which maintain the water levels, containing standing brackish or fresh water. The ditches are especially rich in plants and invertebrates. Almost all areas are grazed and some are cut for hay or silage. Sites may contain seasonal water-filled hollows and permanent ponds with emergent swamp communities, but not extensive areas of tall fen species like reeds; although they may abut with fen and reed swamp communities.

The exact extent of grazing marsh in the UK is not known but it is possible that there may be a total of 300,000 ha. England holds the largest proportion with an estimate in 1994 of 200,000 ha. However, only a small proportion of this grassland is semi-natural supporting a high diversity of native plant species (5,000 ha in England, an estimated 10,000 ha in the UK).

Grazing marshes are particularly important for the number of breeding waders such as snipe *Gallinago gallinago*, lapwing *Vanellus vanellus* and curlew *Numenius arquata* they support. Internationally important populations of wintering wildfowl also occur including Bewick swans *Cygnus bewickii* and whooper swans *Cygnus cygnus*.

2. CURRENT FACTORS AFFECTING THE HABITAT

Losses in the whole UK have been significant in the last 60 years. Losses of grazing marsh from the early 1930s to the mid-1980s include 64% in the Greater Thames, 48% in Romney Marsh and 37% in Broadland. Some of the last remaining unimproved grasslands are highly sensitive to increased nutrient loadings. Unless conservation measures to retain this habitat type are in place, with particular emphasis on the maintenance of water levels, flooding regimes and appropriate grazing or cutting most sites will deteriorate.

The primary threats to grazing marsh are of both a widespread and localised type:

Widespread factors include:

- Ecologically insensitive flood defence works constructed in the past.
- Agricultural intensification.
- Neglect in the form of a decline in traditional management.
- Eutrophication.

Localised effects arise from:

- Industrialisation and urbanisation (particularly in the Greater Thames).
- Saltwater flooding due to sea level rise.

Secondary threats include:

- Groundwater abstraction.
- Pollution of groundwater or surface water.
- Aggregate extraction.

3. CURRENT ACTION

3.1 Legal status

In carrying out their functions the NRA, Water Companies, Internal Drainage Boards and local authorities in England and Wales have a statutory duty to further conservation where consistent with purposes of enactments relating to their functions. These are set out in the Water Resources Act 1991, and the Land Drainage Act 1991. River Purification Boards (RPBs) in Scotland do not have the same duties.

The duty to further conservation applies to the water management functions of the Environment Agency for England and Wales from April 1996, while the pollution control functions of this Agency will have a duty to have regard to the desirability of conserving and enhancing features of special interest. The establishment of the Scottish Environment Protection Agency (SEPA) and the new Scottish water authorities will strengthen conservation duties compared to the predecessor RPBs.

Both the NRA and RPBs have statutory responsibilities for pollution control.

The Water Act (NI) 1972 is currently under review. In Northern Ireland responsibility for water quality, water supply and drainage resides with the Environment Services of DoE(NI), Water Service DoE(NI) and DANI respectively. These bodies also have responsibility for nature conservation interest.

SSSI/ASSIs notified for this habitat may also be internationally important and have been designated as SPAs under the EC Birds Directive and as Wetlands of International Importance under the Ramsar Convention.

3.2 Management, research and guidance

Several ESAs include prescriptions which encourage the management of grazing marsh. These cover around 400,000 ha, of which 50,000 ha of grazing marsh attracts payments of £7.5 million a year. Other incentive schemes such as the Water Fringe element of the Habitat Scheme and the Wildlife Enhancement Scheme in England and Wales contribute towards the management of this habitat. In Scotland the Habitat Scheme has a 'Waterside Habitats' option for watercourses within the watershed of the rivers Don, Dee, Spey and Tweed.

Various guidance has also been issued, including an NCC guide in 1989 on managing drainage channels for nature conservation, a guide on water level management plans issued by MAFF and WOAD in 1992 who also issued notes on environmental procedures on inland flood defence decision making (1992) and coastal defence works (1993). In England and Wales water level management plans are being established for all grazing marsh SSSIs where a drainage body controls a specific structure.

4. ACTION PLAN OBJECTIVES AND PROPOSED TARGETS

- Maintain the existing habitat extent (300,000ha) and quality.
- Rehabilitate 10,000 ha of grazing marsh habitat which has become too dry, or is intensively managed, by the year 2000. This would comprise 5,000 ha already targeted in ESAs, with an additional 5,000 ha.
- Begin creating 2,500 ha of grazing marsh from arable land in targeted areas, in addition to that which will be achieved by existing ESA schemes, with the aim of completing as much as possible by the year 2000.

Grazing marsh is an important habitat for a range of birds, invertebrates and plant communities. There is considerable potential for the enhancement of this biological interest and a target of 5,000 ha is considered achievable provided this is carefully targeted at core areas and where reversing fragmentation is feasible. In some cases this may be in areas where there is potential to recreate this habitat from land currently under arable cultivation. The figure of 2,500 ha could produce significant benefits if targeted carefully.

5. PROPOSED ACTION WITH LEAD AGENCIES

5.1 Policy and legislation

- Take account of the conservation requirements of grazing marsh habitat in developing and adjusting agri-environment schemes. (ACTION: DANI, MAFF, SOAEFD, WOAD)
- Consider extending existing river corridor ESAs at the next review to cover whole floodplains/valley bottoms in relevant catchments. (ACTION: DANI, MAFF, SOAEFD, WOAD)
- Continue to ensure that flood defence works are undertaken in an ecologically sensitive manner (ACTION: DANI, NRA, MAFF, WOAD).
- Continue to notify important sites as SSSI/ASSI by 1998. (ACTION: CCW, DoE(NI), EN, SNH)
- Continue existing programmes for SPAs and/or Ramsar designation by 2004. (ACTION: DoE, DoE(NI), SO, WO)

5.2 Site safeguard and management

- Promote the existing programme of water level management plans for grazing marsh SSSIs in England and Wales and encourage their production in Scotland and Northern Ireland by 1998. Ensure plans are established on all grazing marsh SSSI/ASSIs by 2000. (ACTION: DANI, DoE(NI), NRA, EN, IDBs, LA, SEPA)
- Target Section 39 agreements towards the management of neglected commons and greens and buffer zones around existing important grazing marsh sites and designate 10 such sites by 1998. (ACTION: LAs)
- Management grants to remove secondary woodland from commons with a wetland element should be encouraged. (ACTION: FA)
- Avoid the reseeding of dredged materials where these are unavoidably deposited on grazing marsh areas. (ACTION: NRA, WMA)

5.3 Advisory

- No action proposed.

5.4 International

- Encourage the exchange of data and information on best management practice for grazing marsh through Eurosite, the International Waterfowl and Wetlands Research Bureau and the international voluntary Wader Study Group. (ACTION: JNCC)

5.5 Future research and monitoring

- Support projects which quantify the remaining extent and distribution of grazing marsh in the UK and evaluate the conservation status. (ACTION: CCW, EN, JNCC, SNH)
- Identify and undertake conservation research on areas where rehabilitation and re-creation of grazing marsh could be targeted. (ACTION: CCW, DANI, EN, SNH, SOAEFD, WOAD)

5.6 Communications and publicity

- No action proposed.

COSTINGS

The successful implementation of the action plan will have resource implications for both the private and public sectors. There are a number of difficulties in deriving an accurate assessment of the overall cost to the public sector of maintaining and improving the grazing marsh resource to meet the target. Among these difficulties is the incomplete knowledge of the total area of the resource and that many sites (eg SSSIs) where nature conservation management is undertaken contain other co-existing habitats. However, the data in Table 1 below provide a preliminary estimate of the likely resource costs to the public sector in the years 1997, 2000 and 2010, in addition to existing public expenditure commitments in 1995.

The data are based on the assumption that there are 300,000 hectares of wet lowland grassland to be managed and enhanced through to 2010. It is estimated that £13.1 million will be spent by the public sector during 1995 in maintaining the grazing marsh resource. This expenditure will need to increase by £4.2 million in 1997 and by £13.2 in 2010. In turn this indicates a figure of approximately £87 per hectare per year (including existing commitments) required for management and enhancement costs (by 2010). These figures also are based on the assumption that the proportion of private land under management schemes will increase from the current level of 26% in 1995 to a total of 58% by 2010. The figures also include a public sector land purchase component of 100 hectares each year and a 50% grant for private sector land purchases of 400 hectares each year through to 2010.

It should be noted that the above figures will not necessarily be the net cost to the public sector. While significant increases in environmentally based payment schemes would be required to make payments to land managers there could be some savings in terms of reduced agricultural support payments. Therefore, the net additional cost could be significantly lower than the £13.2 million assessment for 2010.

COSTINGS

HABITAT TYPE: Grazing marsh (£000 per annum)

Area to be maintained and enhanced (Ha)	1997	2000	2010
30,000	4,200	8,400	13,200

PURPLE MOOR GRASS AND RUSH PASTURES (MOLINIA-JUNCUS)
A COSTED HABITAT ACTION PLAN

1. CURRENT STATUS

Purple moor grass and rush pastures occur on poorly drained, usually acidic soils in lowland areas of high rainfall in western Europe. In the UK, they are found in south-west England, particularly in Devon, southern Wales, south-west Scotland, perhaps extending as far north as northern Argyll, and in Northern Ireland, especially Fermanagh. Elsewhere in Europe they are particularly characteristic of the oceanic and sub-oceanic regions of the western seaboard, from Portugal to the Low Countries, extending eastward into central Europe.

Their vegetation, which has a distinct character, consists of various species-rich types of fen meadow and rush pasture. Purple moor grass *Molinia caerulea*, and rushes, especially sharp-flowered rush *Juncus acutiflorus*, are usually abundant. Just as the best examples of lowland heath contain a wide range of plant communities, so the same is true for this habitat: the characteristic plant communities often occur in a mosaic with one another, together with patches of wet heath, dry grassland, swamp and scrub.

Key species associated with purple moor grass and rush pastures include wavy St. Johns-wort *Hypericum undulatum*, whorled caraway *Carum verticillatum*, meadow thistle *Cirsium dissectum*, marsh hawk's beard *Crepis paludosa*, greater butterfly orchid *Platanthera chlorantha*, lesser butterfly orchid *Platanthera bifolia*, marsh fritillary butterfly *Eurodryas aurinia*, brown hairstreak *Thecla betulae*, narrow-bordered bee hawkmoth *Hermaris tityus*, curlew *Numenius arquata*, snipe *Gallinago gallinago*, and barn owl *Tyto alba*.

Purple moor grass and rush pastures are a priority for nature conservation because they are highly susceptible to agricultural modification and reclamation throughout their range. In Devon and Cornwall, where the habitat is known as Culm Grassland, only 8% of that present in 1900 remains, with a staggering 62% of sites and 48% of the total area being lost between 1984 and 1991. In Northern Ireland, between 1990 and 1993, the rate of loss of fen meadow was reckoned to be 3.3% per annum. Fragmentation and isolation of stands have been common.

In Wales it is estimated that there is now about 24,000 ha of lowland purple moor grass and rush pasture. In south west England 530 purple moor grass and rush pastures sites are known to survive on the Culm Measures, covering 3,981 ha, 400 sites on Dartmoor covering 1,000 ha with a further 90 sites covering about 300 ha on the Blackdowns. In Northern Ireland it was estimated that there was about 24,600 ha in 1993. No area estimates are available for Scotland, but the total extent is thought likely to be in the region of 2,000 ha. Thus it is probable that the total extent of the habitat in the UK is now about 56,000 ha. This is thought to be considerably more than survives in the rest of Europe, with the possible exception of the Republic of Ireland.

2. CURRENT FACTORS AFFECTING THE HABITAT

- Agricultural improvement through drainage, cultivation and fertiliser applications.
- Inappropriate management, including overgrazing by sheep and too frequent burning.
- Agricultural abandonment, leading to rankness and scrub encroachment through lack of grazing.
- Fragmentation and disturbance for developments such as housing and road constructions.
- Afforestation, especially in Northern Ireland and Scotland.

3. CURRENT ACTION

3.1 Legal status

In Devon and Cornwall, 27 sites covering 1,100 ha have been notified as SSSIs, and one of these is a National Nature Reserve. In Wales, 93 SSSIs have been selected for various forms of purple moor grass and rush pasture. Collectively, these cover 1,172 ha: a further 630 ha occur on other SSSIs notified mainly for other habitats. One of these Welsh sites is also an NNR. One ASSI in Northern Ireland has been notified primarily for lowland purple moor grass and rush pastures, covering 375 ha, and the habitat probably occurs as a minor component of several others. Five SSSIs (including a composite one), covering 317 ha, have been notified in Dumfries and Galloway, Scotland; it is probable that other Scottish SSSIs also contain the habitat. Thus the total SSSI/ ASSI coverage in the UK currently is about 3,800 ha.

Two sites in Britain have been declared as NNRs.

Types of *Molinia* vegetation in the UK are recognised as examples of *Molinia* meadows on chalk and clay which is listed on Annex I of the EC Habitats Directive. The UK Government has set out its proposals for sites which it considers merit designation as SACs for this type. (Several of these sites are also proposed for the conservation of the marsh fritillary butterfly, which is on Annex II of the Habitats Directive.)

3.2 Management, research and guidance

In south-west England, there are already 170 purple moor grass and rush pasture sites (c. 2,700 ha) under Countryside Stewardship agreements, 54 sites (978 ha) under the Wildlife Enhancement Scheme and 16 sites (161 ha) under Devon County Council agreements. Detailed management guidelines have been produced by EN to assist with these agreements. Some Dartmoor sites are coming under ESA agreements and 9 (covering 85 ha) are already in management agreements with the Dartmoor National Park Authority.

In Wales, there are 553 farms (in three pilot areas) within the Tir Cymen scheme, although the number of these farms containing purple moor grass and rush pasture has not yet been calculated. The total area of marshy grassland under Tir Cymen agreements is 2,655 ha, but this figure includes upland habitats as well as lowland ones.

In Northern Ireland, the West Fermanagh and Erne Lakeland ESA constitutes the most important current initiative to conserve the habitat. Much invertebrate survey work has been carried out by DANI within this ESA. In Scotland, the Stewarty ESA covers one of the main concentrations of purple moor grass and rush pasture in the country.

The Devon Wildlife Trust, with assistance from EN, has produced a map based inventory of sites in Devon, and has run a successful campaign to conserve the habitat, including the production of a newsletter. The Trust manages three sites as nature reserves.

EN has funded preliminary surveys of the extent and types of purple moor grass and rush pasture in Brittany and Galicia.

4. ACTION PLAN OBJECTIVES AND PROPOSED TARGETS

- Secure sympathetic management of at least 13,500 ha of purple moor grass and rush pasture by the year 2000, divided between the four countries as follows: Wales 4,000 ha, England 5,000 ha, Northern Ireland 4,000 ha and Scotland 500 ha.
- Initiate experimental attempts to re-create 500 ha of purple moor grass and rush pasture on land adjacent to, or nearby, existing sites, by the year 2005.

The aim is to secure favourable management for a minimum of 25% of this scarce habitat within the time frame. This is considered to be achievable within the likely resource allocations. Whilst the priority is to secure sympathetic management for the existing resource, where there are real opportunities to reverse fragmentation or to enlarge sites to make management viable, a small figure of 500 ha has been targeted.

5. PROPOSED ACTION WITH LEAD AGENCIES

5.1 Policy and legislation

- Take account of the conservation requirements of purple moor grass and rush pastures in developing and adjusting agri-environment schemes. (ACTION: DANI, MAFF, SOAEFD, WOAD)
- Consider developing and tailoring new incentive schemes in Scotland and Northern Ireland to benefit purple moor grass and rush pasture, to enable the targets for management and re-creation to be met in these countries. (ACTION: DANI, DoE(NI), LAs, SOAEFD)
- Woodland expansion should not be encouraged on the more valuable areas, but some less ecologically valuable sites could be suitable for, for example, new native woodlands. (ACTION: DANI, FA)
- Support local initiatives to find and map purple moor grass and rush pasture sites, and seek to protect and conserve them within development plans by 2000. (ACTION: LAs)

5.2 Site safeguard and management

- Review the extent of SSSI/ASSI coverage and consider notifying further sites as necessary to fill significant gaps. (ACTION: CCW, DoE(NI), EN, SNH)
- Promote the uptake of management agreements with owners and occupiers of SSSIs/ASSIs and other wildlife sites. (ACTION: CCW, DoE(NI), EN, SNH)

5.3 Advisory

- Support and encourage local initiatives to provide advisory booklets, information and other services to owners and managers of purple moor grass and rush pasture. (ACTION: CCW, DANI, DOE(NI), EN, LAs, SNH, SOAEFD, WOAD)
- Encourage the establishment of strategically located nature reserves for management demonstration purposes. (ACTION: CCW, DoE(NI), EN, SNH)

5.4 International

- Encourage surveys in the Republic of Ireland, Portugal and the Low Countries to determine the extent and status of purple moor grass and rush pasture in these countries, so that the international status of the habitat may be fully determined. (ACTION: CCW, DoE(NI), EN, JNCC, SNH)
- Initiate a review of purple moor grass and rush pasture and their conservation in Europe. (ACTION: JNCC)

5.5 Monitoring and research

- Clarify the extent, distribution, composition and status of purple moor grass and rush pasture in Wales, Scotland and Northern Ireland through analysis of existing data and further systematic survey work as necessary. (ACTION: CCW, DoE(NI), SNH)
- Promote the production of site inventories or full coverage habitat surveys, on a county or district basis. (ACTION: CCW, DoE(NI), LAs, SNH)
- Support research into optimal methods of purple moor grass and rush pasture re-creation, especially into nutrient stripping techniques, seed banks and seeding techniques. (ACTION: CCW, DoE(NI), EN, JNCC, SNH)
- Identify former sites adjacent to, or close to, existing sites that are suitable for re-creation, and draw up a strategy to enable the target for re-creation to be met. (ACTION: CCW, DoE(NI), EN, SNH)
- Encourage further surveys of the invertebrates of purple moor grass and rush pasture, and research into the management requirements of key species. (ACTION: CCW, DoE(NI), EN, JNCC, SNH)
- Consider the need for research into the best ways of integrating agriculture and nature conservation on purple moor grass and rush pasture. (ACTION: CCW, DANI, DOE(NI), EN, MAFF, SNH, WOAD)

5.6 Communication and publicity

- Encourage the making of a documentary on the wildlife of purple moor grass and rush pasture, to foster public appreciation of the habitat. (ACTION: CCW, DoE(NI), EN, JNCC, SNH)

COSTINGS

The successful implementation of the action plan will have resource implications for both the private and public sectors. The data in Table 1 below provide a preliminary estimate of the likely resource costs to the public sector in the years 1997, 2000 and 2010, in addition to existing public expenditure commitments in 1995. Figures are provided for estimates based on existing average costs (central) and also from sensitivity analysis to a range of alternative costs (low and high). These alternative figures reflect different payments (and cost) levels and different scheme coverage assumptions.

The data are based on targets whereby 13,500 hectares of existing Lowland purple moor grass and rush pasture pasture habitat will be appropriately maintained and improved and 500 hectares of lowland purple moor grass and rush pasture will be re-established through to 2010. This results in a figure of approximately £92 per hectare per year (central) (including existing commitments) required for management and enhancement costs (by 2010). The figures also are based on the assumption that the area of land under approved management will increase from 60% in 1995 to 100% in the private sector by 2010.

In order to re-establish 500 hectares of lowland purple moor grass and rush pasture pasture additional costs will be as shown in Table 1. It is assumed that the majority of the area can be re-established by 2000 at an average expenditure of approximately £250 per hectare per year (including existing commitments). Ongoing costs to 2010 will comprise management rather than establishment costs and are therefore considerably lower.

It should be noted that the above figures will not necessarily be the net cost to the public sector. While significant increases in environmentally based payment schemes would be required to make payments to land managers there could be some savings in terms of reduced agricultural support payments.

Habitat Type: Lowland purple moor grass and rush pasture (£000 per annum)

Total Area to be maintained and enhanced (Ha)	1997			2000			2010		
	Low	Central	High	Low	Central	High	Low	Central	High
13,500	120	120	120	240	240	240	340	460	580

Area to be re-established (Ha)	1997			2000			2010		
	Low	Central	High	Low	Central	High	Low	Central	High
500	30	40	40	60	70	90	40	50	60

BROADLEAVED AND YEW WOODLAND HABITAT STATEMENT

1. CURRENT STATUS

Britain is one of the least well-wooded countries within Europe. An estimate from the last Forestry Commission census (1985) shows that broadleaved woodland of both native and non-native species, covers approximately 752,000 ha of Britain. The total area is now greater than this because of planting and natural colonisation and is now estimated to be nearer 800,000 ha. Ancient semi-natural broadleaved and yew woodland covers about 1% of the land surface of Britain (302,000 ha).

Broadleaved and yew woodlands can be split into ancient semi-natural woodlands, ancient plantations, recent semi-natural woodland and recent plantations, according to their origins. The plantations and much recent woodland tend to have a high forest structure. That of ancient semi-natural woodland is more varied depending on its past treatment and includes high forest, coppice, wood pasture and parkland. Wood pasture and parkland are covered in a separate Habitat Statement.

The varied climate and geology of Britain combined with their past treatment to produce broadleaved woods which, despite their small size in relation to European counterparts, are structurally complex and support a wide variety of plants and animals. In the UK most native broadleaved woods comprise a mixture of broadleaved species such as ash *Fraxinus excelsior,* hazel *Corylus avellana,* sessile oak *Quercus petraea,* pedunculate oak *Quercus robur,* field maple *Acer campestre,* while in southern Britain beech *Fagus sylvatica,* small-leaved lime *Tilia cordata* and hornbeam *Carpinus betulus* are found. One of three species of conifer which are native to Britain, the yew *Taxus baccata* is generally associated with broadleaved woodlands so is included in this Statement. The conservation of native pine woodland is covered in a separate Habitat Statement. Common juniper *Juniperus communis* is a frequent component of pinewoods. Elsewhere it forms part of scrub associated with a range of different habitat patches.

Broadleaved woodlands are often noted for the wide variety of plants in the ground layer. In particular the UK is part of the Atlantic fringe of Europe and the moist, humid conditions, particularly in western parts of the country, provide ideal conditions for the growth of internationally important communities of bryophytes, lichens, ferns and saproxylic fungi and invertebrates. Another characteristic feature are the spring carpets of bluebell *Hyacinthoides non-scripta* which are unusual to Britain.

Many animal species are also found in broadleaved woodlands. Some of these including the dormouse *Muscardinus avellanarius,* nightingale *Luscinia megarhynchos* and terrestrial invertebrates including rare butterflies such as the heath fritillary *Mellicta athalia,* purple emperor *Apatura iris* and chequered skipper *Carterocephalus palaemon* are both restricted in their range in the UK and on the edge of their distribution in Europe.

2. CURRENT FACTORS AFFECTING THE HABITAT

Broadleaved and yew woodlands are affected by:

- Conversion to other land uses through clearance for localised developments including roads and mineral extraction.

- Inappropriate woodland management, such as the removal of large old trees and uncontrolled grazing of deer and sheep, which leads to a decrease in the structural diversity and reduction in natural regeneration.
- Replacement of native stands by non-native trees.
- Invasion by non-native species such as rhododendron *Rhododendron* spp.
- Excessive disruption through large scale harvesting and other insensitive changes in management regime.
- Reduction of hardwood based industries and demand for wood products through product substitution and loss of traditional markets resulting in loss of species through neglect or unsympathetic management of woodlands.
- Acid deposition, which threatens individual trees within the ecosystem and associated fungi.

3. CURRENT ACTION

3.1 Legal status

Broadleaved and yew woodland receives protection through the SSSI/ASSI series and a number of sites are NNRs. Through these networks of sites representative examples of broadleaved woodland types, throughout their geographical range, are afforded protection. EN, SNH and CCW maintain ancient woodland inventories which detail the occurrence of both designated and non-designated sites.

The international importance of broadleaved woodland is recognised through the EC Habitats Directive with seven broadleaved woodland types and one yew woodland type listed under Annex I of the Directive. The UK Government has proposed that a number of broadleaved woodland sites corresponding to the types listed in Annex I merit consideration as SACs.

National policies set out in the 1985 *Guidelines to the Management of Broadleaved Woodland,* give a presumption against clearance of broadleaved woodland for conversion to another land use. The expansion of broadleaved woodland has been substantial in recent years and the majority of planted broadleaves are of native species.

The UK signed the *Resolution for the Conservation of Biodiversity of European Forests* as agreed in Helsinki (1993). This resolution provides for the enhancement of biodiversity as part of a sustainable forest management programme by integrating the requirements of native, natural and managed woodlands.

3.2 Management, research and guidance

Ancient woodland, especially ancient semi-natural woodland, may receive policy protection in Structure and Local plans. Both ancient and ancient semi-natural woodland must be managed to maintain their special features of environmental and cultural value. The Forestry Authority has produced a series of eight advisory guides on the management of ancient semi-natural woodlands throughout Britain. The advice is intended to help owners and managers to achieve the best practice to secure the woodland's future. The Forestry Authority assesses planting and management schemes (notably Woodland Grant Scheme) against these guidelines.

Important woodland sites may be recognised by Local Authorities as Wildlife Sites and protected by relevant local planning policies which safeguard them from the effects of inappropriate development. In Wales, the broadleaved woodland element of the Habitat Scheme aims to encourage natural regeneration of native woodlands by excluding livestock.

Agricultural Departments encourage the planting of woodland on agricultural land through the Farm Woodland Premium Scheme which offers annual payments (over 15 years, for plantings with over 50% of broadleaved trees) to compensate for income loss. They also offer initial free advice to farmers considering establishing woodlands. Initiatives to create major new mainly broadleaved forests in the UK include the new National Forest, Central Scotland Forest, the Millennium Forest (Scotland) and Community forests around a number of towns and cities. These woodlands are expected to include a high proportion of native species.

Initiatives to restore local wood-based industries include the woodnet project in the Weald, linking wood producers to wood users, and a number of projects to reinvigorate the British-based charcoal industry, such as Cumbrian broadleaves. Small woods projects, designed to reinstate traditional woodland management in neglected broadleaved woodland are also in place. Many of these such as Sylvanus, Esus, Coed Cymru, Anglian Woodlands, Scottish Native Woods and Highland Birchwoods, are joint initiatives between the Forestry Authority and a variety of other statutory agencies.

Many woods are also retained and new areas planted due to landowners interest in game shooting or other sporting and recreation activities.

Felling licences are required for the felling of more than 5 cubic metres of timber in any one quarter. In addition broadleaved woodlands may be covered by Tree Preservation Orders, which are designed to protect individual trees and wooded areas. The Timber Industries are actively promoting the use of home-grown wood in building etc.

EN, CCW and SNH support research into management methods which will restore the conservation value of woodland, as well as more general programmes of survey and monitoring. The Forestry Commission also has a considerable research programme into silviculture and the ecology of broadleaved woods.

- Produce advice on conservation and sustainable broadleaved woodland management for woodland managers and policy makers.
- Encourage research into the effects of natural processes of woodland disturbance and succession and the interactions between herbivores and woodland plant communities.

4. CONSERVATION DIRECTION

Maintain the extent and habitat quality, especially of ancient and semi-natural broadleaved woodland, and expand broadleaved woods, particularly with new native woodland which is linked to ancient and semi-natural woods.

Measures to be considered further include:

- Develop a strategy to implement the *Resolution for the Conservation of Biodiversity of European Forests* as agreed in Helsinki (1993).
- Restore selected ancient woodland sites that have been replanted by converting them back to semi-natural condition.
- Restrict new woodland planting on sites where this would adversely affect the existing conservation value.

PLANTED CONIFEROUS WOODLAND HABITAT STATEMENT

1. CURRENT STATUS

Many woods composed wholly or mainly of conifer species, both native and introduced, have been planted on habitats which had significant biodiversity value as open grounds. Habitat Statements for other habitats such as broadleaved and yew woodland, heath, moor and bog recommend a programme of clearance of plantation woodland to allow recreation of the former habitat. This Statement considers the existing or potential importance for biodiversity of large UK plantations where wholesale restoration is not the main conservation need. It should be considered in conjunction with Statements for other habitats.

Approximately 7% (1,516,000 ha) of Great Britain is covered by conifer woodlands. The stands are usually of a single species, with approximately 40% being sitka spruce, however, at the forest scale species composition is normally mixed: in thinned older stands and at edges and glades, a variety of native trees and shrubs develop as an understorey.. 775,000 ha are managed by Forest Enterprise and 741,000 ha are privately owned.

Many first rotation forests are reaching harvestable age. This provides opportunities to restructure the habitat which will lead to diversification of the plant and animal communities they contain. Second rotation forests are more likely to be planned to take account of nature conservation needs through creating internal forest diversity, in tree and stand age. Many forests also have a number of associated features and habitats that are important for wildlife. Woodland rides and glades for example can be important for vascular plants and invertebrates. They could also provide areas for targeting limited restoration of semi-natural habitat in conifer plantations. Old stands with dead and dying trees, understorey vegetation and open canopies are also important for a variety of species.

A number of GB Red Data Book bird species may occur in plantations. These include goshawk *Accipiter gentilis*, Scottish crossbill *Loxia scotica* and firecrest *Regulus ignicapillus* and in clear-felled or early growth stages nightjar *Caprimulgus europaeus* and woodlark *Lullula arborea*.

2. CURRENT FACTORS AFFECTING THE HABITAT

There is no particular threat to the conifer resource as a whole. However, some factors could either reduce the existing wildlife interest of plantations or mean that potential improvements are not realised. These include:

- Decreases in the structural diversity of stands and forests through insensitive management.
- Clear-felling and replanting that disrupts other elements of the forest ecosystem, for example through erosion or effects on water bodies.

3. CURRENT ACTION

3.1 Legal status

The overall UK policy aims are set out in *Sustainable Forestry: The UK Programme* (1994) and *Biodiversity in Britain's Forests* (1993). An expansion of planted conifer woodland is envisaged, which will increase the diverse benefits that forests can provide. The UK also signed the *Resolution for the Conservation of Biodiversity of European Forests* as agreed in Helsinki (1993). This resolution provides for the enhancement of biodiversity as part of a sustainable forest management programme by integrating the requirements of native, natural and managed woodlands.

In 1986 the Countryside Commission for Scotland proposed that all Local Authorities should undertake the preparation of Indicative Forestry Strategies and in 1987 the Convention of Local Authorities recommended that all Regional Councils should prepare such strategies. These have been produced and are being reviewed. Essentially, Local Authorities draw up maps which direct afforestation onto areas which are known to have a low conservation interest. In England and Wales County Councils have started the process of producing Indicative Forestry Strategies.

There is a strong emphasis on wildlife conservation and management in licences and grants administered by the Forestry Authority. The Forestry Commission, through its Regional Advisory Committees and Environmental Panels, consults conservation specialists on its activities.

3.2 Management, research and guidance

Forest Enterprise is preparing Forest Design Plans with local conservation experts which are subject to Forestry Authority approval. The Forest Design Plans are the major means of delivering biodiversity gains in FE forests through promoting structural diversity and populations of key species.

The Forestry Commission has also produced documents *Forest and Water Guidelines* (1993), *Nature Conservation Guidelines* (1990) and *Landscape Guidelines* (1989) which they use as the basis for prescribing management for wildlife conservation. The Forestry Commission is currently drawing together these, and other environmental guidelines, to produce standards for enhancing the biodiversity of planted forests. These standards will reflect the structural and functional elements of the forest as well as the species interest.

Other practical examples of multi-purpose forest development exist in the National Forest and Community Forest initiatives, and in Woodland Parks, Community Woodlands and Forest Parks.

Some conifer plantations have been notified as SSSI for their bird interest and many others fall within SSSIs notified for other reasons.

Forest Enterprise has initiated a number of restoration schemes, removing trees from heathland, restructuring forests and working to restore native woodlands.

4. CONSERVATION DIRECTION

Maintain and enhance the wildlife potential of the existing conifer resource through continued restructuring and diversification.

Measures to be considered further include:

- Develop a strategy to implement the *Resolution for the Conservation of Biodiversity of European Forests* as agreed in Helsinki (1993)
- Continue to direct the expansion of planted conifers to land of low conservation value (such as derelict industrial and low grade arable land) ensuring habitats of a high nature conservation value are not further threatened - using Indicative Forest Strategies where

available.

- Promote forestry management which enhances conservation value through restructuring and diversification.
- Develop systems of monitoring the biodiversity conservation value of planted conifer woodlands, for example by assessing critical habitat features and selected key or indicator species.

NATIVE PINE WOODLAND HABITAT STATEMENT

I. CURRENT STATUS

Native pinewoods are relict indigenous forests of Scots pine *Pinus sylvestris* var *scotica*, which occur throughout the central and north-eastern Grampians and in the northern and western Highlands of Scotland. They are an important western representative of the European boreal forests in which structure and succession is determined mainly by natural fires caused by lightning. In the past native pine forests may have covered more than 1.5 million ha, however, less than 1% of the former range now remains. The remaining extent of habitat is approximately 16,000 ha.

Native pinewoods occur on infertile, strongly leached, podsolic soils. They do not support a large diversity of plants and animals compared with some more fertile habitats. However, there is a characteristic plant and animal community which includes many rare and uncommon species. The main tree species is Scots pine although birch *Betula* spp., rowan *Sorbus aucuparia*, sessile oak *Quercus petraea*, willows *Salix* spp., and bird cherry *Prunus padus* are also found. Oak occurs mainly in the north-east of Scotland. There is a rich understorey of shrubs including common juniper *Juniperus communis*, aspen *Populus tremula*, holly *Ilex aquifolium* and hazel *Corylus avellana*. Dead rotting wood supports significant bryophyte communities. The field layer is characterised by acid tolerant plants like bell heather *Erica cinerea*, bilberry *Vaccinium myrtillus* and crowberry *Empetrum nigrum*. Many uncommon and rare species are found in this habitat including the specialist hoverfly *Callicera rufa* and the distinctive bird species capercaillie *Tetrao urogallus*, Britain's only endemic bird the Scottish crossbill *Loxia scotica* and rare plants such as twinflower *Linnaea borealis* and one-flowered wintergreen *Moneses uniflora* are also found mainly in the native pinewoods.

2. CURRENT FACTORS AFFECTING THE HABITAT

The primary factor influencing native pinewoods is:

- Lack of natural regeneration due to high grazing levels.

Past threats which must continue to be avoided include:

- Inappropriate forestry management, in particular underplanting with non-native conifer species and clear felling.
- Conversion to other land uses resulting in increased fragmentation and isolation of native pine woods and the associated loss of wildlife interest.

3. CURRENT ACTION

3.1 Legal status

Many of the most important areas of native pinewoods have been notified as SSSIs. Exceptional examples of these were recently proposed by the UK Government as areas that merit designation as SACs under the EC Habitats Directive.

3.2 Management, research and guidance

In 1994 the Forestry Authority completed an inventory of the Caledonian pinewoods which registers the location of native pinewoods, the extent of the woodland and possible regeneration zones. The Report from the Cairngorms Working Party also made strong recommendations for the expansion of remnants of native pinewoods, especially in two areas - Forests of Mar and Strathspey.

A number of Forestry Authority initiatives contribute to the management and recreation of native pinewoods. These include grant aid offered under the Woodland Grant Scheme for regeneration and also for the planting of new native pinewoods within the former natural range of pinewoods. Scots pine of local origin is used for replanting and the Forestry Authority maintains a register of seed sources for use in this scheme. Forest Enterprise also runs a programme of restoration and expansion of native pinewoods and promotes recreational facilities and educational uses through this programme.

The Forestry Authority and SNH are working closely to produce a handbook on pinewood management. The Forestry Authority has also produced a set of advisory guides on the management of ancient semi-natural woodlands throughout Britain, one of which provides advice on the management of native pinewoods.

EC LIFE (Nature) programme funding has been received to assess the resource of native pinewood in Scotland, evaluate the impact of deer grazing and to carry out emergency restoration activities at Glen Affric Forest reserve. This work builds on the Forestry Authority Native Pinewoods Register completed in 1994.

4. CONSERVATION DIRECTION

Maintain and enhance the structure and wildlife interest of native pinewoods and encourage natural regeneration in core areas aiming to restore degenerated areas and to bring them into appropriate management.

Measures to be considered further include:

- Promote the expansion of existing areas of native pinewoods.
- Encourage the protection of small pinewood remnants from grazing pressure and encourage expansion, thereby addressing the historic fragmentation and isolation of pinewoods.
- Restore underplanted pinewoods.
- Follow current guidelines to conserve the genetic integrity of populations of native pinewoods species.
- Take opportunities to produce useable wood.

LOWLAND WOOD PASTURES AND PARKLAND HABITAT STATEMENT

1. CURRENT STATUS

Working lowland wood pastures and parks are those where grazing is still practised at a level that sustains the special features associated with open ground. It is estimated that less than 10,000-20,000 ha of the resource remains in such a working condition. A greater amount of relict wood pastures and parklands exists, however, in either an unmanaged state or as scattered trees with arable or improved pasture around them.

Wood pastures and parklands are believed to have been widespread in lowland landscapes through the mediaeval age and up until the early 19th century, and as such are important for their landscape history and archaeological features. During the 20th century there has been a decline in sites that had survived legal enclosure. The decline is principally due to dereliction and succession to secondary woodland, or conversion to more intensive agricultural or forestry uses. The decline in lowland wood pastures and parks has occurred throughout the lowlands of western Europe. The greatest extent of this habitat in western Europe probably survives in southern England.

Wood pasture and parkland contain large numbers of very old trees particularly ancient pedunculate oak *Quercus robur* and beech *Fagus sylvatica*. They are internationally important for the rare saproxylic invertebrates such as the violet click beetle *Limoniscus violaceus* whose larvae is found inside rotten standing trunks, lichens such as *Lobaria, Lecanactis* or *Sticta* species and fungi such as the hedgehog fungus *Crelophus cirrhatus* and the giant hoof-shaped bracket fungi *Phellinus robustus*, which are associated with the mature bark and dead wood. Acid or neutral grassland also occurs and is an important feature of this habitat.

2. CURRENT FACTORS AFFECTING THE HABITAT

- Changes in rural economies have led to withdrawal of grazing from commons, former Royal Forests and parks.
- Intensification of agricultural management has destroyed the open ground interests on many sites.
- Large old trees are felled and removed from sites; cessation of pollarding may also have reduced the long term survival potential of many old trees.
- Improved recreational access often leads to the clearance, or modification, of ancient trees to make the areas safe as public places. This can also lead to severe erosion of soils and vegetation at key sites.
- On most sites there is a large "generation gap" (very old and young trees present, but few of intermediate age) which leads to a loss of habitat continuity.

3. CURRENT ACTION

3.1 Legal status

Many important wood pastures and parks have been identified as SSSI/ASSIs. Other sites are identified as Wildlife Sites. The UK Government has also set out its commitment to designating some parklands as SPAs and SACs under the EC Birds Directive and the EC Habitats Directive respectively.

3.2 Management, research and guidance

Forest Enterprise is reviewing its management of working wood pastures of the New Forest. This wood pasture system represents the majority of the actively worked resource in the UK and the most extensive area with old oak beech populations in NW Europe.

Grazing regimes are being reinstated at a number of sites including Burnham Beeches (Corporation of the City of London) and Pamber Forest (Hampshire). Plans are well advanced to reinstate grazing in other sites such as Greenham Common (Berkshire), Odiham Common (Hampshire) and Ebernoe Common (West Sussex). Tree management such as pollarding, is being reinstated at some sites, including Burnham Beeches.

Providing guidance on the conservation of parkland and wood pastures is an important element of the statutory agencies' work. The Invertebrate Site Register Habitats Association Module is a key source of data on which advice is based.

EN has established a Veteran Tree Initiative through which they form working partnerships with others involved in parkland management, ensuring that conservation objectives are taken into account. A pilot inventory of the parkland resource for two counties in England has been prepared.

CCW has initiated an inventory project of all parklands in Wales. The project aims to identify parkland sites important in a national, regional or local context for their invertebrate and lichen communities. Survey work in 1994 recorded 25 invertebrate species new to Wales including the beetles *Aeletes atomarius, Ptinella limbata, Cryptophagus labilis* and *Scraptia testacea.*

4. CONSERVATION DIRECTION

Maintain the extent of functioning wood pastures and parks ensuring that the management of important sites takes account of their biological interest. Restore, where appropriate, modified wood pasture and parkland.

Measures to be considered further include:

- Restore management regimes to selected areas of wood pasture and parkland modified by plantation forestry, scrub colonisation, or unsustainable agricultural use such as grazing.
- Protecting wood pasture from inappropriate use, including unsustainable recreation.
- Establish, where restoration of grazing is not appropriate, other systems for maintaining and enhancing the features and species associated with former wood pasture and parkland.
- Compile a UK inventory of the remaining resource of wood pasture and parklands and their associated characteristic plant and animal communities.

BOUNDARY FEATURES HABITAT STATEMENT

I. CURRENT STATUS

There are three main types of boundary feature: hedgerows, walls and ditches, each with a distinctive biological character. Frequently there are linear verges of grassland and other semi-natural habitat associated with these features, particularly along the UK's extensive road network. These features contain a large part of the biodiversity in the countryside and provide opportunities for some species to disperse within otherwise inhospitable countryside.

Hedgerows resemble woodland edge and scrub habitats. They exhibit a wide range of variation and the most important are rich in relicts of ancient woodland. Over 600 plant, 1,500 insect, 65 bird and 20 mammal species are known to live or feed in hedgerows. Particularly in South West England hedges have traditionally been planted on high banks which create a biologically very rich environment. The current UK total, assuming a continued overall net rate of loss through neglect or removal of about 5% pa, may be estimated to be about 450,000 km.

Dry stone walls are most typically found in areas of upland. They provide a habitat for a wide range of flowering plants, ferns, mosses and lichens adapted to rock habitats, including at least one rare moss species known only from dry stone walls in North Yorkshire. Mortared walls of ancient sites such as the Colchester Roman Walls, can also be important for lower plants. Regional variance in field boundaries occur. In Wales, cloddiau (earth banks that are usually stone faced) have an ecological value similar to stone walls. A wide range of invertebrates, reptiles, birds and mammals use dry stone walls for feeding, breeding or shelter.

There are an estimated 112,500 km of dry stone walls in England, half of which are described as derelict. Estimates of the loss of dry stone walls vary, between 7,000 km lost in the period 1947-1985, through to 40,000 km lost in England and Wales in the last 20 years.

In low lying areas where the water table is perennially close to the surface flooded ditches are used as stock proof boundaries to grasslands or as arterial drainage in arable areas. Where land use has been intensive the ditches are the main refuges for aquatic plants and animals and may support nationally important assemblages of rare aquatic plants and animals, such as on the Somerset Levels.

2. CURRENT FACTORS AFFECTING THE HABITAT

Boundary features are adversely affected by both destruction and lack of management.

- The loss of hedgerows and dry stone walls by direct destruction to create larger fields has slowed and some increase in hedgerow extent has taken place. However a large part of the hedgerow and wall resource is unmanaged and gradually disappearing.
- In the case of road verges cessation of management by flail mower and chemicals may have had beneficial effects for wildlife, although where management has ceased rank grassland, scrub and woodland may be replacing more important semi-natural vegetation particularly species-rich grassland.
- The increasing disturbance of roadside verges to lay and maintain services such as gas, electricity and telecommunications.
- Fertiliser run-off and lowering of water tables has adversely affected many drainage ditches.
- Road widening and alignment has resulted in the loss of traditional boundaries and verges.

3. CURRENT ACTION

3.1 Legal status

In the more ecologically impoverished parts of the UK, including parts of Lincolnshire and Cambridgeshire, roadside verges and other boundary features have been specifically protected by designation. Linear features fall within many SSSI/ASSIs and other designated areas including NNRs and LNRs.

3.2 Management, research and guidance

During the period 1991/2 to 1994/5, 3,161 km of hedge restoration work was agreed in England under Countryside Stewardship agreements. This represents an expenditure of £700,000 per annum. In Scotland, SNH provides discretionary grants for the improvement or creation of hedges and other landscape features. SNH has also recently produced a series of leaflets on the management of boundary habitats. In Wales, the Hedgerow Renovation Scheme administered by CCW provides funding for the renovation of selected hedgerows.

Most ESAs offer payments for the restoration and creation of hedges and enhancement of traditional field boundaries (e.g. Exmoor and Pennine Dales). Many local schemes also exist which offer financial incentives, for example, in National Parks.

Further guidance is also available from ADAS and the ITE who recently produced a range of reports for DoE and MAFF on the status, management and wildlife of hedgerows in Britain. MAFF are also currently commissioning further research on hedge management and establishment. The Forestry Commission has published guidance on the establishment of trees in hedgerows. FWAG has produced a Hedge Pack to advise farmers on good hedge management practices.

In 1993 Plantlife launched the Great Hedge Project aiming to create a network of hedges across the country and to foster public interest in hedges.

4. CONSERVATION DIRECTION

Maintain the quantity and quality of boundary features, such as hedgerows, road-side verges, and dry stone walls, protecting features of conservation value and bringing derelict features into appropriate management.

Measures to be considered further include:

- Protect boundary features important for wildlife from damage and destruction.
- Use existing measures such as Countryside Stewardship and Hedgerow Scheme to support the appropriate management of boundary features.
- Extend boundary features to increase cover and connect isolated habitat fragments.
- Develop methodologies for the identification and management of important features, in particular hedgerows and roadside verges.

CEREAL FIELD MARGINS HABITAT STATEMENT

1. CURRENT STATUS

In the landscape of Great Britain tilled land forms 41% of the land area, occupying 44% of land in England, 28% in Scotland and 9% in Wales.

Much of the wildlife interest in arable areas is found at the field edges (or headlands). Some species which were previously considered to be problem weeds are now amongst Britain's rarest plants, for example the corn buttercup *Ranunculus arvensis*, was widespread until the 1960s but is now found in fewer than 25 sites. Other threatened and important species include pheasant's eye *Adonis arnua*, cornflower *Centaurea cyanus*, broadleaved spurge *Euphorbia platyphyllos*, corn parsley *Petroselinum segetum*, shepherd's-needle *Scandix pecten-veneris* and narrow-fruited cornsalad *Valerianella dentata*. Most arable weeds depend on the seed bank and dormancy to ensure that populations survive in years when optimum growth conditions are absent. This means that many can survive, despite spraying and dense crops, reappearing when the right conditions return. These plants in turn attract a range of animals including invertebrates, such as several common grass feeding butterflies and a number of ground beetles (Carabidae), some of which are nationally rare or threatened, mammals and birds. Important features of cereal field margins are outlined more extensively in a separate Costed Habitat Action Plan.

Temporarily and seasonally water-filled hollows in arable fields can be important for a specialised suite of rare vascular plants and bryophytes.

A large number of insects and other invertebrates spend part of their life cycles in cereal fields. Many of these species are a potential food source for birds and mammals. Several birds such as grey partridge *Perdix perdix*, skylark *Alauda arvensis*, corn bunting *Miliaria calandra* and lapwing *Vanellus vanellus* nest in arable areas often selecting crop types according to their structural suitability. Winter stubbles are also used by seed eating birds such as the cirl bunting *Emberiza cirlus* and in Wales the chough *Pyrrhocorax pyrrhocorax*. Many of these species have experienced significant declines, which are associated with changes in agricultural practice.

2. CURRENT FACTORS AFFECTING THE HABITAT

The primary factors which affect the species interest in arable areas are:

- Substantial applications of nitrogen and the widespread use of insecticides and herbicides.
- Removal of hedgerows and other boundary features and small patches of semi-natural habitat.
- Change from spring to autumn sown cereals which has caused loss of feeding opportunities on winter stubbles and loss of suitable conditions in the spring for ground nesting birds.
- Inappropriate husbandry practices, such as spraying out hedge bases.
- Simplification of crop rotation cycle, including a decline in the use of root crops in stock-rearing areas, use of pre-emergence weed killers, and rapid re-seeding of grassland in rotation cycles.
- Improved drainage of large areas of low-lying arable land.
- Loss of arable cultivation from areas where it was traditionally of low intensity, such as in the Western Isles.

3. CURRENT ACTION

In 1987 MAFF initiated a research programme to examine the likely impact of set-aside policy in the UK. From 1988 to 1991 MAFF offered farmers the opportunity to enter five-year set-aside agreements on their arable land. However, changes in the EC's arable support arrangements led to this scheme being closed to new applicants after the 1991 intake. Two basic set-aside options now exist; a six-year rotational set-aside and a flexible set-aside. The set-aside land can be managed in five basic ways; field margins, grasslands, natural regeneration, wild bird cover and growing crops for non-food use, as a means of achieving specific environmental benefits. For example the natural regeneration or grassland option could be used to create sandy grassland or damp lowland grassland in appropriate areas.

Management of former five-year set aside land can be continued in an environmentally beneficial way through one element of MAFF's new Habitats Scheme. Applications for entry into this scheme are assessed in terms of whether the land supports a diversity of plant species, particularly rare arable weeds, or shows evidence of natural reversion to a habitat characteristic for the area such as lowland heathland, or provides a nesting area or feeding ground for key bird species or wild animals or supports a diverse or rare population of invertebrates.

Payments are also available in arable areas for field margins in association with the hedgerow option of the Countryside Stewardship Scheme. Some ESAs also have prescriptions for conservation headlands and the Western Isles ESA has a whole-field arable option.

SNH has a TIBRE project (Targeted Inputs for a Better Rural Environment) which aims to encourage the adoption of new technological applications to reduce the environmental impact of present agricultural operations. EN contributes to similar aims through their Whole Farms Plan Project. CCW's Tir Cymen Scheme, which operates in three pilot areas, is also a whole-farm based scheme with objectives to combine the conservation of existing semi-natural habitats with good farming practice.

The MAFF-led LINK programme on Technologies for Sustainable Farming Systems aims to develop techniques of crop and livestock management which are acceptable environmentally, economically and in terms of animal welfare.

EN has a pesticide policy which seeks a selective reduction in pesticide use to benefit wildlife. The policy is promoted through research to identify the causes of decline in populations of farmland birds and associated development of advice on the environmental effects of pesticides, including pesticide drift.

Much of the current action for maintaining arable species is in the form of advice. To ensure that the advice given is of value there are a number of sources of information produced by FWAG, The Game Conservancy Trust and others. RSPB produced a *Farming and Wildlife Handbook* (1994) which offers guidelines on increasing the wildlife potential of farmland habitats, including arable land. RSPB has also produced a series of *Farmland Bird Management Guidelines*.

Considerable research has been undertaken by The Game Conservancy Trust into improving arable management, particularly for wildlife, and into the status of rare arable flowers. Game management and shooting can be a strong incentive to farmers and landowners to increase the wildlife potential of farmland habitats. The Game Conservancy Trust has also produced a mixture of seeds to farm a "game-crop" which increases potential nesting and holding cover for gamebirds, and can be used by finches and buntings in the autumn and winter when other food supplies are low.

4. CONSERVATION DIRECTION

Maintain existing diversity and distribution of all populations of rare and declining species associated with arable land, where appropriate connecting fragmented populations.

Measures to be considered further include:

- Protect arable areas important for wildlife from inappropriate land use.
- Consider the requirements of rare and threatened species dependent on these areas when negotiating changes to, or reform of, agricultural support schemes.
- Review and use existing measures such as set-aside, ESAs and Countryside Stewardship, to ensure the requirements of key species are taken into consideration.
- Provide farmers with the advice and technology to enable them to manage land for the benefit of wildlife.

IMPROVED GRASSLAND HABITAT STATEMENT

1. CURRENT STATUS

Improved grasslands account for the great majority of all grassland found in rural and urban parts of the UK. They are species-poor, grass dominated swards, often sown for agricultural or recreational use, or created by modification of unimproved grasslands by fertilisers and selective herbicides. They are particularly characterised by the abundance of rye grass *Lolium* spp. and white clover *Trifolium repens*. Sometimes such grasslands are temporary and sown as part of the rotation of arable crops. Where not managed as pasture, improved grasslands are often mown regularly either for silage production or in non agricultural contexts for recreational and amenity purposes.

The biodiversity of improved grasslands is low. Fertiliser use in particular stimulates the growth of competitive grasses and a small number of common broadleaved plants such as common ragwort *Senecio jacobaea* and dock *Rumex* spp. at the expense of other plant species. These grasslands support a very impoverished fauna. Very locally improved grasslands can be of importance for winter feeding waterfowl including internationally important populations of species such as Greenland white-fronted goose *Anser albifrons flavirostris*, barnacle goose *Branta leucopsis* and widgeon *Anas penelope*. Where machine use is infrequent and stocking densities are low such grassland may retain a range of ground nesting birds such as lapwing *Vanellus vanellus* and skylark *Alauda arvensis*, particularly in hill farming areas.

In the past 50 years improved grassland have increased by approximately 90% in area due to the increased intensification of farming. This expansion has been largely at the expense of other habitats of high biodiversity importance, particularly unimproved grasslands, although large areas of moorland and other habitats have also been converted.

In the past two decades the change from hay to silage has stimulated increased agrochemical use on improved grassland, further degrading their already limited biodiversity.

2. CURRENT FACTORS AFFECTING THE HABITAT

- In recent years the area of improved grassland has remained relatively stable. Grass remains one of the cheapest animal feed stuffs and as farm profit margins have decreased this has resulted in an intensification of grassland management on many farms since 1980.
- Attempts to convert improved grassland to species-rich grassland have met with variable but generally limited success due to the residual fertiliser effect, particularly of phosphate.
- A proportion of newly afforested land, particularly in the lowlands has been on improved grassland.
- On improved grassland managed for recreation and amenity, particularly road verges and public open spaces, there is likely to have been some reduction in the intensity of management.
- A high proportion of land restoration on former industrial sites, or associated with civil engineering projects, is to improved grassland.

3. CURRENT ACTION

3.1 Legal status

Areas of improved grassland of international importance as feeding areas for wildfowl are protected within SSSIs and the most important of these area are owned by conservation agencies or NGOs (e.g. Gruinart Flats (Islay), Slimbridge (Gloucestershire), Ouse Washes (Cambridgeshire).

In some situations improved grassland forms an incidental part of mosaics of high quality habitats protected within SSSIs, NNRs and SPAs.

3.2 Management, research and guidance

A number of conservation management schemes (such as the Islay Goose Scheme) involve compensation to farmers for damage caused by wildfowl grazing on improved grasslands.

Some improved grasslands are covered by countryside management schemes, particularly in areas where they are of value for amenity or as components of high quality lowland landscapes.

4. CONSERVATION DIRECTION

Enhance areas of improved grassland which are of importance for wildlife and restore semi-natural vegetation on sites where this would enhance their value for wildlife.

Measures to be considered further include:

- Protect important sites, which include areas of improved grasslands and enhance their potential for wildlife.
- Research methods for recreating semi-natural habitats on areas of improved grassland and establish relevant habitat creation schemes.
- Target activities which would damage semi-natural habitats, including economic development, recreation and some forms of forest planting, to areas of improved grassland which have no potential for restoration to semi-natural habitat.
- Encourage environmentally sensitive farming methods.

UNIMPROVED NEUTRAL GRASSLANDS HABITAT STATEMENT

I. CURRENT STATUS

The vast majority of the grassland found on farms in the UK is now species poor 'improved' grassland which has been modified by extensive fertiliser use and reseeding.

Unimproved (species-rich) neutral grasslands unaffected by agricultural improvement are rare and threatened. There are significantly less than 10,000 ha in England and less than 2,000 ha in Wales. Survey data for Northern Ireland and Scotland are not available but the total UK extent of species-rich neutral grassland is estimated to be less than 15,000 ha.

These grasslands are managed mainly as traditional hay-meadows or pastures and are colourful because they contain a high proportion of broad-leaved herbaceous species relative to grasses. Some characteristic species, such as green-winged orchid *Orchis morio*, snake's head fritillary *Fritillaria meleagris* and adder's-tongue fern *Ophioglossum vulgatum* are now scarce. There are three unimproved neutral grassland types, two of which are unique to the UK, and the third which is otherwise only recorded in Ireland.

Between 1930 and 1984 semi-natural lowland grassland decreased by an estimated 97% in England and Wales. A survey of the Yorkshire Dales National Park, an area rich in upland meadows by national standards, revealed that less than 5% of 3,746 meadows surveyed could be described as herb-rich and less than 2% were protected as SSSI. Worcestershire is one of the main strongholds for lowland neutral grasslands in England but a recent survey has revealed there are only about 500 ha surviving. In Wales approximately 650 ha of neutral grassland occurs on 208 SSSIs illustrating the way in which these grasslands are now confined to numerous small, scattered and often isolated fields.

Most neutral meadows survive in a landscape of hedges and small woods, or in the distinctive upland landscape of stone walls and moorland of northern England. Their conservation importance is partly as a component of these biologically-rich landscapes, for example as feeding areas for moorland birds at certain times of the year and as reservoir of woodland edge species.

2. CURRENT FACTORS AFFECTING THE HABITAT

Neutral grasslands are most affected by changes in agricultural management including:

- Application of artificial fertiliser which has been shown to affect floristic richness adversely at even low levels of application.
- Increased use of slurry, which unlike traditional, occasional, light applications of farmyard manure and lime is detrimental to floristic richness.
- Change from hay to silage production, whereby more frequent cutting reduces seeding opportunities for plants and disrupts the breeding of birds and other animals.
- Change from mowing to spring and summer grazing resulting in the loss of those meadow plants and animals which are intolerant of summer grazing and adapted to traditional cutting management.
- Abandonment and neglect which results in gradual reversion to rank grassland dominated by false oat-grass *Arrhenatherum elatius* and eventually reversion to scrub or secondary woodland of low nature conservation value.

3. CURRENT ACTION

3.1 Legal status

As well as a large number of mostly small and isolated SSSIs selected for their neutral grassland interest, there are a number of neutral grassland NNRs in England such as North Meadow Cricklade (Wiltshire) and Upwood Meadows (Cambridgeshire). Two types of neutral grassland are listed on Annex I of the Habitats Directive: lowland hay meadows and mountain hay meadows, and the UK Government has recently set out its proposals for areas that it considers merit designation as SACs.

3.2 Management, research and guidance

Several ESAs contain neutral meadows and in certain cases, such as the North Pennine Dales and Somerset Levels, the management conditions are designed specifically to protect neutral grasslands.

In England the Countryside Stewardship scheme includes an option for old meadows and pastures in Hereford and Worcestershire, which is primarily focused upon the protection of neutral grasslands, and similar provisions are included in the Tir Cymen scheme in Wales. Several of English Nature's Wildlife Enhancement Schemes have been focused upon neutral grasslands, such as Worcestershire meadows.

4. CONSERVATION DIRECTION

Maintain the extent and quality of species-rich neutral grassland sites in the UK, restore degraded neutral grasslands to buffer sites and restore the range of neutral grassland.

Measures to be considered further include:

- Protect species-rich neutral grassland from inappropriate changes in land use.
- Encourage environmentally sensitive management of neutral grasslands.
- Review and use where appropriate existing measures such as ESAs, Countryside Stewardship and Tir Cymen to encourage appropriate management.
- Develop a fuller understanding of restoration techniques with the aim of expanding remnant patches of unimproved neutral grassland.

ACID GRASSLANDS HABITAT STATEMENT

I. CURRENT STATUS

Acid grasslands are probably one of the most extensive semi-natural habitats in Britain, yet surprisingly little is known about their true extent or conservation management requirements, especially in the lowlands. Estimates suggest that there is in excess of 1,200,000 ha of acid grassland in the uplands but in the lowlands it is unlikely to exceed 30,000 ha. Lowland acid grassland is becoming increasingly rare in Britain. However, in the uplands much acid grassland is often of low biological interest and is the product of poor management of other priority habitats, such as dwarf-shrub heath. Acid grassland also occurs in the montane zone, however, montane habitats are covered by a separate Statement.

Acid grasslands occur on acid rocks such as sandstones, acid igneous rocks and on superficial deposits such as sands and gravels. Although the habitat is typically species-poor a wide range of communities occur in the UK. Large expanses of acid grassland, uniform in character, occur in the uplands. These areas have a limited biodiversity interest, but a proportion contribute to the conservation interest of the moor. In the lowlands, acid grasslands are now rare and particularly in areas such as East Anglia they provide an important reservoir of rare species.

2. CURRENT FACTORS AFFECTING THE HABITAT

In the lowlands this habitat is affected by:

- Agricultural intensification, particularly fertilisation, ploughing and drainage.
- Lack of grazing leading to an invasion by coarse grasses and scrub.

In the uplands the main causes of change are:

- Inappropriate grazing regimes by sheep, cattle, ponies and deer, typically excessive grazing levels at the wrong time of the year, which causes the habitat to become degraded.
- Forestry planting.
- Abandonment and neglect leading to encroachment by bracken *Pteridium aquilinum*.
- Liming, ploughing and reseeding around the lower fringes of upland areas.

3. CURRENT ACTION

3.1 Legal status

Some lowland acid grassland habitat lies within the SSSI network in Great Britain. Large areas are also included within upland SSSIs, although usually only as features of subsidiary interest. However, in Northern Ireland only a small proportion of the estimated 11,787 ha of this habitat is contained in ASSIs.

The application of environmental conditions to livestock headage payment schemes can benefit acid grassland management objectives in the uplands. In 1994 the UK introduced national measures under EC law to limit CAP payments for Suckler Cow Premiums, Sheep Annual Premium Scheme and the Beef Special Premium Scheme. Farmers claiming Hill Livestock Compensatory Allowance can have their payments limited if they overgraze the land. This could help prevent serious deterioration in the growth and quality of vegetation. Overgrazing is a problem associated with upland areas, whilst in lowland areas insufficient grazing is generally the problem.

3.2 Management, research and guidance

Important acid grassland sites may also be recognised as Wildlife Sites and as such are protected by relevant local planning policies.

Non-statutory nature reserves managed by a variety of conservation organisations also include important examples of acid grassland communities. Acid grassland also forms a significant component of a number of ESAs notably Breckland, Pennine Dales, Whitlaw and Eildon, Clun, Exmoor, Lake District, Shetland, and Cambrians.

In Wales the Tir Cymen scheme includes guidance for the appropriate management of acid grassland.

Many examples of acid grasslands, particularly in the uplands, occur on degraded ex-woodland sites of low nature conservation interest. Many of these areas are suitable for afforestation aimed at the establishment of native and non-native woodlands. Other areas may be targeted for heathland restoration.

4. CONSERVATION DIRECTION

Maintain and enhance important areas of acid grasslands, restore areas of degraded acid grassland, in particular to buffer existing important areas.

Measures to be considered further include:

- Identify the true extent and quality of the acid grassland resource.
- Encourage appropriate livestock grazing to conserve the habitat.
- Protect acid grasslands of conservation importance from inappropriate land use and intensification.
- Restore habitat adjacent to important or vulnerable sites.
- Research appropriate methods of managing and restoring acid grasslands in the uplands.

CALCAREOUS GRASSLAND HABITAT STATEMENT

1. CURRENT STATUS

In the UK calcareous grasslands are developed on shallow lime-rich soils most often derived from chalk and limestone rocks. They are widely distributed, from the south Devon coast to Shetland.

It is estimated there are 40,000-50,000 ha of calcareous grassland in the UK. Calcareous grasslands can be found in nearly every county or Scottish district, but are very unevenly distributed. Wiltshire contains close to two thirds of all chalk grassland (approximately 24,000 ha), whilst a majority of all the limestone grassland is found in the counties of North Yorkshire and Cumbria.

Calcareous grasslands contain an exceptional diversity of rare plants, but are particularly characterised by a series of widespread grassland plants which are mainly restricted to lime rich soils. Species include upright brome *Bromus erecta*, blue moor-grass *Sesleria caerulea* and common rock-rose *Helianthemum nummularium*. Due to the high plant variation of these grasslands 13 different types are recognised. These vary from mostly coastal grasslands rich in warmth-loving, southern species, such as hoary rock-rose *Helianthemum canum* and honewort *Trinia glauca,* through to upland and mountain grasslands rich in arctic-alpines, such as spring gentian *Gentiana verna* and mountain avens *Dryas octopetala.*

Scrub is a prominent feature of many sites. In the absence of grazing scrub can spread to replace grasslands, with a negative effect upon the conservation value of the site. With balanced management, however, species-rich scrub-grassland mosaics can be conserved giving increased plant and animal diversity. Certain types of calcareous scrub, such as juniper *Juniperus communis* scrub, and the species-rich hazel *Corylus avellana* scrub of the Derbyshire Dales have a high intrinsic conservation value and are rare.

2. CURRENT FACTORS AFFECTING THE HABITAT

There are no comprehensive data concerning rates of calcareous grassland loss, but in Sussex 25% of chalk grassland was lost between 1966 and 1980. Calcareous grasslands are affected most by changes in management:

- Under-grazing or the complete cessation of management occurs at many lowland sites. It results in reversion to rank grassland and eventually to closed scrub and woodland. In a recent study of lowland calcareous grasslands important for butterflies 60% were found to be ungrazed.
- Overgrazing in the uplands is adversely affecting species-richness with a particular loss of tall herb and shrub species.
- Agricultural intensification in the form of fertiliser use, herbicide application, ploughing and re-seeding may still be damaging or destroying some grasslands.
- Industrial and urban development affects an unknown number of sites, particularly the in-filling of abandoned chalk and limestone quarries and other industrial sites where calcareous grasslands have established naturally after cessation of working.

3. CURRENT ACTION

3.1 Legal status

Calcareous grasslands support a rich and varied invertebrate fauna including many GB Red Data Book species as well as several species afforded protection under Schedule 5 of the Wildlife and Countryside Act 1981. The endemic early gentian *Gentianella anglica*, and marsh fritillary butterfly *Eurodryas aurinia* are both listed on Annex II of the EC Habitats Directive and are found on chalk grasslands. A number of calcareous grassland types are also listed on Annex I of the EC Habitats Directive, including the priority semi-natural dry grassland (important orchid sites) type. The UK Government has set out its proposals for areas that it considers qualify as SACs for these habitat and species interests.

Calcareous grasslands are well represented in the SSSI/ASSI series which includes a high proportion of the total resource. In Wales c. 1,100 ha is notified as SSSI.

Calcareous grasslands are found within in a large number of NNRs including Ben Lawers (Perthshire), Martin Down (Hampshire), Upper Teesdale (Co. Durham) and Parsonage Down (Wiltshire).

3.2 Management, research and guidance

There are four ESAs of particular importance for their calcareous grasslands: South Downs, Breckland, Cotswold hills and South Wessex Downs.

The Tir Cymen and Countryside Stewardship schemes include payment rates for managing calcareous grasslands to agreed prescriptions. Farm Conservation grants are available for positive conservation work and can include activities such as clearing scrub on calcareous grassland.

The MoD is the largest owner of calcareous grassland. The MoD holding on Salisbury Plain (c 12,000 ha) is of outstanding importance as the largest calcareous grassland in Europe and the MoD are taking management measures here, and at other calcareous grassland sites, which contribute to their conservation.

4. CONSERVATION DIRECTION

Maintain calcareous grassland in all parts of the UK where it occurs, restore degraded calcareous grasslands, buffering and linking small, vulnerable or discontinuous sites.

Measures to be considered further include:

- Protect calcareous grassland from inappropriate changes in land use and management.
- Encourage appropriate grazing in lowland areas and reduce the intensity of grazing in the uplands.
- Consider how existing measures, such as ESAs, Tir Cymen and Countryside Stewardship might establish links between fragmented calcareous grasslands; to allow plant and animal dispersal and facilitate grazing management.
- Provide the advice required to manage calcareous grasslands effectively; encourage technological and other innovation to assist in the sympathetic management of calcareous grassland.

LOWLAND HEATHLAND HABITAT STATEMENT

1. CURRENT STATUS

Lowland heathland is characterised by the presence of plants such as heather *Calluna vulgaris*, gorse *Ulex* spp., and cross-leaved heath *Erica tetralix* and is generally found below 300 metres in altitude. Areas of good quality heathland should consist of an ericaceous layer of varying heights and structures, some areas of scattered trees and scrub, areas of bare ground, gorse, wet heaths, bogs and open water. The presence and numbers of characteristic birds, reptiles, invertebrates, vascular plants, bryophytes and lichens are important indicators of habitat quality.

Lowland heathland is a priority for nature conservation because it is a rare and threatened habitat. In England only one sixth of the heathland present in 1800 now remains. The UK has some 58,000 ha of lowland heathland of which the largest proportion (55%) is found in England. The most significant areas for lowland heathland include the counties of Hampshire, Cornwall, Dorset, Surrey, Devon, Staffordshire, Suffolk, Norfolk, Pembrokeshire, West Glamorgan and west Gwynedd. The UK has an important proportion (about 20%) of the international total of this habitat.

2. CURRENT FACTORS AFFECTING THE HABITAT

In the past heathland was lost primarily to agriculture, forestry, mineral extraction and development. Uncontrolled burning has also been a particular threat to bryophyte and lichen-rich heathland. The main factors affecting the habitat at present are:

- Encroachment of trees and scrub and the simplification of vegetation structure due to a lack of conservation management such as light grazing, controlled burning and cutting.
- Nutrient enrichment, particularly deposition of nitrogen compounds emitted from intensive livestock farming, and from atmospheric pollution.
- Fragmentation and disturbance from developments such as housing and road constructions.
- Agricultural improvement including reclamation and overgrazing, especially in Northern Ireland.

3. CURRENT ACTION

3.1 Legal status

Through the Wildlife and Countryside Act 1981, a large proportion of the lowland heathland habitat has been notified as SSSI. Dry heaths (all subtypes) are also listed on Annex I of the EC Habitats Directive and a number of areas that the UK Government consider qualify as SACs for heathland interests have recently been set out.

3.2 Management, research and guidance

The Countryside Stewardship scheme included 9,413 ha of lowland heathland in England by March 1994. This is the only country-wide heathland management and re-creation scheme. A number of counties in England, however, have heathland management projects most of which receive financial support through EN's National Lowland Heathland Programme. A number of other bodies including the National Trust, County Wildlife Trusts and RSPB are also actively involved in heathland management and the Forestry Commission is promoting heathland regeneration within a forest context.

CCW is carrying out a lowland heathland survey in Wales to identify all the remaining important sites and improve management and protection. A survey of the distribution, extent and condition of lowland heathland in Scotland is required.

Management of lowland heathland is carried out through EN's Wildlife Enhancement Scheme which is expected to cover 9,000 ha of heathland by 1997; management agreements are negotiated with SNH over SSSIs containing lowland heathland and also through MAFF's ESAs, notably in Breckland (Norfolk/Suffolk) and West Penwith (Cornwall). In Northern Ireland some lowland heath is managed within DANI's ESAs.

4. CONSERVATION DIRECTION

Maintain and improve by management existing lowland heathland and re-establish lowland heathland where opportunities arise, particularly in areas where this will reduce habitat isolation.

Further details of this conservation direction and the measures required to deliver it are given in the Costed Habitat Action Plan for Lowland Heathland.

GRAZING MARSH HABITAT STATEMENT

1. CURRENT STATUS

Grazing marsh is defined as periodically inundated pasture, or meadow with ditches which maintain the water levels, containing standing brackish or fresh water. The ditches are especially rich in plants and invertebrates. Almost all areas are grazed and some are cut for hay or silage. Sites may contain seasonal water-filled hollows and permanent ponds with emergent swamp communities, but not extensive areas of tall fen species like reeds, although they may abut with fen and reed swamp communities.

The exact extent of grazing marsh in the UK is not known but it is possible that there may be a total of 300,000 ha. England holds the largest proportion of grazing marsh in the UK, with an estimate in 1994 of 200,000 ha. However, only a small proportion of this grassland is semi-natural supporting a high diversity of native plant species (5,000 ha in England, an estimated 10,000 ha in the UK).

Grazing marshes are particularly important for the number of breeding waders such as snipe *Gallinago gallinago*, lapwing *Vanellus vanellus* and curlew *Numenius arquata* that they support. Internationally important populations of wintering wildfowl also occur including Bewick swans *Cygnus bewickii* and whooper swans *Cygnus cygnus*.

2. CURRENT FACTORS AFFECTING THE HABITAT

Losses in the whole UK have been significant in the last 60 years. Losses of grazing marsh from the early 1930s to the mid-1980s include 64% in the Greater Thames, 48% in Romney Marsh and 37% in Broadland. Some of the last remaining unimproved pastures are highly sensitive to increased nutrient loadings. Unless conservation measures to retain this habitat type are in place, with particular emphasis on the maintenance of water levels, flooding regimes and appropriate grazing, most sites will deteriorate.

The primary threats to grazing marsh are of both a widespread and localised type:

Widespread factors include:
- Ecologically insensitive flood defence works built in the past.
- Agricultural intensification.
- Neglect in the form of a decline in traditional management.
- Eutrophication.

Localised effects arise from:
- Industrialisation and urbanisation (particularly in the Greater Thames).
- Saltwater flooding due to sea level rise.

Secondary threats include:
- Ground water abstraction.
- Pollution of ground water or surface water.
- Aggregates extraction.

3. CURRENT ACTION

3.1 Legal status

In carrying out their functions the NRA, Water Companies, Internal Drainage Boards and Local Authorities in England and Wales have a statutory duty to further conservation where consistent with purposes of enactments relating to their functions. These are set out in the Water Resources Act 1991, and the Land Drainage Act 1991. River Purification Boards (RPBs) in Scotland do not have the same duties. Both the NRA and RPBs have statutory responsibilities for pollution control.

The duty to further conservation applies to the water management functions of the Environment Agency for England and Wales from April 1996, while the pollution control functions of this Agency will have a duty to have regard to the desirability of conserving and enhancing features of special interest. The establishment of the Scottish Environment Protection Agency (SEPA) and the new water authorities in Scotland will strengthen conservation duties compared to the predecessor RPBs.

Both the NRA and RPBs have statutory responsibilities for pollution control.

The Water Act (NI) 1972 is currently under review. In Northern Ireland responsibility for water quality, water supply and drainage resides with the Environment Service of DoE(NI), Water Service DoE(NI) and DANI respectively. These bodies also have responsibility for nature conservation interest.

The status of SSSI/ASSIs for this habitat which are also internationally important is recognised by their designation as SPAs under the EC Birds Directive and as Wetlands of International Importance under the Ramsar Convention.

3.2 Management, research and guidance

Several ESAs include prescriptions which encourage the management of grazing marsh. These cover around 400,000 ha of which 50,000 ha of grazing marsh attracts payments of £7.5 million a year. Other incentive schemes such as the Water Fringe element of the Habitat Scheme and the Wildlife Enhancement Scheme in England and Wales contribute towards the management of this habitat. In Scotland the Habitat Scheme has a 'Waterside Habitats' option for watercourses within the watershed of the rivers Don, Dee, Spey and Tweed.

Various guidance has also been issued, including a 1989 NCC guide on managing drainage channels for nature conservation, a guide on water level management plans issued by MAFF and WOAD in 1992 who also issued notes on environmental procedures on inland flood defence decision making (1992) and coastal defence works (1993). In England and Wales water level management plans are being established for all grazing marsh SSSIs where a drainage body controls a specific structure.

4. CONSERVATION DIRECTION

Maintain the existing habitat extent and quality of grazing marsh and rehabilitate areas which have become too dry or intensively managed. Create grazing marsh from arable land in targeted areas.

Further details of this conservation direction and the measures required to deliver it are given in the Costed Habitat Action Plan for Coastal and River Plain Grazing Marsh.

FEN, CARR, MARSH, SWAMP AND REEDBED HABITAT STATEMENT

1. CURRENT STATUS

Fen, carr, marsh, swamp and reedbed are a group of wetland habitats which are widespread and scattered throughout the UK. The UK is also thought to host a large proportion of the fen surviving in the EU. As in other parts of Europe fen vegetation has declined dramatically in the past century.

Fens are peatlands which receive water and nutrients from the soil, rock and ground water as well as from rainfall: they are minerotrophic. Two types of fen can broadly be distinguished: topogenous and soligenous. Topogenous fens are those where water movements in the peat or soil are generally vertical. They include basin fens and floodplain fen. Soligenous fens, where water movements are predominantly lateral, include mires associated with springs, rills and flushes in the uplands, valley mires, springs and flushes in the lowlands, trackways and ladder fens in blanket bogs and laggs of raised bogs. Swamp is characterised by water-table levels that are at, or above, the surface of the vegetation for most of the year. Swamps have a species-poor vegetation in comparison to fens. Marsh is a rather ill-defined term but usually refers to vegetation occurring on mineral soil that has a water table close to the surface for most of the year, but not usually above ground level. Carr is swampy woodland often found in association with fens and marshes. The above habitats often occur together, with areas of open water, ditches and wet grassland.

Fens can also be described as 'poor-fens' or 'rich-fens'. Poor-fens, where the water is derived from base-poor rock such as sandstones and granites occur mainly in the uplands, or are associated with lowland heaths. They are characterised by short vegetation with a high proportion of bog mosses *Sphagnum* spp. and acid water (pH of 5 or less). Rich-fens, are fed by mineral-enriched calcareous waters (pH 5 or more) and are mainly confined to the lowlands and where there are localised occurrences of base-rich rocks such as limestone in the uplands. Fen habitats support a diversity of plant and animal communities. Some can contain up to 550 species of higher plants, a third of our native plant species; up to and occasionally more than half the UK's species of dragonflies, several thousand other insect species, as well as being an important habitat for a range of aquatic beetles.

In intensively farmed lowland areas fens occur less frequently, are smaller in size and more isolated than in other parts of the UK. There are, however, exceptions to this. The UK's largest continuous area of base-poor fen, the Insh Marshes in the floodplain of the River Spey in Scotland, covers an area of 300 ha, the calcareous rich fen and swamp of Broadland covers an area of 3,000 ha and Lough Erne system in Fermanagh has extensive areas of fen and swamp. In some lowland areas such as the Scottish borders and southern Northern Ireland there are concentrations of small fens of particular importance.

Reedbeds are fens or swamps dominated by stands of the common reed *Phragmites australis*. There are about 5,000 ha of reedbeds in the UK, but of the 900 or so sites contributing to this total, only about 50 are greater than 20 ha, and these make a large contribution to the total area - and are mostly concentrated in SE England. Reedbeds are amongst the most important habitats for birds in the UK. They support a distinctive breeding bird assemblage including 6 nationally rare GB Red Data Birds the bittern *Botaurus stellaris*, marsh harrier, *Circus aeruginosus*, crane *Grus grus*, Cetti's warbler *Cettia cetti*, Savi's warbler *Locustella luscinioides* and bearded tit *Panurus biarmicus*, provide roosting and feeding sites for migratory species (including the globally threatened aquatic warbler *Acrocephalus paludicola*) and are used as roost sites for several raptor species in winter. Five GB Red Data Book invertebrates are also closely associated with reedbeds including red leopard moth *Phragmataecia castanaea* and a rove beetle *Lathrobium rufipenne*.

2. CURRENT FACTORS AFFECTING THE HABITAT

Fens are dynamic semi-natural systems and in general, management is needed to maintain open-fen communities and their associated species richness. Without appropriate management (e.g. mowing, grazing, burning, peat cutting, scrub clearance), natural succession will result in scrub and woodland. Current factors affecting this habitat type are:

- Small total area of habitat and critically small population sizes of several key species dependent on the habitat.
- Loss of area through drying caused by excessive water abstraction and, in the past, drainage and conversion to intensive agriculture.
- Lack of or inappropriate management of existing fens and reedbeds leading to drying, scrub encroachment and succession to woodland.
- Eutrophication causes an increased growth and dominance of vigorous plant species, can lead to a loss of biodiversity and may cause reed death.
- Pollution of freshwater supplies to fens and reedbeds: siltation may lead to drying; toxic chemicals may lead to loss of fish and amphibian prey for key species; accumulation of poisons in the food chain may also cause reed death.
- Most of the important reedbeds are found on the coast of eastern England, where relative sea-level rise is predicted to lead to the loss of significant areas of coastal habitat.

3. CURRENT ACTION

3.1 Legal status

Most of the more significant fens and reedbeds are notified as SSSI/ASSIs and many are notified as Wetlands of International Importance under the Ramsar Convention and as SPAs under the EC Birds Directive. Several of the larger fens and reedbeds are managed as NNRs by EN and CCW, and as reserves of the RSPB and County Wildlife Trusts. Several types of fen are listed on Annex I of the EC Habitats Directive including transition mire, poor and rich fen, alkaline fens (rich-fen). A number of fens have been proposed by the UK Government as possible SACs under this Directive.

3.2 Management, research and guidance

CCW has an active programme of positive management focused on NNRs and undertake active management to restore favourable conditions on key fen sites.

EN's 3 year, £200 000 *Action for Bittern* project, part of its Species Recovery Programme provides funding for reedbed rehabilitation and extension in England.

RSPB has a priority programme for reedbed rehabilitation on their reserves and are creating new reedbeds on land of low nature conservation interest purchased by the society.

The Broads Authority conduct a fen and reedbed management programme within their executive area in association with EN, who provide management agreements to owners/occupiers for reedbed management.

The statutory conservation agencies have negotiated several management agreements on SSSIs to help secure sympathetic reedbed management and have worked with key partners using EU Life funding to create an extensive reedbed on former peat workings in the Somerset Levels.

RSPB/EN/Broads Authority/British Reedgrower's Association published a leaflet *Reedbed Management for Bitterns* and the management guide *Reedbed Management for Commercial and Wildlife Interests Handbook* to encourage the management and creation of reedbeds.

Statutory conservation agency and RSPB staff provide advice to a range of reedbed owners on appropriate management, rehabilitation, extension and creation.

Voluntary and statutory agency staff monitor (and licence the monitoring of) the population size and productivity of key reedbed species.

NRA have been encouraged to incorporate reedbed and fen protection, management or creation in their catchment and shoreline management plans.

Many reedbeds are or will be subject to water-level management plans prepared by flood defence operating authorities under a MAFF and Welsh Office initiative.

4. CONSERVATION DIRECTION

Maintain the existing area of fen, carr, marsh swamp and reedbed habitats and identify those that are suitable for restoration. Create new reedbeds on land of low conservation importance. Further details of this conservation direction and the measures required to deliver it are given in the Costed Habitat Action Plan for Reedbeds and the Costed Habitat Action Plan for Fens.

LOWLAND RAISED BOG HABITAT STATEMENT

1. CURRENT STATUS

Peatlands can be divided into two types: ombrotrophic peatlands which are fed exclusively by precipitation inputs (rain, snow etc.) and minerotrophic peatlands which are additionally fed by surface ground water and/or streams. Two types of ombrotrophic peatlands are recognised, blanket bogs and lowland raised bogs. This Statement outlines the conservation status of lowland raised bogs in the UK.

Intact lowland raised bogs are one of Europe's rarest and most threatened habitats. They occur throughout the UK in flat low-lying locations or basins. Since around the start of the 19th Century the extent of primary, active lowland raised bog has decreased from 95,000 ha to 6,000 ha, a decline of 94%. The remaining 6,000 ha resource is scattered across a large number of small sites.

Lowland raised bogs are recognisable within landscapes as gently sloping raised mounds of peat. They consist of a deep accumulation (up to 10m) of water logged peat and, when intact, a surface covered by a living layer of plants and mosses known as the acrotelm. As the surface of the bog is raised above the local water table the only source of water and nutrient feeding the bog becomes direct rainfall (ombrotrophic systems). Lowland raised bogs can be classified as primary or secondary depending on the degree of damage the bog has been subjected to. Primary raised bogs are those in which the dome is intact and usually dominated by an actively growing and *Sphagnum* rich surface pattern with an undisturbed acrotelm. A secondary bog is one which has been damaged due to peat extraction or other activities, but where the water table has (or may have) stabilised because the drainage pattern has become blocked. Under these conditions the surface vegetation may be dominated by a secondary growth of *Sphagnum* spp. and bog cottongrass *Eriophorum* spp. Secondary bogs may be either active or degraded (ie: laying down peat, or capable of restoration): both types are considered to be of European conservation importance.

The characteristic plants of raised bogs, mainly heaths *Erica* spp., cotton grasses and bog mosses, are all specially adapted to live in water logged, nutrient poor conditions. The abundance of some *Sphagnum* species is of critical importance to the development of the bog (typically *Sphagnum papillosum* together with species such as *Sphagnum magellanicum*). The growth of *Sphagnum* species help to create the strongly acidic conditions of ombrotrophic peat and associated bog pools. Zonation of the environmental conditions controls the distribution of the species, and this can create distinctively undulating and often colourful vegetation pattern on the bog surface.

Lowland raised bogs not only support plants but also a distinctive range of animals including nightjars *Caprimulgus europaeus*, many wetland birds and dragonflies. Rare and localised invertebrates such as the large heath butterfly *Coenonympha tullia* are also found on some lowland raised bogs.

2. CURRENT FACTORS AFFECTING THE HABITAT

The primary factors affecting lowland raised bogs are:

- Planning permissions for peat extraction and horticultural use or peat extraction for fuel.
- Mineral extraction (for deposits under peat)
- Lowering, or fluctuations, in the water levels resulting from forestry planting and drainage.

The secondary factors affecting lowland raised bogs are:

- Legacy of past use and misuse, including drainage, grazing and burning

3. CURRENT ACTION

3.1 Legal status

A large proportion of the UK lowland raised bog resource as been notified as SSSI/ASSI and a number of sites have also been declared as NNRs. In Scotland and Northern Ireland there is a continuing programme of notification to ensure that all key areas which meet the SSSI selection guidelines are notified. Raised bogs, both active and degraded, are also listed on Annex I of the EC Habitats Directive and the UK Government has recently set out its proposals for areas that it considers qualify as SACs under this Directive.

3.2 Management, research and guidance

In 1990, the NCC issued a Peat Policy giving strong commitment to the protection of lowland peatlands. This commitment has been carried forward by the country conservation agencies who support moves by industry to use sustainable growing-media based on recycled organic materials.

Conservation bodies in the UK have also received funding through the EC LIFE (Nature) Programme, for projects that develop techniques for the management and restoration of peatbogs. One such project is run by the Scottish Wildlife Trust. It has set out to produce an inventory of the lowland raised bogs resource in Scotland and to develop/promote management techniques.

DoE has also recently funded work which assessed the opportunities and potential for the restoration of peatlands. This work resulted in the production in 1995 of the report *Restoration of Damaged Peatlands* (HMSO).

MAFF has prepared guidance on water level management plans and has issued a timetable for their production for relevant SSSIs in England and Wales. The NRA is also preparing management plans for river catchments in England and Wales. Water level management plans will play an important role in the conservation of lowland raised bogs.

4. CONSERVATION DIRECTION

Safeguard remaining areas of *primary* lowland raised bog and with appropriate management ensure that the full functioning hydrological units supporting the habitat are maintained. Safeguard and restore key areas of *secondary* lowland raised bog which, although modified, still contain sufficient representation of species typical of active raised bogs or the required environmental features that favour peat development.

Measures to be considered further include:

- Promote alternatives to peat and moss in horticulture and in energy generation.
- Evaluate existing measures for conserving and managing lowland raised bogs.

- Protect lowland raised bogs from inappropriate uses by identifying them in Mineral and other plans, and in Forest Indicative Strategies.
- Promote an understanding and appreciation of lowland raised bogs.
- Encourage the restoration of degraded lowland raised bogs.

STANDING OPEN WATER HABITAT STATEMENT

1. CURRENT STATUS

Standing open waters include natural systems such as lakes, meres and pools, as well as man-made waters such as reservoirs, ponds and gravel pits. Their size varies from 38,500 ha (Lough Neagh) to ponds a few metres across. The open water zone lies beyond the limits of swamp vegetation, but may contain submerged, free-floating or floating-leaved vegetation. Standing waters are usually classified according to their nutrient status and this can change naturally over time. There are three main types of standing waters. These are: oligotrophic (nutrient poor), eutrophic (nutrient rich) and mesotrophic (an intermediate), although gradations between these types occur. Other types include dystrophic (highly acidic), marl lakes, brackish water lakes, turloughs and other temporary water bodies.

Oligotrophic waters are poor in plant nutrients and are typical of northern and western Britain, although they also occur on some heathland sites in the south. Their waters are clear because plankton is sparse, and the biomass of lower plants and animals is low. Typical plants are water lobelia *Lobelia dortmanna*, alternate water-milfoil *Myriophyllum alterniflorum* and bog pondweed *Potamogeton polygonifolius*. The invertebrate fauna is dominated by insects such as mayflies and caddisflies in the littoral zone whilst fish include brown trout *Salmo trutta* and arctic charr *Salvelinus alpinus*.

Eutrophic waters are naturally rich in plant nutrients and are typical of lowland Britain. These waters support large amounts of vegetation and a wide variety of animals. Many of them are important breeding and wintering sites for waterfowl. Eutrophic waters are often clouded with abundant plankton; characteristic plants are duckweeds *Lemna* spp., yellow water-lily *Nuphar lutea*, spiked water-milfoil *Myriophyllum spicatum* and fennel pondweed *Potamogeton pectinatus*. The fish are largely coarse species such as roach *Rutilus rutilus*, bream *Abramis brama* and pike *Esox lucius*. The invertebrate fauna is diverse and includes snails and crustaceans.

Mesotrophic waters are intermediate between oligotrophic and eutrophic waters, and potentially have the highest biodiversity of any lake type.

Dystrophic types are highly acidic and low in oxygen content and occur in peaty areas. They contain a restricted fauna and flora which is often dominated by *Sphagnum* species. In contrast, marl waters which are rich in lime and contain low concentrations of phosphorus, are dominated by stoneworts *Chara* species. These species require the clear water typical of this type of system. Slightly saline water bodies occur in some coastal areas.

2. CURRENT FACTORS AFFECTING THE HABITAT

The principal factors affecting standing open waters are:

- Eutrophication caused primarily by nitrates or phosphates in sewage or fertiliser run-off.
- Acidification may occur locally in areas with sensitive geology and soils, as a result of atmospheric deposition of pollutants.
- Pollution from organic matter, silt, heavy metals and thermal discharges.
- Lowering of water levels caused by over abstraction of surface or ground water, or by drainage.
- Urbanisation and in-filling of ponds.
- Hydro-electricity generation causing water fluctuations in some Scottish lochs.
- Poor management on multiple use water bodies where activities (e.g. recreation, fish farming) are not sensitively managed (e.g. by zoning), and where surrounding habitats are inappropriately managed or neglected.
- Changes in surrounding land use that alter the water table, change the pollution load, or degrade or remove valuable adjacent habitat.

3. CURRENT ACTION

3.1 Legal status

In carrying out their functions the NRA, Water Companies, Internal Drainage Boards and Local Authorities in England and Wales have a statutory duty to further conservation where consistent with purposes of enactments relating to their functions. These are set out in the Water Resources Act 1991, and the Land Drainage Act 1991. River Purification Boards (RPBs) in Scotland do not have the same duties. Both the NRA and RPBs have statutory responsibilities for pollution control.

The duty to further conservation applies to the water management functions of the Environment Agency for England and Wales from April 1996, while the pollution control functions of this Agency will have a duty to have regard to the desirability of conserving and enhancing features of special interest. The establishment of the Scottish Environment Protection Agency (SEPA) and the new water authorities in Scotland will strengthen conservation duties compared to the predecessor RPBs.

The Water Act (NI) 1972 is currently under review. In Northern Ireland responsibility for water quality, water supply and drainage resides with the Environment Service of DoE(NI), Water Service DoE(NI) and DANI respectively.

There is a network of standing water SSSI/ASSIs in the UK, some of which are also NNRs. Others are designated as SPAs under the EC Birds Directive or as Ramsar Sites, because of their bird populations or because they represent excellent examples of aquatic habitats. A series of dystrophic, eutrophic and oligotrophic standing waters have also been proposed by the UK Government as SACs under the EC Habitats Directive.

3.2 Management, research and guidance

The statutory conservation agencies are funding several lake research projects. These include the Scottish freshwater loch survey, the CCW lake survey, palaeolimnological studies funded by CCW and EN and the environmental audit of a number of lakes within SSSIs in England. A comprehensive botanical and chemical survey has already been carried out for the majority of lakes in Northern Ireland.

The Anglesey Wetland Strategy, an informal conservation liaison between NRA, CCW, RSPB, ADAS and the North Wales Wildlife Trust, monitors and manages the lakes on Anglesey. Various partnerships also contribute to lake restoration objectives (e.g. in the Broads). A Voluntary Pond Conservation Group has been established with support from EN and the NRA.

MAFF guidance on water level management plans has been prepared and a timetable issued for plans to be produced for relevant SSSIs in England and Wales, which include some open water habitats.

Large areas of standing open waters have been created as part of restoration schemes following mineral extraction or as part of post-industrial restoration schemes. These areas can make a significant contribution to the nature conservation interest in particular areas.

DoE(NI) are presently preparing a cross border Water Quality Management Strategy (WQMS) for the Lough Erne catchments. It is proposed to start work on a WQMS for Lough Neagh during 1996.

4. CONSERVATION DIRECTION

Maintain and improve the conservation interest of standing open waters, through the use of integrated management plans, and the sensitive management of adjacent land. Create new standing open waters, of maximum wildlife benefit, where possible.

Measures to be considered further include:

- Introduce Statutory Water Quality Objectives where appropriate.
- Prepare water level management plans for the benefit of wildlife, particularly with respect to key sites where appropriate.
- Develop integrated catchment management plans.
- Use existing measure such as the Countryside Stewardship Waterside Landscape option, to support the appropriate management of open waters and their associated habitats.
- Reduce acid emissions to reduce damage to open waters from acid rain.
- Carry out Environmental Assessments of developments which will have an impact on open waters and their associated habitats.

RIVERS AND STREAMS HABITAT STATEMENT

1. CURRENT STATUS

In their natural state rivers are dynamic systems, continually modifying their form. However in many cases their ability to rejuvenate and create new habitat has been reduced or arrested by flood defence structures and impoundments. Few rivers in the UK have not been physically modified by man and such rivers represent a very valuable resource. Erosion of banks has also been caused by canalization and the removal of tree cover in historic times. Such activities have resulted in changes in the frequency and magnitude of flooding, altering seasonal patterns of flows and hydrograph form. In addition, flow regulation has altered patterns of sediment transport and nutrient exchange in river systems. Any resulting eutrophication can have detrimental effects on floodplain habitat which still retains some connection with the main stream.

The mosaic of features found in rivers and streams supports a diverse range of plants and animals. For example, riffles and pools support aquatic species, and exposed sediments such as shingle beds and sand bars are important for a range of invertebrates, notably ground beetles, spiders and craneflies. Marginal and bankside vegetation support an array of wild flowers and animals. Rivers and streams often provide a wildlife corridor link between fragmented habitats in intensively farmed areas.

The plant and animal assemblages of rivers and streams vary according to their geographical area, underlying geology and water quality. Swiftly-flowing upland, nutrient-poor rivers support a wide range of mosses and liverworts and relatively few species of higher plants. The invertebrate fauna of upland rivers is dominated by stoneflies, mayflies and caddisflies, while fish such as salmon *Salmo salar* and brown trout *Salmo trutta* will almost certainly be present. In contrast, lowland nutrient-rich systems are dominated by higher plants, and coarse fish such as chub *Leuciscus cephalus*, dace *Leuciscus leuciscus* and roach *Rutilus rutilus*. Where nutrient levels are artificially raised, the occurrence of algae increases.

2. CURRENT FACTORS AFFECTING THE HABITAT

The primary threats to rivers and streams are:
- Pollution including eutrophication and acidification.
- Excessive ground water and surface water abstraction.
- Construction of dams and reservoirs.
- Water transfer schemes between rivers.
- Land drainage and flood defence works which if not sensitively carried out, can reduce stream habitat and isolate streams from their floodplains.
- Inappropriate bank management, including overgrazing.
- Introduction of invasive plant and animal species.
- Industrial, housing and hydro-electric power scheme development within the floodplain.

3. CURRENT ACTION

3.1 Legal status

In carrying out their functions the NRA, Water Companies, Internal Drainage Boards (IDBs) and Local Authorities in England and Wales have a statutory duty to further conservation where consistent with purposes of enactments relating to their functions. These are set out in the Water Resources Act 1991, and the Land Drainage Act 1991. River Purification Boards (RPBs) in Scotland do not have the same duties. Both the NRA and RPBs have statutory responsibilities for pollution control.

The duty to further conservation applies to the water management functions of the Environment Agency for England and Wales from April 1996, while the pollution control functions of this Agency will have a duty to have regard to the desirability of conserving and enhancing features of special interest. The establishment of the Scottish Environment Protection Agency (SEPA) and the new water authorities in Scotland will strengthen conservation duties compared to the predecessor RPBs.

The Water Act (NI) 1972 is currently under review. In Northern Ireland responsibility for water quality, water supply and drainage resides with the Environment Service of DoE(NI), Water Service DoE(NI) and DANI respectively.

Environmental Assessment legislation requires all works with the potential to have a significant effect upon the environment to be subject to formal impact assessment. In the context of river engineering works this includes new, improvement and heavy maintenance works. The Environmental Statement on the extent of the impacts is open to public scrutiny.

Ministers can direct IDBs in England and Wales in order to prevent serious damage to conservation sites of national and international importance. Local Authorities in England and Wales have a statutory duty to further conservation when carrying out improvement works, so far as is consistent with the purposes of the Land Drainage Act 1991.

In Northern Ireland there are unlikely to be any new works e.g. drainage schemes on rural watercourses and Environmental Impact Assessment Regulations are in place to deal with situations where maintenance works are liable to have a significant effect on the environment. In England, some 27 river SSSIs will be notified by March 1998, representing 3% of main river length. A programme for SSSI notification of rivers in Scotland is also being pressed forward and in Wales further notification of rivers as SSSI is under review. The NRA and EN have agreed through a 'Memorandum of Understanding' to produce joint conservation strategies for SSSIs.

Under the EC Habitats Directive the UK Government is still considering areas which might qualify as SACs for a number of riverine interests listed on Annex II.

3.2 Management, research and guidance

A number of agricultural support schemes are in place which aim to benefit watercourses. These include some ESA prescriptions, the Countryside Stewardship Scheme (aimed at creating buffer strips), the Habitat Scheme Water Fringe Option (aimed at buffer streams upstream of SSSIs), and the Habitat Improvement Scheme in Northern Ireland which is relevant to some 'scheduled' waters.

Management plans are being prepared by the NRA for 163 river catchments in England and Wales. Each plan will be the subject of a public consultation exercise which is due to be completed in 1998.

MAFF guidance on Water Level Management Plans has been prepared and a timetable issued for their production for relevant SSSIs in England and Wales which includes some rivers and streams.

In February 1995, the Secretary of State for the Environment announced a pilot scheme regarding Statutory Water Quality Objectives, which includes a small number of rivers. Water Quality standards that maintain the special conservation interest of streams and rivers, with particular emphasis on combating artificial nutrient enrichment, should be widely implemented. In Northern Ireland, Catchment Water Quality Management Strategies are being developed.

A small number of rivers, mainly in England, have been identified as targets for phosphate stripping from their sewage effluent, and two demonstration river restoration projects are currently in operation, with funding from NRA, EN, EC LIFE and others.

Flood defence works should be carried out in an environmentally sympathetic way, enhancing degraded rivers wherever the opportunity arises. Technical guidance for environmentally-sensitive flood defence works is contained in *The New Rivers and Wildlife Handbook*, published jointly by the NRA, RSPB and the Wildlife Trusts in 1994. Guidance on best practice procedures to be followed by flood defence operating authorities has been issued by MAFF; this guidance aims to ensure that environmental issues are afforded due consideration when flood defence works are being planned, designed and implemented.

The Forestry Commission also produced a revised version of the *Forest and Water Guidelines* in 1993.

The Forestry Authority, NRA and statutory conservation agencies are currently appraising the value of floodplain forests. This appraisal will underpin any future revaluation of the requirements for a forest floodplain creation scheme.

The Forestry Commission is also about to start experimental research into the role of coarse woody debris in modifying the physical habitat of upland streams, and also to evaluate the potential of coarse woody debris accumulations for increasing habitat quality and diversity for macro-invertebrates.

A new methodology for assessing the conservation value of rivers at a catchment scale in the UK has been developed. Known as SERCON this computer-based system will increase the rigour and repeatability with which evaluations can be carried out. The NRA is developing a classification of river reaches based on habitat features applicable to the UK as a whole.

4. CONSERVATION DIRECTION

Maintain and improve the quality, state and structure of all UK rivers and streams and their associated floodplains. Restore degraded river and streams taking account of water quality and quantity, structure and hydraulic connection with the floodplain.

Measures to be considered further include:

- Introduce Statutory Water Quality Objectives, especially for phosphates.

- Use Water Level Management Plans and water abstraction licensing procedures for the benefit of wildlife, particularly with respect to key sites.
- Implement integrated catchment management plans.
- Use existing measures, such as the Countryside Stewardship Waterside Landscape option, to support the appropriate management of rivers, streams and their associated habitats, in particular floodplains.
- Reduce acid emissions to reduce damage to rivers and streams from acid rain.
- Review the powers and duties of water management institutions to manage water for nature conservation objectives.

CANALS
HABITAT STATEMENT

1. CURRENT STATUS

Construction of canals in the UK took place predominantly between 1750 and 1830, although some were built much earlier and others later. The main concentration of canal construction was in the Midlands linking this area to London. Outlying areas often only had local canals. British Waterways currently owns 2,012 miles (including some river navigation) of canals, representing 52% of the canal network in Britain.

Canals can be important for wildlife. Those which no longer carry heavy boat traffic often support highly diverse assemblages of plants and animals and may support nationally scarce species such as the floating water-plantain *Luronium natans* and grass-wrack pondweed *Potamogeton compressus*. The wetland habitats are inter-related with the margins, towpath and hedge or other boundary features which also contribute shelter and emergence sites for aquatic animals. Canal tunnels may provide excellent roosting and breeding sites for bats. The associated habitats are often rich in species, some of which are relicts from formerly widespread habitats such as unimproved grassland, marsh and carr.

2. CURRENT FACTORS AFFECTING THE HABITAT

The primary threats to the wildlife interest of canals are:

*   Large-scale restoration projects, including marina developments; pollution (including eutrophication, oil, industrial and mine water).
*   Excessive abstraction and infilling.
*   Increased usage by powered boats.
*   Urbanisation including landscaping, planting bulbs and non-native trees.
*   Surfacing wide paths, clearing scrub and carr.
*   Lack of appropriate management.

3. CURRENT ACTION

3.1 Legal status

British Waterways has a duty to further the conservation and enhancement of natural beauty and the conservation of plants, animals and geological or physiographical features of special scientific interest and to balance this against a requirement to develop. Restoration works involving large scale earth moving require planning permission and removal of trees may require a felling licence. DANI have a similar responsibility for canals in Northern Ireland.

The conservation importance of canals is recognised by the statutory nature conservation agencies who have notified 65 canal related SSSIs in Great Britain. The floating water-plantain is listed on Annex I of the EC Habitats Directive, and the UK Government is considering proposals for SACs for this species.

3.2 Management, research and guidance

British Waterways and the statutory conservation agencies have carried out surveys of a number of key canals and in 1986 agreed a report 'Management of canal SSSIs' with the Nature Conservancy Council.

4. CONSERVATION DIRECTION

Maintain the existing environmental quality of all canals (remaindered, derelict and navigable) in the UK and enhance the wildlife interest of the habitats associated with key canals through upgrading and improving water quantity, water quality and the restoration of bank-side features.

Measures to be considered further include:

*   Implement Statutory Water Quality Objectives.
*   Carry out Environmental Assessments for maintenance, management and restoration work, and development affecting canals and their associated habitats.
*   Use existing measures, such as the Habitats Scheme, to support the appropriate management of associated habitats.
*   Encourage the effective management of all canals, using water level management plans and water abstraction licensing procedures for the benefit of wildlife, particularly in respect to key sites.

MONTANE HABITAT STATEMENT

I. CURRENT STATUS

Montane habitat (approximately 600,000 ha) is found in areas which lie above the natural level of tree development, above 611m, throughout much of the uplands but descending in exposed areas of the north and west. These alpine and subalpine areas represent some of the most natural and undisturbed habitats in the UK. In the exposed climate of the north west Highlands and islands of Scotland, the potential natural tree line occurs at much lower altitudes and here plant and animal communities of the montane zone can occur almost down to sea level. Such areas are included in this habitat category wherever they contain characteristic montane plant communities. Over 90% of the montane habitat in the UK is in Scotland.

Montane habitat comprises many different kinds of habitat supporting a wide range of plant and animal communities. In less disturbed areas of the uplands montane plant communities include a range of near-natural dwarf-shrub heaths, moss-heath and grasslands. Late-lying snow patches have characteristic bryophyte and lichen communities with prime examples in the Cairngorms and Ben Nevis, and on other Highland ranges. Plant communities of tall-herbs, arctic-alpine willows *Salix* spp., spring flushes, rock crevices and screes are widespread. Freshwater seepages, rills, streams and pools provide another range of habitats. The whole assemblage of habitats supports a high diversity of plant and animal species. Of particular importance are relict arctic-alpine species, lower plants and invertebrates. Montane areas contain important concentrations of endemic species.

Montane areas are also important for a number of breeding bird species including golden eagle *Aquila chrysaetos*, golden plover *Pluvialis apricaria*, purple sandpiper *Calidris maritima*, snow bunting *Plectrophenax nivalis*, and dotterel *Charadrius morinellus*.

2. CURRENT FACTORS AFFECTING THE HABITAT

Montane areas are under a similar range of threats as other upland areas, except that the poor soils and extreme climate renders them unsuitable for forestry or intensive agriculture. However, the fragile and vulnerable nature of the vegetation and soils in montane areas renders them especially susceptible to:

- Overgrazing by sheep and deer in the Scottish Highlands and by sheep south of the Highlands which has caused the loss of much alpine and subalpine dwarf-shrub heath, scrub, herb-rich vegetation and moss-heaths.

- Increasing recreational pressure from walkers and skiers accelerated by the summer use of ski uplift facilities, causing damage to fragile vegetation and soils.

- Fires started in the sub-montane zone which spread up into the montane shrub heaths and cause destruction of vegetation and soils.

- The long-term effects of pollution such as acidification and global warming resulting in the possible loss of species which will be unable to recolonise.

3. CURRENT ACTION

3.1 Legal status

Many of the most important montane areas are protected as SSSI or NNR and in England and Wales some important sites are included within National Parks. In addition, some montane areas are covered by ESAs, such as the Lake District ESA.

The importance of montane habitats has been acknowledged by identification of some key sites as candidate SPAs under the EC Birds Directive; several key sites as NNRs; and the Cairngorms as a proposed World Heritage Site. A number of montane habitats, including alpine and sub-alpine heaths, are also listed on Annex I of the EC Habitats Directive. The UK Government has set out its proposals for areas which it considers qualify as SACs for these interests.

3.2 Management, research and guidance

The Scottish Office has recently announced the establishment of the Cairngorms Partnership. This is intended to co-ordinate the work of owners, other groups with an interest in the area, relevant agencies and local people, to ensure its protection and enhancement.

NGOs are devoting considerable resources to the conservation of the most important montane sites. For example, The National Trust for Scotland owns and manages Ben Lomond and Ben Lawers and the Mar Lodge Estate in the Cairngorms. The National Trust in Wales owns a substantial part of Carneddau, the RSPB has acquired a portion of the Cairngorm plateau, and the John Muir Trust has recently bought part of the Cuillin Hills of Skye.

4. CONSERVATION DIRECTION

Minimise further deterioration to the resource of near natural montane and high altitude moorland; restore areas of scrub, herb and moss cover and minimise damage and disturbance.

Measures to be considered further include:

- Carry out surveys to identify remnant areas of near-natural montane communities.

- Reduce grazing pressure from deer.

- Encourage lower levels of sheep grazing and burning management to maintain montane vegetation.

- Protect montane areas from inappropriate development and discourage disturbance and damage to montane areas from inappropriate forms and levels of use, including recreational uses.

- Consider the need for studies to investigate the effects of acid deposition on montane communities.

UPLAND HEATHLAND HABITAT STATEMENT

I. CURRENT STATUS

Upland heath lies below the montane zone (which begins above the 'potential woodland limit' at c. 600-750m) and above the upper edge of enclosed agricultural land, usually around 300-400m, but descending to near sea-level in northern and north-western Scotland. This habitat type is present on 1,144,000 ha in England and Wales, 53,000 ha in Northern Ireland and 2,514,000 ha in Scotland. Dwarf-shrub heaths have international conservation significance and are largely confined to the British Isles and the western seaboard of Europe.

Upland heath is generally dominated by dwarf shrubs such as heather Calluna vulgaris, bilberry Vaccinium myrtillus, crowberry Empetrum nigrum, bell heather Erica cinerea and in the west gorse Ulex gallii. Other communities particularly in the wetter north and west may be dominated by mixtures of cross-leaved heath Erica tetralix, purple moor-grass Molinia caerulea and Sphagnum bog mosses where drainage is impeded. Of the 3.7 million ha of upland dwarf shrub habitat 1.6 million ha are of less than 50% heather dominance. Upland heath contains mosaics of dry heath, wet heath and blanket bog.

Upland heather moorland is usually found in areas with over 100 cm of precipitation per annum, on nutrient-poor acid soils which are peaty podsols or shallow peat. Variation in the vegetation communities is broadly due to climate, but is also influenced by factors such as altitude, aspect, slope, maritime influences and management practices (including grazing pressure and burning regime).

This is prime habitat for a suite of bird species including red grouse Lagopus lagopus, twite Carduelis flavirostris, golden plover Pluvialis apricaria and wide ranging species such as hen harrier Circus cyaneus and merlin Falco columbarius.

Some forms of upland heath are very rich in bryophyte and lichen communities, especially in the oceanic west. Upland dwarf-shrub heaths are derived from former woodlands or areas of scrub with a dwarf-shrub rich ground flora, these woodlands and scrubs now being relict by and large. Under low intensities of land use and management the dwarf-shrub heath provides a refuge for many of the associated species of the original woodland ground layer.

2. CURRENT FACTORS AFFECTING THE HABITAT

The main factors affecting upland heathland are:

- Inappropriate management of sheep (and more locally in Scotland of red deer Cervus cervus). Heavy grazing is incompatible with maintaining upland heath cover and diversity and with preventing heather and shrub damage. There have been marked losses of heather, a trend sometimes exacerbated by excessive burning.
- Afforestation (commercial) leading to direct loss of dwarf-shrub habitat; and natural woodland regeneration which retains and enhances elements of the original dwarf-shrub habitat in the woodland ground layer.
- Conversion to more intensive forms of agriculture, such as pasture improvement, particularly at lower elevations.
- Poorly managed muirburn may be a threat to the lower plant communities of upland heath.
- Acidification from atmospheric deposition.

3. CURRENT ACTION

3.1 Legal status

Large tracts of moorland are notified as SSSI/ASSI some of which are also SPAs under the EC Birds Directive. Under Annex I of the EC Habitats Directive two upland heath types are listed and the UK Government has set out its proposals for areas that it considers merit designation as SACs. Much moorland has other designations such as National Park, NNR and National Scenic Area which confer varying degrees of protection.

3.2 Management, research and guidance

Most upland heath is privately owned in the form of large estates, though substantial areas are publicly owned, for example crofting land owned by private landowners and SOAEFD or land belonging to Forest Enterprise and large public companies. Only a very small proportion is held by nature conservation bodies, or indeed managed specifically for nature conservation. Some SSSIs are managed sympathetically by means of Management Agreements, and recently agri-environment and other schemes have been used to help protect and improve heather moorland habitats, encourage lower stocking levels and more appropriate management practices.

ESAs such as the Lake District, North Peak, Exmoor, Dartmoor and the Shropshire Hills include substantial areas under agreement to reduce stock intensities and introduce sympathetic management of moorland.

Most moorland is managed for sheep or for shooting of grouse, and is maintained by rotational burning. Red deer 'forest' takes in much upland heath, and this is burnt less systematically. Deer stalking and grouse shooting by visitors to Scotland generates over £20 million per annum and is an important element of the rural economy.

SNH has worked closely with the Agriculture Department on the development of the heather moorland (extensification) scheme and in conjunction with SOAEFD is undertaking further research into the influence of grazing in the uplands. SNH is also undertaking research on the characteristics and impacts of muirburn.

In the Welsh uplands CCW are also assessing the extent of overgrazing, and are developing strategies for habitat restoration.

The National Trust for Scotland will also receive funding through the EC LIFE (Nature) Programme to develop grazing management plans for four upland sites, in its ownership, that have been identified as possible SACs. This project will collate existing information on habitat distribution at the four sites, set objectives for the establishment of an ideal grazing regime and recommend suitable monitoring procedures to assess whether the objectives are met. It will also develop a general methodology for the production of grazing management plans for any upland site.

The Brecon Beacons National Park Authority, backed by CCW, has received funding through the EC LIFE (Nature) Programme for a pilot project on common land management in upland Wales. The project is investigating methods of improving management and reconciling different interests for a category of land with high landscape, wildlife, recreation and agricultural values.

4. CONSERVATION DIRECTION

Maintain the extent, enhance the quality and restore upland dwarf-shrub heath as part of upland mosaics and transitions of semi-natural and natural habitats appropriate to soils and climate.

Measures to be considered further include:

- Encourage sympathetic management of upland heath for wildlife, notably for a greater structural diversity and for the rich lower plant communities.
- Promote demonstrations and advice on good muirburn practices.
- The need for studies to investigate the effects of acid deposition on upland heath communities.
- Encourage measures which reverse habitat fragmentation of upland heath vegetation.
- Reduce grazing pressure from red deer and sheep by reducing their numbers.
- Protect upland heaths from inappropriate development by identification in relevant development plans and in Forest Indicative Strategies.

BLANKET BOG HABITAT STATEMENT

1. CURRENT STATUS

Peatlands can be divided into two types: ombrotrophic peatlands which are fed exclusively by precipitation inputs (rain, snow etc.) and minerotrophic peatlands which are additionally fed by ground water and/or streams. Two types of ombrotrophic peatlands are recognised, blanket bogs and lowland raised bogs. This Statement outlines the conservation status of blanket bogs.

Blanket bog occurs in the wettest parts of the UK and is found in the north and west of Britain, extending from Devon in the south to Shetland in the north. The total area of blanket bog in the UK is approximately 1.5 million ha, of which by far the largest proportion is found in Scotland. A major part of the total resource of blanket bog in the European Union occurs in the UK.

Blanket bog is a mantle of peat which develops in areas with a typically oceanic climate; cool with high, regular inputs of rainfall. Blanket bog complexes support other widespread features such as flushes, where water is channelled over the surface or where there is a general surface seepage. In Britain bog systems can be shown to have been accumulating peat for as much as 10,000 years, but blanket bogs are generally speaking of more recent origin, being between 2,000-7,000 years old. The peat forms not only in wet hollows but also over large expanses of the undulating land surface, on slopes of up to 30%, hence the descriptive name blanket bog. The prevalence of hard, acidic rock and base deficient soils favours development of the living surface of acidophilous ('acid-tolerant') plant communities in which the genus *Sphagnum* is abundant. As well as being dominated by carpets of the bog moss *Sphagnum*, a wide range of ericoids including heather *Calluna vulgaris*, cross-leaved heather *Erica tetralix*, bilberry *Vaccinium myrtillus* and crowberry *Empetrum nigrum* may be present on the hummocks together with common cottongrass *Eriophorum angustifolium* and *Trichophorum cespitosum*. Heather and or *Eriphorium vaginatum* are often dominant over large areas, but various mixtures of species occur. There is substantial ornithological interest with species such as golden plover *Pluvialis apricaria*, dunlin *Calidris alpina*, greenshank *Tringa nebularia* and red-throated diver *Gavia stellata* nesting at internationally high densities.

'Active' blanket bogs are those in which the peat is still capable of accumulating through growth and impeded decay of *Sphagnum* and *Eriophorum*-rich communities. In the far north and west of the UK, the surface often displays areas of dramatic patterning, consisting of variously shaped bog pools separated by sometimes quaking peat ridges. Within blanket bog terrain a variety of peatland communities may be found in ecologically and hydrologically important transition zones between mineral and peat soils.

2. CURRENT FACTORS AFFECTING THE HABITAT

Factors which influence the structure and flora composition of blanket bog habitats include:

- Moorland drainage (very widespread).
- Previous planting of trees, mainly non-native species, over extensive tracts of blanket bog.
- Commercial peat extraction for horticultural use.
- Domestic peat extraction for fuel.
- Natural erosion processes.
- Grazing and uncontrolled burning which can lead to increased erosion and the loss of characteristic bog species.
- Acidification from atmospheric deposition.

3. CURRENT ACTION

3.1 Legal status

Large tracts of blanket bog receive statutory protection through SSSI/ASSI, SPA and NNR designations. Active blanket bog is also listed as a priority habitat on Annex 1 of the EC Habitats Directive. Occurrence in National Park, National Scenic Area and ESA also offers a degree of protection to the UK resource.

3.2 Management, research and guidance

An estimate of the blanket bog resource in Great Britain is being carried out through the National Peatlands Resource Inventory (NPRI) resourced by SNH, and work undertaken by DoE (NI). The NPRI maps and assesses the peatland resource using satellite imagery and soil map information, backed up by field validation.

SNH currently operates a Peatland Management Scheme which offers financial assistance to encourage maintenance of sympathetic land management on peatland SSSIs in Caithness and Sutherland. At the end of March 1995, 53,473 ha of blanket bog had been entered into the scheme. The Tir Cymen Scheme in Wales includes blanket bog as a component of moorland and includes specific guidelines for the management of bogs. Some ESAs, such as the Lake District and North Peak, also include management of blanket bogs as a component of moorland.

Conservation bodies in the UK have also received funding from the European Union, through the EC LIFE (Nature) Programme, for projects that develop techniques for the management and restoration of peatbogs. One such project is led by RSPB and has set out, through land acquisition and management, to secure key areas of active blanket bog and to restore the conservation value of some marginal areas.

4. CONSERVATION DIRECTION

Minimise deterioration and promote appropriate management of areas of active blanket bog which retain their hydrological characteristics and rehabilitate areas of damaged blanket bogs where the hydrological integrity is suitable for restoration (e.g. drain blocking).

Measures to be considered further include:

- Develop national inventories and agree a UK framework for identifying the extent and quality of the resource, the factors affecting the habitat and action required to conserve it, in line with international obligations.
- Protect blanket bogs from inappropriate uses by identifying them in Mineral and other Plans, and in Forest Indicative Strategies.
- Promote alternatives to peat as sources of energy and alternatives to moss for use in horticulture.
- Examine further the role of peatlands as carbon sinks.

- Examine further the functional role of peatlands as dominant factors in catchment dynamics - major sources of drinking water, maintenance of water quality, prevention of soil erosion.
- Secure cross-sector Government Department policies for sustainable utilisation of extensive peatland resources, based on principles of conservation.
- Encourage appropriate grazing, burning and other management of blanket bogs.

MARITIME CLIFF AND SLOPE HABITAT STATEMENT

I. CURRENT STATUS

Seacliffs are formed at the junction between the land and the sea where a break in slope is formed by slippage and/or erosion by the sea. Slopes vary between 15° and vertical, vary in their height and their geology. Approximately 4,000 km of the coastline is cliff.

Exposure to the wind and salt spray is one key determinant of the vegetation type which develops along maritime cliffs and slopes. The exposure is greatest on the south-west and northern coasts. The long fetch generates high waves and swell and the prevailing winds help deliver salt spray to the cliff face and cliff tops. Variation in the vegetation is also determined by the geology of the cliff or slope, which changes from the vertical hard granites, sandstones or limestone in the north and west to the soft rock cliffs formed from sand and clay deposits, often derived from glacial material, in the south and east of Britain. The "hard" rock cliffs are resistant to wave action and weathering takes place slowly, allowing the vegetation to develop on ledges or crevices, or where a break in slope allows soils to accumulate. The "soft" rocks are much more unstable and landslip is common. On soft rock cliffs the key determinants of vegetation are the degree of instability and the wetness of the soil.

The plant communities of the hard rock cliffs in the north, which are exposed to the extreme exposure of the north Atlantic are characterised by roseroot Sedum rosea and Scots lovage Ligusticum scoticum, where the cliffs are vertical and drenched in sea spray. Cliffs may also support sea campion Silene maritima and thrift Armeria maritima and in some of the richer areas Arctic species such as purple saxifrage Saxifraga oppositifolia and moss campion Silene acaulis are found. These exposed cliffs are also important breeding grounds for a range of birds including the auks: black guillemot Cepphus grylle, razorbill Alca torda, and guillemot Uria aalge.

In southern areas the vegetation of hard rock cliffs is formed by communities of thrift Armeria maritima, rock samphire Crithmum maritimum and buck's-horn plantain Plantago coronopus occur. They may also include the rare curved hard-grass Parapholis incurva and the sea lavender Limonium recurvum. On relatively sheltered, dry, calcareous cliffs on the south coast, wild cabbage Brassica oleracea is found on crumbling edges and sloping ledges. This species is rare in Britain and is found in association with other rare species such as early spider orchid Ophrys sphegodes and Nottingham catchfly Silene nutans.

The vegetation of coastal cliffs or slopes forms a transition from maritime species to terrestrial communities further inland. These inland types may be dominated by acid heath or calcareous grassland. Occasionally in the more steep and inaccessible slopes woodland may survive such as in the 'Denes' of north east England or the western slopes of some of the Scottish sea lochs.

Soft rock cliffs are important for some invertebrates, eg: the bee wolf Philantus triangulum and the mining bee Lasioglossum laticeps.

2. CURRENT FACTORS AFFECTING THE HABITAT

Factors which influence maritime cliff and slope habitats are:

- Cultivation of cliff top vegetation which has truncated the natural zonation between maritime and terrestrial vegetation resulting in a loss of plant species diversity.
- Eutrophication associated with agricultural run-off leading to a loss of plant species diversity.
- Lack of grazing is causing scrub encroachment leading to the loss of maritime grassland communities.
- Trampling can cause loss of plant species diversity and the creation of access paths from cliff top locations to the shoreline can increase erosion.
- Increased levels of disturbance may adversely affect nesting birds.
- Coast protection works may prevent the removal of eroded material by the sea and obscure important rock exposures. This may also be to the detriment of the plant and invertebrate communities that are dependent upon the unstable surface.
- Cliff-top developments also destroys cliff top habitat and may result in the prevention of the natural retreat of cliffs, as artificial coast protection walls are built.

3. CURRENT ACTION

3.1 Legal status

A number of coastal cliff and slope sites are internationally important for their bird interest and the vegetation they support. Areas have therefore been designated as SPAs under the EC Birds Directive and also the Government has recently identified a list of 12 areas that it considers merit designation as SACs under the EC Habitats Directive Annex I type 'Vegetated sea cliffs of the Atlantic and Baltic coasts'. These areas are representative of cliffs on northern coasts, such as Stromness Heath and Coast, as well as cliffs and limestone slopes in the southern part of the UK, such as the Limestone Seacliffs of South-West Wales.

3.2 Management, research and guidance

The UK Government has set out its commitment to promote the sustainable use of the coast. The objective is to encourage the management of all aspects of the human use of the coast to yield the greatest benefits to the present population whilst maintaining the potential of coastal systems to meet the needs of future generations.

A number of landscape designations encompass cliff habitats. Thirty-four percent of the coastline of England and Wales is designated as Heritage Coast, 20 of the 39 Areas of Outstanding Natural Beauty and 5 of the 10 National Parks in England and Wales contain a coastal element and 31 National Scenic Areas in Scotland include the coast. Other designations such as World Heritage Sites and Biosphere Reserve may include important cliff sites although an audit of the exact extent of Maritime cliff slope covered by these designations is required.

Management of maritime cliffs and slopes is undertaken by, among others, the National Trust who are major land owners and managers of coastal areas in South West England and South West Wales. The encouragement of non-statutory shoreline management plans, by Government and the statutory nature conservation bodies, will also contribute to the conservation of these habitats.

4. CONSERVATION DIRECTION

Maintain and manage in a natural state, including the great range of variation in habitat, hard rock cliffs and extensive soft rock cliff systems, whilst taking into consideration the need for essential coastal defence works.

Measures to be considered further include:

- Evaluate the existing measures for conserving and managing maritime cliff and slope.
- Protect cliff habitats of conservation importance from inappropriate uses.
- Protect remaining localities where specialised algal communities have colonised the splash zone of chalk cliffs.
- Implement strategies for managing the coastal zone at local, regional and national levels.
- Review the powers and duties of coastal authorities for safeguarding this habitat.
- Encourage further survey work and research into the ecology of this habitat type.

SHINGLE ABOVE HIGH TIDE MARK HABITAT STATEMENT

1. CURRENT STATUS

Shingle beaches are widely distributed around the 18,000 km length of UK coastline. In England and Wales it is estimated that 30% of the coastline is bordered by shingle. In Scotland, although shingle is found in the southwest, northeast and northern Isles, it often grades into rock and cliff habitats.

The term shingle is applied to any sediment ranging in grain size between 2mm (large sand grain size) and 200mm. Shingle beaches form in high energy environments where the sea can move and pile up pebbles on the shore, above the tideline. Five types of shingle beach have been recognised

- Fringing beaches (strand of shingle in contact with the land).
- Spits (occur where coasts have an irregular outline).
- Barriers (similar to spits but occur at estuary mouths or in bays)
- Cuspate forelands (series of large, parallel ridges formed as shingle piles up against a fringing beach or spar)
- Barrier islands (shingle deposits in shallow water).

The origin of coastal shingle varies according to location. In southern England much of the shingle is composed of flint which has come from the active erosion of chalk cliffs. In western and northern Britain the shingle may be deposited on the coastline by rivers or glacial outwash. Glacial sediments deposited on the seabed may also be reworked by wave action and deposited on the coastline.

Vegetation will establish on shingle beaches when there is a matrix of finer material such as sand or silt and the structure is stable. The hydrological regime is also important. Stable shingle structures are rare with only about 4,200 ha of stable or semi-vegetated shingle in Great Britain. Shingle vegetation is characterised by a wide range of plant communities which vary in their composition depending on their positioning in relation to the sea. On the seaward edge herb-rich open pioneer stages form and include species such as sea-kale *Crambe maritima*, sea pea *Lathyrus japonicus*, thrift *Armeria maritima*, yellow horned-poppy *Glaucium flavum* and sea holly *Eryngium maritimum*. Where parallel ridges occur the vegetation usually exhibits a distinctive pattern reflecting that of the ridge system. Grassland, heath, scrub and moss and lichen-dominated vegetation of old, stable, shingle occurs further inland. Shingle beaches which are exposed to extreme environmental influences support no vegetation.

Many species of invertebrates are also dependent on the shingle vegetation. These include the rare jumping spider *Euophrys browningi* which shelters in cast-up whelk shells and uncommon terrestrial species such as the millipede *Thalassisobates littoralis* and the woodlouse *Stenophiloscia zosterae*. Bird species such as the arctic tern *Sterna paradisaea* and the smallest terns to nest in Britain, the little tern *Sterna albifrons*, use shingle areas as their breeding grounds.

2. CURRENT FACTORS AFFECTING THE HABITAT

The main factors influencing this habitat are:

- Unmanaged recreational access to shingle resulting in disturbance and compaction of the surface by vehicles, destruction of ridge systems, trampling of the unique plant communities and disturbance to ground nesting birds.

- Coastal defence infrastructures which impact on the sediment supply reaching shingle structures.
- Onshore gravel extraction which destroys both the surface structure of the shingle and the associated wildlife communities.

3. CURRENT ACTION

3.1 Legal status

Nearly 200 SSSI/ASSIs include shingle features, although it has been estimated that only 22 of these contain significant areas of stable or semi-stable vegetation. Several shingle sites have also been declared NNRs or are managed as LNRs. Many of the most important SSSIs have also been declared SPAs under the EC Birds Directive. The UK Government has also set out its proposals for SACs that will contribute to the protection of coastal shingle vegetation. Perennial vegetation of stony banks are listed on Annex I of the EC Habitats Directive. Non-statutory shoreline management plans are also being encouraged in England and Wales by Government Departments and the statutory conservation agencies.

3.2 Management, research and guidance

In 1987 the Nature Conservancy Council commissioned a GB wide survey of shingle structures. The project surveyed almost 60 vegetated shingle beaches and resulted in the production of maps and written descriptions of the plant communities.

Conservation bodies have also received funding from the European Union, through the EC LIFE (Nature) Programme, for shingle conservation and restoration projects. One such project at Orfordness, a 16 km shingle spit on the Suffolk coast, is managed by the National Trust. The project aims to re-establish damaged shingle structures by introducing appropriate grazing regimes and controlling damaging recreational activities.

4. CONSERVATION DIRECTION

Maintain important shingle structures and the processes by which shingle structures are formed.

Measures to be considered further include:

- Implement strategies for managing the coastal zone at local, regional and national levels.
- Avoid damaging sites of conservation importance due to gravel and sand extraction.
- Avoid disrupting the dynamics of shingle beach processes by coastal defence and other construction works.
- Discourage disturbance and damage to important shingle areas from inappropriate forms and levels of use, including recreational uses.
- Review the powers and duties of coastal authorities for safeguarding this habitat.

BOULDERS AND ROCK ABOVE THE HIGH TIDE HABITAT STATEMENT

1. CURRENT STATUS

Areas of boulders and rocks above the high tide mark are those found in the upper limits of the littoral zone, a zone only wetted by wave splash and salt spray. This habitat is of particular interest for its coastal lichens, with variations reflecting the local geology and topography. Lichen species found include the scrambled egg lichen *Fulgensia fulgens*, ciliate strap lichen *Heterodermia leucomelos* and the southern grey physcia *Physcia tribacioides*, amongst others. There are also many characteristic coastal vascular plants including common scurvygrass *Cochleria officinalis* and sea lavender *Limonium recurvum* and bryophytes. Rocky coastlines also form important breeding colonies for the grey seal *Halichoerus grypus* which are among the rarest seals in the world. In Scotland the common seal *Phoca vitulina* also breeds on rocky coastlines, although its breeding grounds are more characteristically associated with sandflats and estuaries. Boulders and rocks form an important habitat type for wintering bird species such as the distinctive turnstone *Arenaria interpres* and purple sandpiper *Calidris maritima*. Breeding bird species associated with this habitat type include the rock pipit *Anthus petrosus*. The habitat has a distinctive vertebrate fauna consisting of some terrestrial species such as bristle-tails, *Petrobius maritimus* and large sea slater woodlice, *Ligia oceanica* on rock surfaces and in crevices, and several species of very small woodlice (eg: *Metatrichoniscoides celticus* and *Miktoniscus patiencei*) under large boulders, as well as some marine species like limpets, *Patella* species, winkles, *Littorina* species and sandhoppers, *Amphipoda*.

The coastline of Britain extends over some 18,000 km of which approximately 6,700 km is rocky at the high tide mark. Of this, 84% occurs in Scotland.

2. CURRENT FACTORS AFFECTING THE HABITAT

Factors influencing this habitat type include:

- Tabilisation of the foot of naturally eroding cliff faces which can result in a loss of rock exposures and the plant and insect communities which are dependent on them.
- In certain areas and at certain times, recreational access can lead to the disturbance of rock nesting birds. Trampling may also be detrimental to plant life.
- Damage from coastal defence works.

3. CURRENT ACTION

A number of landscape designations include rock and boulder habitats, although the exact amount is currently unknown: 20 of the 39 Areas of Outstanding National Beauty, 5 of the 10 National Parks in England & Wales contain a coastal element; 31 National Scenic Areas in Scotland include the coast.

4. CONSERVATION DIRECTION

Maintain rock and boulder habitats above the high tide mark in a natural state, by allowing the natural processes which lead to their formation to continue.

Measures to be considered further include:

- Protect coastal boulder and rock habitats of conservation importance from inappropriate uses.
- Implement strategies for managing the coastal zone at a local, regional and national level.
- Review the powers and duties of coastal authorities for safeguarding this habitat.
- Develop guidelines for coastal management to discourage damage or disturbance to this habitat.

COASTAL STRANDLINE HABITAT STATEMENT

1. CURRENT STATUS

Strandline vegetation is annual vegetation which colonises accumulations of drift material and gravels rich in nitrogenous organic matter at or near the high water mark. Strandlines are open in nature and support few species. Those species which are able to colonise can withstand periodic disturbance and are tolerant of seawater inundation as the beaches are often overtopped by the tide or subject to spray from the waves breaking over the beach. Periodic "cleaning" of the beach during winter storms may be important in removing excess litter and help to retain open conditions under which the strandline species thrive but where more aggressive species fail to colonise. Storms may, however, displace the shingle plant communities associated with the strandline and recolonisation may take several years to occur as the stability returns.

Strandlines may be precursors to other coastal habitats such as sand dunes or are found within saltmarsh or shingle. There is currently no estimate of the amount of strandline in the UK. Such an estimate would be difficult to arrive at because of the highly transitory nature of the habitat which may develop on any coastline.

Characteristic, vascular plant communities of strandlines include species such as sea sandwort *Honckenya peploides*, saltwort *Salsola kali* and sea rocket *Cakile maritima*, sea holly *Eryngium maritimum* and sea beet *Beta maritima*. Some rare and scarce species may also be found such as shore dock *Rumex rupestris* in the south-west and the oysterplant *Mertensia maritima* in the north.

The accumulations of rotting organic matter on the strandline support various assemblages of invertebrates, depending on the composition, humidity and state of decay of the material. Some specialised species such as the woodlouse *Armadillidium album* and the ground beetle *Nebria complanata* are found beneath the upper drift lines of foredunes and saltmarsh and one scarce beetle *Aphodius plagiatus*, is associated with the rotting algae and plant litter on dune strandlines. Other species are associated with driftwood and either bore into the timber, such as the wharf borer beetle *Nacerdes melanura* or find shelter, like the large ground beetle *Broscus cephalotes*, under larger pieces of driftwood or objects such as fishboxes and items of plastic.

2. CURRENT FACTORS AFFECTING THE HABITAT

The best areas of strandline vegetation are supported on flat, slightly mobile beaches with little or no human disturbance. Maintenance of the strandline requires minimal interference but a balance has to be struck between beach cleaning activities and the conservation requirements of important strandlines. Some of the current factors known to affect the habitat include:

- Human disturbance may affect the development of a species-rich invertebrate fauna and damage the vegetation.
- Clearance of important strandline vegetation and debris when beaches are cleaned up.
- Marine pollution, including oil and litter.
- Coastal squeeze and loss of sediment supply which can result from sea defence works and are likely to destroy strandline habitat.

3. CURRENT ACTION

Little action specific to strandline habitats has been carried out. However, actions taken which benefit other coastal habitats such as shingle, sand dunes and saltmarshes are likely to be of benefit to strandline habitat.

Guidance on best practice procedures to be followed by flood defence operating authorities has been issued by MAFF; this guidance aims to ensure that environmental issues are afforded due consideration when flood defence works are being planned, designed and implemented.

4. CONSERVATION DIRECTION

Maintain naturally occurring strandline habitat within sites which as a whole have been identified as being of national and international importance for coastal habitats and species.

Measures to be considered further include:

- Avoid damaging of sites of conservation importance by sand extraction.
- Incorporate information on the occurrence and structure of strandlines in inventories of coastal habitats.
- Encourage the development of conservation guidelines for strandlines which discourages their removal or disturbance especially when carrying out beach cleaning activities.
- Promote shoreline management plans which permit the natural functioning of coastal sediment processes.
- Encourage reductions in inputs of marine contaminants stemming from human activities.
- Encourage further ecological studies of this habitat.

MACHAIR
HABITAT STATEMENT

I. CURRENT STATUS

Machair is a distinctive sand dune formation which is only found in the north and west of Scotland (around 5,000 ha of machair) and in western Ireland. It is estimated that more than two thirds of the global extent of machair is found in Scotland.

Machair supports extensive grazing regimes and unique traditional forms of cultivation which rely on a low-input low-output system of rotational cropping. It is this system which sustains rich and varied dune and arable weed plant communities. The traditional management provides habitat for important breeding wader populations through the creation of periodically disturbed open ground. Machair supports a rich invertebrate fauna, providing almost the only calcareous habitat in extensive areas of acidic soils and rocks. The globally threatened corncrake *Crex crex* is also found on machair habitat.

By definition, machair soils develop from wind deposited shell-sand blown inland by prevailing winds from coastal beaches and mobile dunes over a plain of impermeable rock. Machair habitats comprise the dry grassland, damp grassland (seasonally waterlogged), marsh (permanently waterlogged) and standing water (lochs) habitats that occur on this shell-sand. Typically, between the inland (eastern) margin of machair and the adjoining peatland habitats, there is a 'blackland' transition zone with dark peaty soils supporting acid grassland or heath vegetation. The rich and diverse habitat mosaic typical of machair systems results from the wide combination of conditions found along four environmental gradients: wetness (dry to wet), soil pH (5-9), salinity (fresh to saline) and human disturbance (ploughing).

2. CURRENT FACTORS AFFECTING THE HABITAT

The move away from the traditional cattle based agriculture associated with crofting towards a less labour intensive system based on sheep is the main factor affecting this habitat. Within this the main elements of change are:

- Earlier cutting of grass for silage rather than hay, which prevents seeding of flowering plants and destroys nests of characteristic birds such as the corncrake.
- More intensive grazing, combined with a switch from cattle to sheep, which leads to a closely-cropped sward that is unsuitable for many species.
- Increased use of fertilisers and pesticides, leading to a loss in variety of species.
- Lack of grazing leading to rank, species poor vegetation.

3. CURRENT ACTION

3.1 Legal status

Much of the machair area in Scotland is crofted land. Crofting communities enjoy unique forms of management and land tenure, which have been protected since the passing of the Crofters Act 1886. Their status has been enhanced by a series of subsequent acts which were consolidated under the Crofters (Scotland) Act 1993.

Some of the most important machair sites for nature conservation have been notified as SSSIs. Machair is also listed on Annex I of the EC Habitats Directive and the UK Government has recently set out its proposals for a number of areas which merit designation as SACs. Some areas of machair are also proposed SPAs under the EC Birds Directive.

Machair areas are designated as Less Favoured Areas (LFAs). Farmers are therefore eligible for a range of support measures including two aimed specifically at crofters (relating to agricultural grants and building grants/loans). The European Commission takes a close interest in rural development in crofting areas. UK and EU agricultural support payments are disbursed by SOAEFD, and bodies such as SNH, the Red Deer Commission and Local Enterprise Councils are involved to an extent in maintaining the wider environmental interests of machair.

3.2 Management, research and guidance

Schemes relating to conservation are also in place, although they are small in scale compared with agricultural support schemes. These include ESA schemes, covering the Uists, Benbecula and Vatersay, and the Argyll Islands, an environmental element of the Agricultural Business Improvement Scheme and SSSI management grants.

The RSPB has joined SNH and the Scottish Crofters' Union to set up and administer a 'Corncrake Initiative'. This scheme provides financial incentives to manage machair meadows to attract and hold corncrakes. A parallel scheme to encourage farmers to provide uncultivated field corners for corncrakes was introduced in Balranald in 1994, and will be developed to include larger areas of the Western Isles and the Inner Argyll Islands in 1995.

4. CONSERVATION DIRECTION

Maintain and enhance, through appropriate agricultural use, a mosaic of species diverse short grass, tall herbaceous vegetation and rotationally cultivated soil with its associated field weeds and semi-natural habitats.

Measures to be considered further include:

- Maintain traditional crofting use of machair which sustains the habitat and associated species.
- Use existing measures, such as ESAs, to support appropriate management of machair.
- Research the feasibility and methods of restoring damaged machair.
- Promote a wide understanding and appreciation of this habitat.

SALTMARSH HABITAT STATEMENT

1. CURRENT STATUS

There are about 45,000 ha of saltmarsh habitat in the UK. The habitat is widely distributed around the UK covering nearly 1,700 km (about 10%) of the coast. However, just ten sites account for 60% of the total resource. Historically large areas of saltmarsh have been lost as a result of land claim.

Saltmarsh is a highly productive habitat which develops along sheltered coasts with soft, shallow shores which provide protection from strong wave action. 95% of saltmarsh in Great Britain is found within estuaries. It represents a transition from sand and mudflat areas on the lower marsh, where the vegetation is frequently flooded by the tide, through to the upper saltmarsh where creeksides and depressions or pans occur. Here the plant communities are less frequently inundated and for shorter durations. In the uppermost areas of saltmarshes there may be transitions to brackish or freshwater marsh or to dune vegetation or vegetation overlying shingle structures. Characteristic saltmarsh species include annual sea-blite *Suaeda maritima*, glasswort *Salicornia* spp., common saltmarsh-grass *Puccinellia maritima*, the sea rush *Juncus maritimus*, sea aster *Aster tripolium*, sea-purslane *Atriplex portulacoides* and sea lavender *Limonium* spp. The exact species composition of saltmarsh communities varies along a north/south gradient in the UK. Many invertebrates, including GB Red Data Book and nationally scarce species are confined to saltmarsh. Areas with high structural and plant diversity, particularly where freshwater seepages provide a transition from fresh to brackish conditions, are particularly important for invertebrates.

Saltmarshes are also important habitats for wintering and passage birds and can become even more important under certain grazing regimes. Notable bird species include barnacle goose *Branta leucopsis*, and twite *Carduelis flavirostris*. Saltmarshes are important for breeding waders in some areas.

The often intimate relationship between saltmarsh vegetation and other coastal habitats means their management cannot be divorced from actions to conserve other habitats such as shingle structures, sand dunes and intertidal flats.

2. CURRENT FACTORS AFFECTING THE HABITAT

The main factors that influence saltmarsh include:

- Combination of rising relative sea levels and maintenance of sea defences resulting in 'coastal squeeze'. This increases both erosion of the lower saltmarsh edge and the loss of upper saltmarsh habitats.
- Construction of coastal defences along with dredging activities which may disrupt sediment dynamics.
- Construction and enlargement of sea walls and associated works and/or land claim, resulting in the loss of the upper saltmarsh and transitional communities.
- Pollution, particularly from oil, and any subsequent clean-up operation.
- Grazing regimes can affect plant species diversity.
- Nutrient supply, freshwater flows and the morphology of the estuary.
- Cordgrass *Spartina anglica* colonisation.

3. CURRENT ACTION

3.1 Legal status

A large proportion of the saltmarsh in Britain is notified as SSSI. It is estimated that approximately 51% of saltmarsh in north Scotland, 83% in east and southeast Scotland, 89% in northeast, east and southeast England, 79% in south and southwest England and 87% in Wales are notified. The majority of Northern Ireland's saltmarsh is ASSI and almost all is likely to be included in ASSIs in the future.

The UK Government has set out its commitment to promoting the sustainable use of the coast. A number of initiatives contribute to this aim. These include the publication of planning policy guidance notes (PPG 20) for coastal areas, and a Strategy for Flood and Coastal Defence in England and Wales.

3.2 Management, research and guidance

Various coastal management and policy fora are now in place and include the Affordir Group in Wales, EN's Estuaries Initiative, and SNH's Focus on Firths. Both Countryside Stewardship and Tir Cymen specifically target saltmarsh and include management prescriptions which are aimed at maintaining and enhancing both grazed and ungrazed saltmarshes. By the end of 1993, 3,312 ha of saltmarsh had been entered into Countryside Stewardship in England and 84 ha into Tir Cymen in Wales. A saltmarsh option was introduced under the Habitat Scheme in 1994 which offers a payment per hectare for farmers who reintroduce tidal influence to agricultural land behind the sea defences. MAFF and EN are already testing the optimum conditions and the best techniques for re-establishing saltmarsh in conjunction with managed set-back of coastal defences. A large scale MAFF research project is underway at Tollesbury Fleet (Essex) and a smaller scale project at a National Trust site, Northey Island, (Essex).

Non-statutory shoreline management plans are also being encouraged in England and Wales by Government Departments and the statutory conservation agencies.

4. CONSERVATION DIRECTION

Maintain and enhance the area and quality of saltmarsh and its constituent communities in the UK. Prevent further habitat loss to land claim and reverse poor habitat management.

Measures to be considered further include:

- Pilot the creation of new saltmarsh habitats to replace unavoidable losses from sea level rise or where appropriate opportunities arise through coastal defence setback or behind existing defences.
- Avoid disruption of the dynamics of saltmarsh processes by coastal defence and other construction works.
- Review the powers and duties of coastal authorities for safeguarding this habitat.
- Implement strategies for managing the coastal zone at local, regional and national levels.
- Encourage reductions in marine contaminants stemming from human activities.
- Encourage appropriate levels of grazing on sand dune systems.
- Encourage research projects into the ecology of saltmarsh habitat.

SAND DUNE HABITAT STATEMENT

I. CURRENT STATUS

Sand dunes in the UK develop on coastlines where there is an adequate supply of sediment within the size range 0.2 to 2.0 mm. The critical factor is the presence of a sufficiently large beach which dries out at low tide and where the sand grains are blown onto the land by the action of wind. Vegetation prevents the sand from further dispersal.

Sand dunes are widely distributed around the UK coastline. There are 31,436 ha in Scotland, 9,276 ha in England and 6,406 ha in Wales. 43 sites in Great Britain exceed 50 ha and are considered to be of national importance as dune habitats. A further two sites are of importance in Northern Ireland.

Dune systems comprise several distinct features:

- 'Foredunes' are actively building or growing dunes, found in areas receiving large quantities of blown sand. The continual burying by sand restricts the number of plants that can survive but provides ideal conditions for the growth of the sand-binding marram grass *Ammophila arenaria* and in northern areas lyme-grass *Leymus arenarius*. Sand couch grass *Elymus farctus* is also a frequent component of the early stages of colonisation especially where salt spray reaches the upper parts of the beach. Many GB Red Data Book and nationally scarce species of invertebrates are often associated with the bare, open sand in the areas of early succession of dune development.

- 'Yellow dunes' are more stable and an increasing number of annuals and perennials occur in the associated vegetation. In the south sea bindweed *Calystegia soldanella* and sea-holly *Eryngium maritimum* are often present.

- 'Dune grassland' occurs as a more stable form of dune develops. The occurrence of sand-binding marram grass is less frequent and gives way to plant species that are associated with calcareous grassland. Dune grassland may be species-rich and contains species that are typically associated with inland areas including in the south, pyramidal orchid *Anacamptis pyramidalis*, and in the north Scottish primrose *Primula scotica*, mountain avens *Dryas octopetala* and common juniper *Juniperus communis*.

- 'Dune slacks' are areas of wetland within the dune system including peatlands on the inner edges of some dunes and the swampy edges of open water. Where the grass is closely grazed by rabbits important populations of some rare or scarce plants can occur, such as the fen orchid *Liparis loeselii* and the petalwort *Petalophyllum ralfsii*. Dune slacks, and the less stable foredunes, are important for fungi which form mycorrhizal associations with colonists such as the sand-binding marram grass.

- 'Dune heath' is found on stable areas of acid or lime-deficient dunes. The exact composition of the plant community varies around the coast, but heather *Calluna vulgaris* is almost always present. Bell heather *Erica cinerea*, western gorse *Ulex gallii*, crowberry *Empetrum nigrum* and sheep's-fescue *Festuca ovina* may also be present. Dune heaths differ from most inland heaths because they also contain characteristic sand dune plants such as sand sedge *Carex arenaria*.

- 'Dune scrub' develops in both dry and wet areas of the dune system. The scrub on dry dunes is dominated by sea buckthorn *Hippophae rhamnoides* and in the wetter dune slack areas it is normally dominated by willow *Salix* spp. or birch *Betula* spp. In Wales much of the dry dune scrub is dominated by gorse *Ulex europaeus* and blackthorn *Prunus spinosa*.

2. CURRENT FACTORS AFFECTING THE HABITAT

- In some instances, such as Sefton Coast, coastal defence works and direct extraction of sand from dunes for building purposes has arrested the formation of new dunes seaward of existing ones due to the loss of sediment supply.

- Increasing sea levels are causing steepening of the foreshore and increased wave attack at the base of dune systems.

- Afforestation restricts dune development and also changes the nature of the dunes making them more acidic. Changes in the water tables arising from afforestation can also affect the characteristic vegetation for some distance from the plantation.

- Increasing tourism in coastal areas results in pressures from the development of public amenities and increasing levels of visitor pressure which leads to trampling of the vegetation, erosion of the dune systems and disturbance of breeding birds.

- Inappropriate grazing management of dune systems also leads to a reduction in the diversity of plant species. It can also lead to excessive amounts of nutrients within the dune system, favouring nitrophilous weeds and result in eutrophication of dune slacks.

- Spread of non-native species such as the New Zealand pirri-pirri burr *Acaena novae-zelandiae* and in Wales sea buckthorn can lead to a loss of plant and invertebrate diversity.

3. CURRENT ACTION

3.1 Legal status

A large number of sand dune areas are notified as SSSI/ASSI. A number of sand dune species, including the sand lizard *Lacerta agilis* and the natterjack toad *Bufo calamita* are protected under the Wildlife and Countryside Act 1981. A number of sand dune species, such as seaside centaury *Centaurium littorale*, are also protected under the Nature Conservation and Amenity Lands (Northern Ireland) Order 1985.

Ten coastal sand dune types are also listed on Annex I of the EC Habitats Directive and the UK Government recently set out its proposals for areas which it considers merit designation as SACs.

The UK Government also set out its commitment to promoting the sustainable use of the coast. A number of initiatives contribute to this aim. These include the publication of planning policy guidance notes (PPG 20) for coastal areas, and the MAFF/Welsh Office Strategy for Flood and Coastal Defence in England and Wales.

3.2 Management, research and guidance

The statutory conservation agencies have commissioned a series of botanical surveys of the major British coastal habitats. This programme aims to establish the size, location and quality of the main coastal habitats; to allow the impact of development proposals to be assessed, particularly on sites of national importance; to provide guidance on the management of coastal habitats and to investigate the role of physical and biological processes in the maintenance of natural and semi-natural coastal habitats. As part of this programme a sand dune inventory of Great Britain was undertaken, the results of which have been published in three volumes by JNCC.

A *Sand Dune Inventory of Europe* was published by JNCC and the European Union for Coastal Conservation (EUCC) in 1991. The production of this inventory required the co-operation of a wide variety of people involved in dune conservation throughout Europe.

The EU, through the EC LIFE (Nature) Programme, also contributes to the conservation of sand dune systems in the UK. In 1995, funding to support the preparation of a conservation strategy for the Sefton Coast dune area was secured. Through this project restoration management of the dune habitat and heathland will be carried out together with species recovery work of endangered species.

4. CONSERVATION DIRECTION

Maintain the extent and enhance the habitat quality of sand dune systems, and ensure the continuation of natural processes which create dune systems.

Measures to be considered further include:

- Protect sand dune habitats of conservation importance from inappropriate uses.
- Implement strategies for managing the coastal zone at local, regional and national levels.
- Review the powers and duties of coastal authorities for safeguarding this habitat.
- Reduce the impact of sea level rise including replacing unavoidable habitat losses.
- Reduce the damage resulting from the introduction of non-native species.
- Encourage appropriate levels of grazing on sand dune systems.

SALINE LAGOONS HABITAT STATEMENT

1. CURRENT STATUS

Lagoons in the UK are bodies of saline water, natural or artificial, partially separated from the adjacent sea. They retain a proportion of their sea water at low tide and may develop as brackish, fully saline or hyper-saline water bodies. The total area of UK lagoons is 1,300 ha, and the largest lagoon is in excess of 450 ha: the rest are much smaller and some may be less than 1 ha. Lagoons contain soft sediments which often support tassel weeds and charophytes as well as filamentous green and brown algae. In addition, lagoons contain invertebrates rarely found elsewhere. They also provide important habitat for waterfowl, marshland birds and seabirds. The invertebrate fauna present can be divided into three main components: those that are essentially freshwater in origin, those that are marine/brackish species and those that are more specialist lagoonal species. The presence of certain indigenous and many specialist plants and animals make this habitat important to the UK's overall biodiversity.

There are several different types of lagoons, ranging from those separated from the adjacent sea by a barrier of sand, or shingle ('typical lagoons') to those arising as ponded waters in depressions on soft sedimentary shores to those partially separated from the sea by a rocky sill or artificial construction such as a sea wall. Sea-water exchange in lagoons occurs through a natural or man-modified channel or by percolation through or overtopping of the barrier. The salinity of the systems are determined by various levels of fresh water input from ground or surface waters. The degree of separation and the nature of the material separating the lagoon from the sea are the basis for the distinguishing several different physiographic types of lagoon.

2. CURRENT FACTORS AFFECTING THE HABITAT

The processes which lead to the natural development of some types of lagoons are generally inhibited by human coastal activities. It is probable that the formation of new lagoons will not keep pace with the process of lagoon loss. Current factors affecting this habitat type include:

- Saline lagoons are naturally transient; salinity regimes change as succession leads to freshwater conditions and eventually to vegetation such as fen carr. Some formerly saline sites are now freshwater.
- The bar-built sedimentary barriers of 'typical' coastal lagoons tend to naturally move landwards with time. Lagoons behind them will eventually be in-filled as bar sediments approach the shore.
- Pollution, in particular nutrient enrichment leading to eutrophication, can have major detrimental effects. This may result from inputs to the lagoon or the waters supplied to the lagoon.
- Artificial control of water (sea and fresh) to lagoons can have profound influences on the habitat.
- Many lagoons are often seen as candidates for in-filling or land claim as part of coastal development.
- Some coastal defence works can prevent the movement of sediments along the shore and lead to a weakening of the natural coastal structures within which many coastal lagoons are located.
- The impact of coastal defences will be compounded by the effects of sea level rise. It has been estimated that about 120 ha of coastal lagoons in England alone (10% of the existing resource) will be lost in the next 20 years, mainly as a consequence of sea level rise.
- Sea level rise also presents an opportunity for the reinstatement of saline waters to freshwater lakes which once were coastal lagoons, thereby allowing the creation of new lagoonal habitat.

3. CURRENT ACTION

3.1 Legal status

In Great Britain 10 species of invertebrate and plant associated with lagoons are protected under the Wildlife and Countryside Act 1981. However, no lagoonal species are listed for protection under the Nature Conservation and Amenity Lands (Northern Ireland) Order 1985.

Of the 177 sites of lagoons surveyed in England, just over 50 % occur within existing SSSIs and about 10% occur within NNRs and as many in LNRs. Fewer examples are found in Wales where only about four lagoons are recognised (there remain some un-surveyed potential sites in Clwyd). A survey currently under way in Scotland is expected to identify about 130 lagoons. A preliminary study suggests that there may be 30 lagoonal habitat sites in Northern Ireland (of these only a few small perched salt marsh pools are thought to be natural in origin). They will all eventually fall within the ASSI/SPAs network.

Internationally important lagoons have been designated, for their bird interest, as SPAs under the EC Birds Directive. Coastal lagoons are also listed as a priority habitat on Annex I of the EC Habitats Directive and the UK Government has recently set out its proposals for sites which it considers merit designation as SACs under this Directive.

3.2 Management, research and guidance

Coastal groups are currently preparing shoreline management plans for defined lengths of coast. The production of these plans will require identification of key habitats, including coastal lagoons, and confirmation of their management requirements.

Certain lagoons have an established research base and study group.

4. CONSERVATION DIRECTION

Maintain and enhance the current number, area (1,300 ha) and distribution of coastal lagoonal habitats across their geographical range by allowing natural processes to create new lagoons and accepting that some losses will arise through natural succession.

Further details of this conservation direction and the measures required to deliver it are given in the Costed Habitat Action Plan for Saline Lagoons.

ISLANDS AND ARCHIPELAGOS HABITAT STATEMENT

1. CURRENT STATUS

Islands or island archipelagos in the UK include mainly rocky coasts with a wide range of aspects in a small area usually in seas away from the immediate influence of the mainland coast. Around their coasts are habitats ranging greatly in their exposure to wave action and strength of tidal currents. Deep rock surfaces often occur. Sediment types are likely to be varied with coarse clean sediments off exposed coasts and muddy coarse sediments off sheltered coasts. This habitat statement considers the marine environment around the islands and archipelagos.

There are hundreds of islands around the UK mainland. They are common off western coasts and particularly numerous off the coasts of north and west Scotland. Shetland, Orkney and the Western Isles are the largest island groups. Other examples are the islands of St. Kilda, the Inner Hebrides, Anglesey, the Pembrokeshire islands, the Isles of Scilly, Lundy, the Isle of Wight and the Farne Islands. The Isles of Scilly are the only Lusitanian semi-oceanic archipelago in Europe. In addition there are numerous rocky outcrops which form islands around the British Isles.

The types of marine habitat and communities which fringe islands vary according to location and surrounding conditions. There are examples in extremely exposed islands (Fair Isle), current swept islands (Rathlin Island and Firth of Lorne) and very sheltered inshore islands (the Isle of Sheppy). Due to their separation from the mainland many islands are less susceptible to the effects of human disturbance and as a result they may support important bird or seal colonies. Examples of such island groups include St. Kilda and Grassholm where significant populations of gannets *Sula bassana,* occur and the Farne Islands where large populations of grey seals *Halichoerus grypus* are found. Other notable species include the endemic Lundy cabbage *Coincys wrightii* and the associated flea beetle *Psylliodes luridipennis,* the lesser white-toothed shrew *Crocidura suaveolens* found on the Scilly Isles and the Orkney vole *Microtus arvalis.*

Islands off the west coast of Britain are often very rich in oceanic lower plant species. Particularly notable are the oceanic and Lusitanian lichens found on the Isles of Scilly. Many of the western Scottish islands, such as St. Kilda, also have unique plant communities which are northern outliers of southern-oceanic species.

2. CURRENT FACTORS AFFECTING THE HABITAT

Activities influencing these habitats are:

- Total fishing effort (boats, gear, efficiency) has increased, particularly close inshore where there was a relatively pristine environment, and can damage fringing habitats and sediment around islands and their associated communities.
- Dredging, disposal of the material and aggregate extraction cause local damage to benthic communities as well as creating sediment plumes which may effect the biology of a wider area.
- Areas intensively used by shipping, or where conditions are particularly hazardous for navigation, are at risk from shipping accidents and threats of pollution. Ships often shelter in the lee of islands and may release pollutants through operational discharges.

- Licensing of areas for oil and gas extraction brings a further risk of pollution to some island groups should the areas be developed.

3. CURRENT ACTION

3.1 Legal status

There is a range of national and international legislation and agreements designed to protect the oceans. The UN Law of the Sea Convention (UNCLOS) provides a comprehensive framework for the regulation of all ocean space. Within the framework more specific agreements exist, for example, on dumping at sea through the London Convention 1972 and on shipping through MARPOL. The UK has also signed the OSPAR Convention for the protection of the marine environment of the north-east Atlantic which covers the prevention of pollution from land-based sources by dumping and incineration and from off-shore sources. The Convention also provides for an assessment of the quality of the marine environment. These agreements are given effect by a variety of statutes in the UK.

The report of Lord Donaldson's enquiry into the prevention of pollution from merchant shipping recommended, among other things, that "marine environmental high risk areas" (MEHRAs) be established. These would be areas of high environmental sensitivity which were also at risk from shipping. When established MEHRAs would be one of a number of ship routing measures designed to reduce the risks of pollution. The EU started a similar initiative in 1993 to encourage the identification of Marine and Coastal Environmentally Sensitive Areas.

A quality status report for the North Sea was published in 1993. It was drawn up by scientists from all the littoral states and represents the most thorough assessment of the health of the sea that has been undertaken. It is part of a wider assessment of all waters covered by the OSPAR Conventions which is to be completed by the year 2000.

Many islands are SSSI/ASSIs or NNRs but the boundaries of these designations do not extend below low mean water mark. Those with important seabird colonies may be designated as SPAs under the EC Birds Directive. A number of the marine habitats listed on Annex 1 of the EC Habitats Directive may occur in these areas and the UK Government has recently set out its proposals for SACs.

3.2 Management, research and guidance

The UK has three Marine Nature Reserves (MNRs), two of which surround islands - Lundy and Skomer. In the case of Lundy Island MNR the Devon Sea Fisheries Committee have introduced bylaws to control certain activities. There are areas where trawling, dredging, and the use of nets is prohibited as well as limits on potting. A colour zoning scheme has been developed to present the information in an easily understood format. Interpretative material is available, a management plan is in place and there is a resident warden. The Skomer MNR has an interpretation centre, marine conservation officers, and information describing the features of the reserve available to the public. Fisheries are limited to commercial activity hence the collection of crustaceans by divers is prohibited. In addition, there is a ban on the collection of scallops by dredging and other means. Bylaws have been introduced to prevent the reckless disturbance of wildlife.

Monitoring of marine communities or particular species takes place in both reserves.

The Isles of Scilly Marine Park, established in 1989, is overseen by the Isles of Scilly Environmental Trust, and a voluntary code of conduct aimed at shore visitors, divers, yachtsmen, boat operators, anglers and fishermen is in operation. Off the Northumberland coast, the local authority aims to promote marine conservation and produce educational materials about St Mary's Island. The National Trust and other non-governmental organisations own or manage islands and, in some cases, are trying to include marine issues in their management plans. The RSPB, for example, as owner of Ramsey Island, is developing an island management plan which also includes the adjacent waters and the National Trust is involved with the management of an important grey seal colony which haul out on some of the Farne Islands.

In 1994 EN identified 27 important areas for marine wildlife around England, some of which include islands and their adjacent marine habitats. In some of these there are existing management initiatives. EN encourages the development and testing of management methods using a voluntary approach in conjunction with existing regulatory controls. Twenty nine Marine Consultation Areas have been identified in Scotland. These are sites where SNH wish to be consulted prior to approval of activities which may damage the marine interest of the sites. Most are sealochs but also include islands in many cases.

The International Maritime Organisation (IMO) have recommend that defined zones around the Smalls (south-west Wales), Isles of Scilly and Fair Isle are 'Areas to be Avoided' by shipping. This is intended to minimise the risk of shipping accidents and should, in turn, reduce the risk from marine pollution resulting from such incidents. Following the grounding of the M.V. Braer, the shipping industry and the Department of Transport identified a number of voluntary "no-go" areas. Most of these centre around or involve islands.

4. CONSERVATION DIRECTION

Maintain and enhance the quality of marine habitats and communities surrounding islands and archipelagos.

Measures to be considered further include:

- Identify islands and archipelagos in UK waters which support marine habitats and species of national and international importance.

- Include representative examples of islands, archipelagos, and their fringing marine habitats, in the UK network of marine protected areas.

- Promote research in order to improve our understanding of the dynamics and sensitivity of marine habitats around island ecosystems.

- Promote codes of good practice on the use of island waters.

- Encourage Coastal Zone Management; closely linking marine and terrestrial features and activities on islands.

- Assess the nature and extent of fisheries in sensitive sites.

INLETS AND ENCLOSED BAYS HABITAT STATEMENT

I. CURRENT STATUS

Marine inlets, including sounds, straits and narrows are a common feature of the coastline of the UK and are particularly numerous along the west coast of Scotland and the outlying Scottish Islands. Of the various distinctive types fjords and fjards are a feature of northern Britain, while rias occur on southern coasts. There are good examples of all three types in the UK; Loch Seaforth and Loch Sunart (fjords), Loch Maddy and Loch Roag (fjards) and Milford Haven, the Fal Estuary, Salcombe Estuary and the Helford River (rias). Voes are similar physiographic features to rias but are only present in Shetland. Loch Gairloch and Loch Caolisport are typical of the more open sealochs while good examples of enclosed bays and harbours are Pagham and Poole, on the south coast of England. Sounds and straits are channels of water between two land features and typically open at both ends to the open coast. Narrows are restricted channels typically with strong tidal currents that are usually a feature of marine inlets such as sealochs.

Several important species and benthic communities are found in marine inlets and bays, although they also occur in other marine habitats. These include *Serpula vermicularis* reefs, seapens such as *Funiculina quadrangularis*, *Pennatula phosphorea* and *Virgularia mirabilis*, the file shell *Limaria hians*, the burrowing anemone *Pachycerianthus multiplicatus*, horse mussel *Modiolus modiolus* and native oyster *Ostrea edulis*. Beds of maerl, *Ascophyllum nodosum*, ecad *mackaii* and *Zostera* spp., are also key elements of these habitat types.

2. CURRENT FACTORS AFFECTING THE HABITAT

Signs of damage, change and deterioration in the quality of marine habitats and species can be seen in many marine inlets and enclosed bays:

- Development of anoxic conditions and bacterial mats under fish farms.
- Mobile bottom fishing gear has and can damage seabed communities such as maerl, horse mussel, scallop and file shell beds, and areas colonised by seapens.
- Discharge of sewage causes localised pollution. Poor water quality can also be a problem due to the retention and concentration of discharges and run-off from surrounding land leading to nutrient enrichment and the accumulation of persistent chemicals.
- Build up of tributyl tin, a component of anti-fouling paints has resulted in the decline of various species, most notably the dog whelk. There has been some recovery since a ban was imposed on its use for small craft but it remains at significant levels in some inlets.
- In Britain there have been changes in the species composition of marine inlets following colonisation by non-native species. Introductions have primarily occurred as a result of international maritime traffic and unintentional introductions associated with mariculture.
- Concentration of vessel traffic in some inlets brings an increased risk of pollution.
- Maintenance dredging of shipping lanes and dumping of the collected material, together with other developments can increase the sediment load in the water column leading to reduced water quality for algae and smothering of the benthos.
- Proposals for barrages, development of coastal superquarries, increased recreational use of inlets with associated coastal development and the threat of sea level rise.

3. CURRENT ACTION

3.1 Legal status

In carrying out their functions the NRA, Water Companies, Internal Drainage Boards and Local Authorities in England and Wales have a statutory duty to further conservation where consistent with purposes of enactments relating to their functions. These are set out in the Water Resources Act 1991, and the Land Drainage Act 1991. River Purification Boards (RPBs) in Scotland do not have the same duties. Both the NRA and RPBs have statutory responsibilities for pollution control.

In Northern Ireland responsibility for water quality, water supply and drainage resides with the Environment Service of DoE(NI), Water Service DoE(NI) and DANI respectively.

Deposits in the sea are controlled by a system of licences issued under the Food and Environment Protection Act 1985 with the intention of protecting the marine environment. Additionally, operational discharges are controlled by the Convention for the Prevention of Pollution from ships (MARPOL), and the UK shipping regulations.

Parts of some inlets and enclosed bays are cited on lists of statutory designations (e.g. SSSIs/ASSIs) however, in the majority of cases, the sites have been designated for a terrestrial interest. Protection afforded by the notification is currently limited to areas above low water (the precise boundary varies between Scotland and other parts of the UK).

Inlets and bays are defined as 'Large Shallow Inlets and Bays' on Annex I of the EC Habitats Directive. The UK Government has set out its proposals to consider 7 such areas as SACs for this interest. Some inlets and bays also meet the criteria necessary to qualify as SPAs under the EC Birds Directive and/or Wetlands of International Importance under the Ramsar Convention.

3.2 Management, research and guidance

In Northern Ireland Strangford Lough is a MNR.

The Helford River has been a voluntary marine conservation area since 1987. There are education interpretation and monitoring activities. A trial reintroduction of seagrass *Zostera marina* to an area where it was abundant earlier this century and studies on cockling, bass fisheries and bait digging along the River have been conducted.

Twenty nine Marine Consultation Areas have been identified in Scotland and many of these are sealochs. These are sites where Scottish Natural Heritage wishes to be consulted prior to approval of activities which may damage the marine nature conservation interest of the sites.

In 1994 English Nature identified 27 important areas for marine wildlife around England. These include a number of marine inlets such as Plymouth Sound, Dartmouth and the Salcombe estuary. These are areas where English Nature will develop and test management methods using a voluntary approach in conjunction with existing regulatory controls.

The International Maritime Organisation (IMO) has recommended a deep water route to the west of the Outer Hebrides to reduce the risk of marine pollution from shipping accidents in the Minch. This is a voluntary arrangement at present.

Guidance on best practice procedures to be followed by flood defence operating authorities has been issued by MAFF; this guidance aims to ensure that environmental issues are afforded due consideration when flood defence works are being planned, designed and implemented.

A report of Scottish sealochs published by JNCC in 1994 notes that each sealoch surveyed had an individual character and most had biotopes or species of some interest. Surveys of harbours, rias and estuaries in southern Britain (carried out as part of the Marine Nature Conservation Review by JNCC) have also identified sites of high nature conservation importance. Similar information is available for Northern Ireland from sublittoral surveys completed in 1986.

4. CONSERVATION DIRECTION

Maintain and manage the variety of habitats, communities and species of inlets and enclosed bays, as well as seeking improvement of areas which have been damaged or degraded.

Measures to be considered further include:

- Encourage integrated coastal zone management through collaboration and co-operation between the many interests concerned with marine inlets.
- Include inlets and bays of international, national and regional importance within a network of protected areas.
- Avoid reduction in water quality from direct and indirect discharges, run-off or inappropriate use.
- Minimise the risk of the introduction of non-native species through quarantine regulations and controls on the discharge of ballast.
- Guide inappropriate development away from these sites or the adjacent coastal land.
- Reduce damage to benthic communities and species found in inlets and bays, especially where they are particularly fragile, vulnerable or unusual and where this has already occurred examine the feasibility of re-establishment or restoration.

OPEN COAST HABITAT STATEMENT

1. CURRENT STATUS

The open coast includes the coast itself and waters out to six miles from the baseline. The extensive areas of open coast around the UK support a variety of marine wildlife and habitats. Intertidal areas include relatively rare habitats, such as chalk foreshores which form only 0.6% of the British coastline, but which constitute the largest expanses of intertidal chalk found in northern Europe. Biogeographic differences occur with the rocky shores of south-western England which are richer in species than those to the north and east. Much of the sublittoral zone adjacent to open coast is a mixture of rock and sediment but there are notable areas where one type dominates. St. Kilda is renowned for its sublittoral cliffs, caves, tunnels and archways, the 'Sarns' of Cardigan Bay are reefs of boulders, mobile cobbles and pebbles, the seabed adjacent to the Northumberland coast is a mixture of rock grading through to sands further offshore while the seabed adjacent to East Anglia is typified by soft sediments.

Open coasts are those subject to fully saline conditions and often strong wave action. Both intertidal areas and subtidal areas out to the approximate limits of coastal influence are included. Where there is a gradually sloping seabed and no large input of estuarine water, this is likely to be approximately 5 km from the low water mark or deeper than 50m. Where estuarine plumes extend offshore or where there are offshore features such as reefs, turbid water, accelerated or reduced tidal flows, and localised shelter from wave action this habitat is likely to be found further offshore.

Benthic habitats may be of rock or sediment or a mixture of both. Rocky shores are generally dominated by algae in wave-sheltered conditions and by limpets, barnacles and mussels where there are wave-exposed conditions. Sediment shores may be narrow fringing habitats or constitute extensive intertidal flats. The communities present reflect sediment type and can be highly impoverished in mobile sediments, to very rich in sheltered mixed sediments. There is a distinct zonation of communities on both rocky and sediment intertidal areas, reflecting mainly the degree of immersion and emersion by the tide. In the subtidal, zonation on rock is brought about primarily by the attenuation of light, with well-lit areas dominated by kelp forests, extending in deeper water to rocks colonised by animal communities where light is insufficient for algae to dominate. The different communities found on, and in, sediments are determined mainly by the sediment type which, in turn, is largely a reflection of wave and current action.

A number of species important for commercial fisheries are also key elements of the total wildlife value of open coast habitats. Examples include plaice *Pleuronectes platessa*, Dover sole *Solea solea*, lobster *Homarus gammarus*, prawn *Palaemon serratus* and scallops *Pecten maximus* and *Aequipecten opercularis*.

2. CURRENT FACTORS AFFECTING THE HABITAT

Activities which have damaged or disturbed marine habitats and wildlife along open coasts include:

- Bottom fishing gears, especially trawled gear, operating close inshore, which can damage fragile species and can damage or disturb communities in rocky areas as well as on soft sediment.

- Soft rock coastlines have been especially affected in some areas by development that has subsequently required protection from erosion.
- Sediment structure has changed on some beaches following extensive bait digging.
- Localised changes in benthic communities have been linked to uncontrolled discharge and dumping of material in the marine environment.

Intertidal habitats and wildlife of open coasts are affected by:

- Discharge of pollutants, possible nutrient enrichment from diffuse land based sources as well as sewage outfalls.
- Disturbance through collection of algae and marine animals, such as peeler crabs or bait digging, land claim, litter, and coastal protection.
- Non-native species such as the vigorously growing alga jap weed *Sargassum muticum* or the slipper limpet *Crepidula fornicata* may alter the local balance of ecology.

In the nearshore environment factors which should be considered are:

- Aggregate extraction which causes direct damage to important sand and gravel communities.
- The development of inshore blocks for oil and gas exploration which could adversely affect the habitat through discharge of chemicals, disturbance to wildlife and direct damage to the seabed should construction not be properly managed in the vicinity of installations.

3. CURRENT ACTION

3.1 Legal status

In carrying out their functions the NRA, Water Companies, Internal Drainage Boards and Local Authorities in England and Wales have a statutory duty to further conservation where consistent with purposes of enactments relating to their functions. These are set out in the Water Resources Act 1991, and the Land Drainage Act 1991. River Purification Boards (RPBs) in Scotland do not have the same duties. Both the NRA and RPBs have statutory responsibilities for pollution control.

In Northern Ireland responsibility for water quality, water supply and drainage resides with the Environment Service of DoE(NI), Water Service DoE(NI) and DANI respectively. These bodies also have responsibility for nature conservation interest.

Deposits in the sea are controlled by a system of licences issued under the Food and Environment Protection Act 1985 with the intention of protecting the marine environment. Additionally, operational discharges are controlled by the Convention for the Prevention of Pollution from ships (MARPOL), and the UK shipping regulations

There are several hundred coastal SSSIs/ASSIs and in most cases the boundaries include the foreshore. Bylaws prohibit certain activities to safeguard the conservation importance of the foreshore of some SSSIs. Although some SSSIs and NNRs have offshore boundaries the limit of statutory protection does not currently extend below the low water mark.

Areas which include sea caves, sandbanks, reefs, mudflats & sandflats, categories listed on Annex 1 of the EC Habitats Directive could qualify as SACs. The UK Government has already set out its proposals for a number of areas to be designated under this Directive.

Under the Bonn Convention UK contributes to the conservation of small cetaceans. In April 1992 the UK Government signed the Agreement on the Conservation of Small Cetaceans of the Baltic and North Seas (ASCOBANS). Under this agreement the range states co-operate in both research and management to conserve small cetaceans in the Baltic and North Sea. The statutory conservation agencies and Environment and Fisheries Departments contribute to the implementation of this agreement in a number of ways including recommending Sites of Conservation Interest, providing marine environment advice, and supporting research which reviews population data and contributes to the understanding of the impact of by-catches.

A quality status report for the North Sea was published in 1993. It was drawn up by experts from all the littoral states and represents the most thorough assessment of the sea that has been undertaken. It is part of a wider assessment of all waters covered by the OSPAR Conventions which is to be completed by the year 2000.

3.2 Management, research and guidance

In 1994 EN identified 27 important areas for marine wildlife around England. Most of these include stretches of open coast. They are areas where EN wish to develop and test management methods, using a voluntary approach in conjunction with existing regulatory controls. EN has also recently established a voluntary reserve grant scheme and in 1994/5 they made £50,000 available to run the scheme. The primary aim of this grant is to substantially increase the number of voluntary reserves by working through local groups.

Three voluntary marine conservation areas include stretches of open coast. These are at St. Abbs Head (Borders), North Devon, and Purbeck (Dorset). Voluntary codes of conduct are promoted at these sites to conserve marine habitats and wildlife. Part of the Skomer and Lundy MNRs also come under the category of open coast but is discussed in more detail in the Statement dealing with 'Islands and archipelagos'.

Stretches of coast in England and Wales have been defined as Heritage Coast. Although primarily concerned with land management there has been an interest in conservation of foreshore and adjacent waters in some areas. This is particularly the case at Ceredigion, where a marine Heritage Coast has been identified, and on the Purbeck coast, where the Heritage Coast scheme has supported the voluntary marine conservation area off Kimmeridge.

Non-statutory shoreline management plans are also being encouraged in England and Wales by Government departments and the statutory nature conservation agencies.

In 1993 as part of the EU's initiative on marine and Coastal Environmentally Sensitive Areas the statutory agencies submitted to Government Departments a list of environmentally sensitive sites subject to heavy shipping traffic. In addition, the report of Lord Donaldson's enquiry *Safer Ships, Cleaner Seas* recommended that Marine Environmental High Risk Areas - MEHRAs be established. The statutory agencies are encouraging Government to conduct a comprehensive monitoring exercise to check that vessels are avoiding MEHRAs.

Guidance on best practice procedures to be followed by flood defence operating authorities has been issued by MAFF; this guidance aims to ensure that environmental issues are afforded due consideration when flood defence works are being planned, designed and implemented.

4. CONSERVATION DIRECTION

Maintain the wildlife interest of open coast habitats around the UK.

Measures to be considered further include:

- Prepare coastal zone management plans for stretches of open cast and adjacent seas and encourage the development of a single, co-ordinated framework for management of protected areas which span the coastal zone.

- Examine the representation of open coast habitats in the current network of protected areas and extend this, if necessary, to ensure that there is adequate coverage and protection of sites representative of each marine biogeographic zone.

- Promote shoreline management plans which take account of the environmental interests of the coastline and the coastal process which are essential to their maintenance.

- Prepare management plans for species that support commercial fisheries in the UK and enable control and regulation where these relate to inshore fisheries.

- Consider options for restoration of damaged or degraded areas of open coast.

- Define Statutory Water Quality Objectives for coastal waters.

OPEN SEA WATER COLUMN HABITAT STATEMENT

I. CURRENT STATUS

Open seas are defined as those beyond six miles from baselines. The area they cover is vast. For this Statement the off-shore limit has been taken to be the extent of UK controlled waters (200 miles).

The coastal seas which cover the continental shelf around Britain have a very different ecology from those of the open ocean. The close proximity of the sea-bed, land/sea interactions, the dominance of tidal flows, and in some areas riverine inputs, strongly influence mixing and nutrient supplies and hence the productivity regime. These seas are further subdivided. Shelf sea fronts at the interface between stable water masses of significantly different temperatures (or salinities). They can be areas of high phytoplankton growth which support dense populations of zooplankton and hence fish, seabirds and cetaceans. The North Sea, to the north of the tidal front which extends eastwards from Flamborough Head, has a very different ecology and is inhabited by assemblages of species that are distinct from those of the southern North Sea. The southern North Sea is also influenced both by the relatively small inflow of water from the English Channel and the outflows of the great European rivers. To the north the dominant influence is from Atlantic water flowing around northern Scotland and from over the shelf-break to the east of the Shetlands. Along Britain's west coast the gradients are more related to latitude and the flow of the residual currents, so the Celtic Sea is distinct from the coastal sea off the Hebrides.

The open ocean beyond the shelf-break is not as clearly geographically defined, and there are latitudinal gradients (produced primarily by changing thermal regime) in the assemblages and ecological characteristics of the pelagic communities, which result in the ecology of the seas to the north of Scotland being distinct from those in the south off the South-western Approaches but the changes are clinal rather than being stepped. The dominant flow through the Irish Sea is northwards.

The ecology and associated animal and plant communities of open seas are quite distinct. The species richness of neritic waters is quite low, but the quantities of animals are often very high. Oceanic waters are locally richer in species but the populations tend to be smaller. In terms of global diversity, the pelagic animal communities of the open ocean are relatively poor in species, because the main ocean currents ensure that the species have immense geographical ranges.

2. CURRENT FACTORS AFFECTING THE HABITAT

There is limited information on changes in quality of this habitat but several issues need to be considered:

- Cargo ships which take on sea water ballast in coastal waters can transfer non-native species to another bio-geographic area when they discharge their ballast. This is the subject of ongoing research in the UK.
- Discharge of contaminants from anthropogenic sources.
- Over exploitation of fish stocks. This may influence the habitat by the removal of top predators or the removal of the prey species of others.

3. CURRENT ACTION

3.1 Legal status

The quality of coastal waters is relevant to the open seas, and bodies with a statutory duty are covered by that habitat statement.

There is a range of national and international legislation and agreements designed to protect the oceans. The UN Law of the Sea Convention (UNCLOS) provides a comprehensive framework for the regulation of all ocean space. Within the framework more specific agreements exist, for example on dumping at sea (through the London Convention 1972) and on shipping (through MARPOL). The UK has also signed the OSPAR Convention for the protection of the marine environment of the north-east Atlantic, which covers the prevention of pollution from land-based sources by dumping and incineration, and from off-shore sources. The Convention also provides for an assessment of the quality of the marine environment. These agreements are implemented in the UK by a variety of statutes.

A quality status report for the North Sea was published in 1993. It was drawn up by experts from all the littoral states and represents the most thorough assessment of the sea that has been undertaken. It is part of a wider assessment of all waters covered by the OSPAR Conventions which is to be completed by the year 2000.

The ecology of open sea systems and the high incidence of migratory species necessitates an international approach to conservation. This is recognised by UNCLOS 1985 and the UN Agreement on Straddling Stocks, Fish Stocks and Highly Migratory Fish Stocks (August 1985). The latter urges regional management. EU fisheries are managed through the CFP. The CFP includes the proscription of certain fishing methods. Other international bodies and agreements (eg: the IWC, CITES and ASCOBANS) protect other marine species, including imposing a moratorium on whaling.

3.2 Management, research and guidance

In 1993 as part of the EU's initiative on marine and Coastal Environmentally Sensitive Areas the statutory agencies submitted to Government Departments a list of environmentally sensitive sites subject to heavy shipping traffic. In addition, the report of Lord Donaldson's enquiry *Safer Ships, Cleaner Seas* recommended that Marine Environmental High Risk Areas - MEHRAs be established.

4. CONSERVATION DIRECTION

Maintain and enhance the richness and quality of the open sea environment.

Measures to be considered further include:

- Improve co-ordination between competent and relevant authorities operating in the marine environment in the management of activities and uses of the open sea.
- Continue to assess the environmental impact of activities taking place in the open sea.
- Improve the quality of coastal waters.

- Assess the contribution which a network of marine protected areas in the open sea might make to species and habitat conservation.
- Work through the IMO to minimise the environmental impacts of shipping.
- Continue to implement international conventions, agreements and declarations to which the UK is committed.

SHELF BREAK HABITAT STATEMENT

1. CURRENT STATUS

The shelf-break lies along the margin of the continental shelf to the west of Britain and Ireland, generally at a depth of about 200m, where the sea-floor suddenly drops steeply away into the deep ocean. Here, as the tides impinge on the continental margin, resonances are set up in the water which can result in high growth of phytoplankton during the summer. This creates a region of high productivity which is sometimes clearly visible in satellite images, and often marked by dense concentrations of seabirds, shoals of fish and cetaceans. Echosounders often reveal large and extensive patches of intense back-scatter from pelagic fishes and macroplankton. The break is a migration route for whales and the spawning grounds for several commercial fish stocks.

Species richness peaks along the front which is the boundary between the more abyssal seabed communities and the communities which inhabit the shallow shelf seabed. Oceanic waters mix with and displace shelf waters and eddying results in discrete boluses of ocean water moving up onto the shelf. The shelf break is evident in the benthic inhabitants on the seabed but there is exchange of many pelagic species; fish, reptiles, mammals and plankton. There are also a range of both pelagic and benthic species which occur almost exclusively in the vicinity of the shelf-break.

In the South-western Approaches the slope at the shelf-break is intercepted by deep canyons, and an immense embayment, the Porcupine Seabight. To the north of the Seabight the slope becomes almost straight until it curves around to the north of Ireland. Then, offshore of the Hebrides, it becomes almost straight again. A near-seabed current flows northwards, at about a knot, just offshore of the shelf-break.

2. CURRENT FACTORS AFFECTING THE HABITAT

There is little information on the quality of this habitat. The main activities which may affect the quality are:

- Commercial fishing which removes large numbers of top predators as well as disturbing benthic habitats with bottom gears which can operate at these depths.
- Oil and gas installations have the potential for localised impacts.

Some activities, such as fishing, may also support populations of other species, for example, discards (including offal) may support populations of gannets *Sula bassana* and fulmars *Fulmaris glacialis*.

3. CURRENT ACTION

3.1 Legal status

There is a range of national and international legislation and agreements designed to protect the oceans. The UN Law of the Sea Convention (UNCLOS) provides a comprehensive framework for the regulation of all ocean space. Within the framework more specific agreements exist, for example, on dumping at sea through the London Convention 1972 and on shipping through MARPOL. The UK has also signed the OSPAR Convention for the protection of marine environment of the north-east Atlantic which covers the prevention of pollution from land-based sources by dumping and incineration and from off-shore sources. The Convention also provides for an assessment of the quality of the marine environment. These agreements are given effect by a variety of statutes in the UK.

3.2 Management, research and guidance

There is currently no conservation management specifically directed at this habitat. However, an increasing amount of research is being undertaken.

4. CONSERVATION DIRECTION

Maintain the richness and diversity of the three shelf-break regions in UK waters.

Measures to be considered further include:

- Gain a better understanding by identifying the species and communities associated with these ecosystems, the contribution they make to oceanic biodiversity and the factors that affect them. Including the identification of areas that may require some degree of protection.
- Develop a system for environmental assessment of activities taking place in the vicinity of the shelf break.
- Develop techniques for conserving communities and wildlife associated with this habitat.
- Improve water quality in inshore waters in order to reduce possible inputs of contaminants to shelf-break systems.
- Encourage international co-operation and collaboration over the development and implementation of suitable management measures for the conservation of shelf-break regions.
- Build an awareness, both nationally and internationally, of the ecological significance of these systems to marine processes.

OFFSHORE SEABED HABITAT STATEMENT

1. CURRENT STATUS

Thousands of square kilometres of UK waters can be defined as offshore seabed which is away from the immediate influence of coastal features and processes (beyond six miles from baselines). The area includes a variety of habitats but it is dominated by soft sediments. It includes deep areas which are below the thermocline, and therefore thermally stable, to shallow offshore banks.

The strength of wave action on the seabed (in depths to 30-40m), the residual currents, eddies and gyres (which also influence greater depths), and the sediment supply collectively determine the seabed sediment type which, in turn, strongly influences the composition of the burrowing (infaunal) community. The species present are mainly polychaete worms, echinoderms, bivalve molluscs and crustacea. The epifauna species, including crustacea and echinoderms, are less dependent on sediment type. Hard substrata are rare but may include sediment concretions formed by leaking gases and reefs of horse mussels, *Modiolus modiolus*. In deep water (generally >200m) reefs of the coral *Lophelia pertusa* occur particularly offshore of north-western coasts.

2. CURRENT FACTORS AFFECTING THE HABITAT

Changes in the quality of offshore seabed are sometimes difficult to determine or link to specific events or activities. Despite this there are numerous instances of localised change as well as widespread effects.

Changes may arise from:

- Use of bottom fishing gears which mobilise and sort sediments and cause damage to epifauna and infauna in the near surface sediment.
- Discards of under-size fish and bycatch during normal fishing operations.
- Aggregate extraction.
- Extensive littering of the seabed from various sources.
- Operational discharges around existing oil and gas installations results in localised pollution. Possible persistence of some chemicals in sediments may have some long-term impacts.

3. CURRENT ACTION

3.1 Legal status

There is a range of national and international legislation and agreements designed to protect the oceans. The UN Law of the Sea Convention (UNCLOS) provides a comprehensive framework for the regulation of all open space. Within the framework more specific agreements exist, for example, on dumping at sea through the London Convention 1972 and on shipping through MARPOL. The UK has also signed the OSPAR Convention for the protection of the marine environment of the north-east Atlantic which covers the prevention of pollution from land-based sources by dumping and incineration and from off-shore sources. The Convention also provides for an assessment of the quality of the marine environment. These agreements are given effect by a variety of statutes in the UK.

A quality status report for the North Sea was published in 1993. It was drawn up by scientists from all the littoral states and represents the most thorough assessment of the health of the sea that has been undertaken. It is part of a wider assessment of all waters covered by the OSPAR Conventions which is to be completed by the year 2000.

Environmental Assessment is a statutory requirement. Government departments assess the potential impacts of oil, gas and aggregate extraction and dumping of dredgings prior to licensing. Conditions can be attached to licences to minimise any environmental impact or a license may be refused on environmental grounds.

Areas which can be defined as sandbanks that are slightly covered by seawater all the time or reefs are currently being considered by the UK Government as possible SACs under the EC Habitats Directive. Following up a commitment from the Fourth International Conference on the Protection of the North Sea, the European Commission are to consider a proposal before 1997 for the establishment, on an experimental basis, of undisturbed areas in the North Sea for scientific purposes in order to assess the recovery and redevelopment of the marine ecosystem.

3.2 Management, research and guidance

Government fisheries departments and marine laboratories are involved in the development, promotion and enforcement of measures concerned with the management of fisheries. These can be used to assist the conservation of marine wildlife and habitats found offshore. The UK Fisheries Departments have a programme investigating the process of fish capture including the processes which stimulate fish to escape from nets. There are also programmes to study the effect of towing fishing gear on the sea bed and on the benthos. MAFF and the Crown Estate Commission are also studying the effects of aggregate extraction on seabed communities. The results of these investigations will assist with the development of commercial fishing gear and management decisions to minimise the impact of these activities on offshore seabed.

Permitted discharges from oil and gas installations are identified as part of the licensing conditions. The Offshore Chemicals Notification Scheme is a voluntary arrangement to control the use of chemicals, but is only partly implemented. The feasibility of mandatory controls, with the support of computer modelling to predict environmental risk, is being tested at the moment. SOAEFD are monitoring more extensive areas of the sea and sea bed, rather than the immediate vicinity of installations.

4. CONSERVATION DIRECTION

Maintain and enhance the habitats and wildlife of offshore seabed.

Measures to be considered further include:

- Increase our knowledge of the offshore seabed through research and mapping of seabed types.
- Research and monitor improvement or deterioration or damage of the habitats and wildlife of offshore seabed.
- Minimise as far as practicable the impact of commercial activities on the offshore sea bed.
- Incorporate examples of offshore seabed habitats into the UK network of marine protected areas.
- Use existing legislation, such as FEPA, and risk assessment for the use of chemicals in the offshore

oil and gas industry.

- Continue to monitor any impact of dump sites on marine habitats, communities and wildlife and take action as appropriate.
- Where possible seek to restore damaged and degraded areas of offshore seabed.
- Continue to examine options for the establishment of 'undisturbed areas' of seabed.

LIMESTONE PAVEMENTS HABITAT STATEMENT

1. CURRENT STATUS

Limestone pavements are a scarce and non-renewable resource. They were formed by the scouring action of ice sheets over exposures of limestone during the ice age which ended some 10,000 years ago. Since then water action has widened the cracks in the pavements to form a complex pattern of crevices known as *grikes* between which are massive blocks of worn limestone called *clints*.

The habitat is widely scattered in the UK, on Carboniferous limestone in Wales, Northern England and Northern Ireland, and Durness limestone in Scotland. The total area in the UK of this habitat is less than 3,000 ha with the largest areas occurring in North Yorkshire and Cumbria, and smaller areas in Lancashire, Wales, Scotland and Northern Ireland. The UK holds a significant proportion of the resource of this habitat within the European Union.

Limestone pavements are of both geological and biological importance. The vegetation is rich in vascular plants, bryophytes and lichens and varies according to geographical location, altitude, rock type and the presence or absence of grazing animals. Limestone pavement vegetation also contains unusual combinations of plants, with woodland and wood-edge species well-represented in the sheltered grikes. The clints support plants of rocky habitats or are often unvegetated. In the absence of grazing scrub may develop. In oceanic areas scrub over limestone pavement is important for epiphytes.

2. CURRENT FACTORS AFFECTING THE HABITAT

A comprehensive GB-wide survey undertaken in 1975 estimated that 61% of the total limestone pavement area was intact and only 3% of the remaining pavements were undamaged. There have been no recent estimates of change. Some damage has, however, continued in the intervening years and, as it is irreversible, the resource has been further reduced.

The main factors affecting limestone pavement areas are:

- Illegal or incidental removal of pavements.
- Legal removal of pavements under extant planning permissions.
- Overgrazing of upland pavements and abandonment of lowland pavements.

3. CURRENT ACTION

3.1 Legal status

Under section 34 of the Wildlife and Countryside Act 1981, limestone pavement is subject to protection measures that are additional to the normal SSSI provisions. Pavements of special interest (for wildlife, geology or physiography) can be notified to the local authority, who may then make a Limestone Pavement Order (LPO) to protect the pavement. Once an LPO is in place, removal of rock becomes a criminal offence under the Wildlife and Countryside Act 1981. ASSIs can also be declared in Northern Ireland under the Nature Conservation and Amenity Lands Order (NI) 1985.

The most important limestone pavement areas have been notified as SSSIs. Exceptional examples of these were recently proposed by the UK Government as areas that merit designation as SACs under the EC Habitats Directive.

3.2 Management, research and guidance

In 1989 the Nature Conservancy Council along with the Countryside Commission and local authorities, set up a Limestone Pavement Project. The project set out to survey all the pavements in North Yorkshire, Lancashire and Cumbria and to notify all those of special interest to relevant local planning authorities. The project was completed in 1994. English Nature and the Countryside Commission consider that most of the pavements of "special interest" under the terms of the Wildlife and Countryside Act, 1981 should now be protected by a Limestone Pavement Order made by the Local Planning Authority. The implementation of these Orders is being monitored by the Limestone Pavement Forum, a consortium of local authority and statutory agencies.

Voluntary sector organisations, concerned at the continued damage (both legal and illegal) to limestone pavements established the Limestone Pavement Action Group in 1994, to highlight the issue of the damage caused to this irreplaceable habitat by demand for the use of water-worn stone in rockeries, and to campaign for better protection for pavements.

All of the limestone pavement in Northern Ireland is within Fermanagh ESA.

4. CONSERVATION DIRECTION

Protect the extent and quality of limestone pavement.

Further details of this conservation direction and the measures required to deliver it are given in the Costed Habitat Action Plan for Limestone Pavement.

URBAN HABITAT STATEMENT

1. CURRENT STATUS

Urban wildlife habitats include buildings and hard surfaces but for the purposes of this Habitat Statement they are defined as greenspaces and the associated ecological niches found within built up areas. Greenspaces can be divided into four distinct categories:

i.   Remnants of ancient natural systems, such as woodland, wetland, freshwater and estuarine.

ii. Pre-industrial rural landscapes with arable land, meadows, heathland, grazing marshes and villages.

iii. Managed greenspaces. These include town parks, pocket parks, amenity grassland, private gardens and planted shrubberies. They can, depending on their structure, management and planted species, support a large number of wild species of invertebrate and birds especially in the suburbs. These include regionally and nationally uncommon species, including for example juniper fauna which has adapted to garden junipers.

iv. Naturally seeded urban areas or industrial sites such as demolition sites, disused railway lands or unexploited industrial land. These areas can be particularly rich in species, often reflecting the complex mixture of features. In the early stages of colonisation ephemeral species are favoured and include many uncommon species including some bees and wasps for which urban areas are now their stronghold and early successional carabid beetles. Later stages of succession - short perennial, tall ruderal and then through to woodland - equally contain many uncommon invertebrates with flies, bees, wasps, including some parasitic species and sawflies. The lichens of disused land include several rare species. Both plant and animal communities contain recently established species, some of which are virtually confined to urban areas but a few of which have also established in rural situations.

The rural remnants (i) and (ii) above are not considered further in this Habitat Statement.

An important characteristic of urban areas as a whole, as well as of the greenspaces they hold, is their mosaic of habitats. It is this intimate mosaic of habitats within sites which gives rare ground-nesting bees and wasps and protected species such as the great-crested newt *Triturus cristatus* the mixture of breeding site, foraging areas and shelter they need within relatively small areas. This needs to be repeated across urban areas in general if they are to maintain viable populations.

2. CURRENT FACTORS AFFECTING THE HABITAT

The main factors which alter the overall structure of urban habitats are:

- Simplification of park management and reclamation or redevelopment of disused land to a uniform landuse.

- Development encroachment onto parks, old cemeteries, long abandoned sites and large established suburban gardens.

- Management of greenspaces such as clearing of shrubs, filling in ponds and levelling land with hillocks and hollows making them less attractive to wildlife.

- Changes in industrial processes and mining activities and the end of many producing large quantities of waste means that the distinctive communities and uncommon species associated with many waste and spoil tips will decline.

3. CURRENT ACTION

3.1 Legal status

Some protection is given to urban habitats where these are notified as SSSI/ASSIs or declared as NNRs or LNRs, and analogous areas in Country Parks in Scotland. However, for the majority of urban wildlife areas the protection comes from outside the conservation legislation, notably planning policies in local plans.

3.2 Management, research and guidance

A number of schemes can be used to enhance the wildlife interest of urban areas. Community Action for Wildlife provides assistance to local community groups in England who wish to manage urban areas for their wildlife potential. In the central belt of Scotland the Countryside in and Around Towns (CAT) projects are aimed at improving the local natural heritage in and around settlements and people's access to, and enjoyment of, these areas.

Current interest in planning for sustainable cities and for low cost management of existing open spaces could help to maintain or improve local biodiversity. Derelict and disused urban areas may also be eligible to receive funding through Derelict Land Grants in England. In Scotland land reclamation falls largely to Scottish Enterprise National and Highlands and Islands Enterprise and local authorities. In Wales grants are administered by the Welsh Development Agency. Although these schemes provide grants for development projects designed to restore derelict land some consideration should be given to the additional environmental benefits that can be achieved.

Grants in the region of £700,000 were given by CCW in 1994/95 for work on urban and urban fringe with roughly 60% going to Groundwork Trusts and Local Authorities.

SNH is soon to publish its urban policy framework promoting conservation, enhancement, enjoyment and awareness of the natural heritage in and around settlements through engaging the community and building partnerships.

Urban habitats also have considerable potential for local people to take part in enjoyable activities which benefit nature conservation and enable them to take action for the local environment. These areas also form an important education resource informing people of wildlife interests, natural processes and conservation management. The framework provided by Local Agenda 21 is appropriate and important.

4. CONSERVATION DIRECTION

Maintain the existing diversity and extent of wildlife in all urban areas, expanding the range and distribution of rare and common species and enabling this resource to be utilised as an educational tool.

Measures to be considered further include:

- Survey and evaluate the full range of urban habitats (including buildings) in terms of their importance in maintaining wildlife interest.
- Protect sites important for wildlife from changes in landuse.
- Encourage the integration of green networks (incorporating a full range of wildlife habitats) in planning and developments within the urban environment.
- Implement strategies to enable the use of vacant and derelict land, either temporarily or permanently as wildlife habitats.
- Incorporate the conservation and enhancement of wildlife into the management of urban greenspace.
- Encourage community action to survey, plan for and manage wildlife habitats.
- Promote wild space in urban areas as an educational resource to inform communities about local wildlife in the context of the wider environment.

Printed in the United Kingdom for HMSO
Dd 0301857   C30   12/95   3400/4   340041   47/34154